VERNON I. CHEADLE

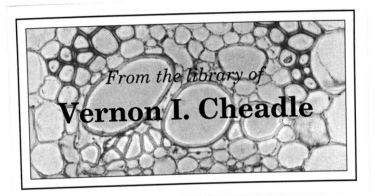

PRINCIPLES
of
PALEOBOTANY

WILLIAM C. DARRAH

ASSOCIATE PROFESSOR OF BIOLOGY
GETTYSBURG COLLEGE

SECOND EDITION

THE RONALD PRESS COMPANY · NEW YORK

Library of Congress Catalog Card Number: 60–6147

Dedicated to the memory of

Paul Bertrand

1879-1944

Devoted Scientist——Inspiring Teacher——Steadfast Friend

PREFACE

Twenty years have elapsed since the publication of the first edition of *Principles of Paleobotany*. The purpose now, as then, is to provide a general introductory survey of the field of paleobotany for the nonspecialist. The book is intended as a text in one-semester and one-quarter undergraduate and graduate courses in paleobotany, plant evolution, and phylogeny, and as supplementary reading in courses in plant morphology.

The many developments in paleobotany since 1939 have materially altered major points of view. A vast Carboniferous coal-ball flora has been found in the United States; undisputable microfossils have been recognized in Cambrian and Proterozoic rocks; the Triassic has yielded angiosperms; the Mesozoic conifers have been reinterpreted, and the finding of a number of obscure, previously unknown groups of gymnosperms and primitive tracheophytes has cast doubts upon popular theories nurtured for many years.

Attempts have been made to summarize these newer discoveries and to suggest their implications. Emphasis, however, is placed upon classic work, even when recent monographs are available, to retain a historical point of view and to convey a sense of the cumulative nature of scientific knowledge as well as the continuity of life. Living descendants, disappearing floral elements, relict phenomena, and the process of floral change are repeatedly considered. A limited number of forms are described in a conventional manner to illustrate the nature of fossil remains. The gross aspects of representative floras are portrayed in a wide selection of landscape reconstructions. Various techniques and interpretations have been employed in the development of these restorations; hence, some inconsistencies are evident.

The concepts and methods developed by paleobotanists to interpret the fossil plant record are used throughout the book to acquaint the student with the conceptual nature of contemporary science. Man has always attempted to interpret the world in which he lives. The study of fossil organisms is merely an extension of this insatiable intellectual curiosity. Perhaps the greatest single contribution of paleontology is the proof that fossil organisms can be interpreted by the same concepts as existing organisms, and, conversely, extinct organisms give meaning and answers to problems of living organisms.

The bibliographies include three types of suggested supplementary readings—general background, where desirable; classic papers, even if technical and not always accessible; and a small number of references to current research in critical groups. Throughout the text, passing references are made to the general work of well-known paleobotanists without citations to specific publications. This has been done for the sake of brevity. Full references are readily available in the *Geologic Literature of North America* published by the United States Geological Survey.

Grateful acknowledgement is due Dr. Frans Verdoorn, Director of the Biohistorical Institute in Utrecht and Consulting Editor for the Chronica Botanica books, for his many favors during the preparation of the manuscript for this edition, and to the many colleagues who, over the years, have continued to send me separates of their publications.

WILLIAM C. DARRAH

Gettysburg, Pennsylvania
    January, 1960

CONTENTS

1 BIOLOGICAL AND GEOLOGICAL PRINCIPLES 3

2 HISTORY AND AIMS OF PALEOBOTANY 13

3 PALEOBOTANICAL TECHNIQUES 20

4 EARLY PLANT RECORDS: THALLOPHYTES 32

5 THE PSILOPSIDA 41

6 OTHER DEVONIAN PLANTS 57

7 THE LYCOPSIDA 67

8 THE SPHENOPSIDA 83

9 PTEROPSIDA: FERNS 97

10 THE PTERIDOSPERMS 114

11 CARBONIFEROUS FLORAS 124

12 THE PALEOBOTANY OF COALS 141

13 CORDAITALES AND GINKGOALES 154

14 BENNETTITALES AND CYCADALES 166

15 THE CONIFERALES 178

16 MESOZOIC FLORAS 190

17 ORIGIN OF THE ANGIOSPERMS 205

18 UPPER CRETACEOUS FLORAS 217

19 CENOZOIC FLORAS 229

20 ORIGIN OF THE EXISTING FLORA 238

21 POLLEN ANALYSIS AND FLORISTICS—KEYS TO FLORAL CHANGE . 248

22 FOSSIL PLANTS AND EVOLUTION 261

23 A REASONABLE PHYLOGENY 270

INDEX 281

PRINCIPLES
of
PALEOBOTANY

1

BIOLOGICAL AND GEOLOGICAL PRINCIPLES

Paleobotany is the study of the history of the plant kingdom. It deals with problems concerning the vegetation of the geologic past and with the many different kinds of plants which have populated the earth. The living plant kingdom has behind it the heritage of a billion years. The present vegetation of the earth owes its composition and distribution to circumstances of earth history.

The materials of paleobotany are fossils. A fossil may be defined as any tangible evidence of former life, not necessarily prehistoric, but conventionally so considered. The word "fossil" is derived from the Latin verb "to dig" and implies the usual occurrence of fossils in the earth.

In the living plant there are various structures which are resistant to rapid decay and which are liable to preservation by burial in sediment. An infrequent but striking method of fossilization may accompany burial by volcanic ash. The destruction of Herculaneum and Pompeii during the violent eruption of Vesuvius in A.D. 79 is well known. Pompeii was covered to a depth of several feet above the house tops, and Herculaneum was buried under many feet of mudstreams. Excavations by archeologists have shown that the hot ash destroyed the plant and animal bodies, although natural moulds were formed in the sediment. Lifelike plaster casts of humans and dogs have been prepared from them. In 1902, the eruption of Mont Pelée, on the island of Martinique, enveloped the town of St. Pierre. Specimens of carbonized rice, bread, and spaghetti have been collected from the ruins. If the ash had been cool, carbonization would not have occurred; instead, nearly airtight burial would have resulted. Burial by volcanic ash is relatively uncommon, but paleobotanists have been able to study the process in two recent eruptions, Katmai in Alaska (1912) and Parícutin in Mexico (1943). (Dorf, 1951.)

3

Two major factors are involved in this mode of preservation: rapidity of burial and prevention of normal decomposition. A combination of these factors frequently occurs under other circumstances, such as burial in stagnant water, complete burial under fine-grained sediment, or rapid infiltration by mineral substances, in any of which the quantity of available oxygen is diminished.

Whatever the initial circumstances, many plant structures are preserved as fossils, with a greater or lesser amount of structural detail, by the relatively simple process of burial under conditions that retard or prevent microbial and autolytic decomposition.

KINDS OF FOSSIL PLANTS

1. Petrifactions or mineralized plants. In this group are included those fossils preserving the external form, the internal structure, and sometimes substance of the original plant. Examples: coalballs, silicified wood.

2. Incrustations. These are fossils with the external form as a cast. The internal structure is not preserved, and the carbonaceous material is usually completely lost. Example: leaves in tufa.

3. Compressions. The external form of the plant is modified by vertical pressure of the sediments with which it is surrounded. Most of the so-called carbonizations are compressions.

4. Compactions or mummified plants are plants, or plant fragments, compressed by vertical pressure. Masses of plant fragments without intervening matrix, such as are found in peat and coal, are large-scale compactions. Most of the deformations observed in this type of fossilization are caused by the pressure of one fragment against another. Frequently remarkable conditions of preservations are found in compactions.

5. Impressions. The forms impressed by fossils of the incrustation or compression types on the matrix are usually termed impressions.

Fossils are usually found in fine-grained sediments such as shales and sandstones. These consolidated sediments represent the muds and sands in which the plants were buried. Most plants, of course, decay completely and quickly, and it is only in exceptional cases that the delicate parts of organisms are preserved. As a general rule, a plant which falls into water becomes saturated and soon sinks to the bottom where the progress of decay is retarded. If, instead of progressive but complete destruction, the tissues are incompletely decomposed, the accumulating sediment may enclose residual structures and arrest further decomposition.

Sometimes the plant bodies or plant parts are buried under conditions in which not only is decay retarded, but in addition the water carries dissolved mineral substances. Such circumstances result in petrifaction or mineralization. Silicified wood may reveal the minute detail of the ornamentation of cell walls, or calcified nodules may preserve the nuclei in the cells of a developing megaspore.

Some kinds of plants are more liable to preservation than others, and some are of such delicate form and structure that they are seldom encountered as fossils. Calcareous algae are frequent fossils. The protoplasts are not preserved, but the calcified parts are diagnostic enough to permit accurate identification. On the other hand, fungi are infrequently observed as fossils, but their ravages can be detected in a great many petrifactions.

ASSUMPTIONS OF MODERN GEOLOGY

It should be apparent that paleobotany is both a geological and a biological science. Within the past fifty years, the biological aspect has engaged the attention of most paleobotanists. There are a number of fundamental concepts which have largely directed the philosophical approach to our subject. These may be considered briefly.

It is a basic assumption of modern geology that the various forces which now act upon the earth are the same as those which shaped the face of the earth in the past. Rains descend and erode the land, brooks and rivers transport their burden of sediment into places where this burden is deposited. This process of tearing down and building up is the simplest aspect of inevitable and universal earth change. There are other factors which cause profound modifications in the aspect of the earth, such as wind, ice, freezing, vulcanism, subsidence, and even organisms, but erosion and deposition go on continuously. To be sure, the rates at which these processes accomplish their work may have been much slower or faster in past times, but the result is always the same: old land surfaces are constantly being worn down while new land is being formed.

In the many millions of years of earth history, great mountain chains have been formed only to disappear by denudation and erosion. Even the configuration of entire continents has undergone extensive modification.

The multitudinous earth changes and the biological changes correlated with them readily lend themselves to rather natural chronologic groupings, "eras" and "periods." In each period of earth history certain plants and animals occupied the inhabitable environments. Many years ago the English geologist William Smith observed that there was a definite order in which fossil floras and faunas occurred: that the lower or older strata contain the most primitive and extinct organisms, while the higher strata contain fossils which become increasingly like those living at present. This orderly succession of geological and biological events is now almost universally accepted as primary data of natural science. Only those persons with strong prejudices antagonistic to a great age for the earth deny this basic concept in geology.

The birth of the earth was an astronomical event. Astronomers and geologists are by no means agreed on how the formation of the earth took place. It is outside of the scope of paleobotany to enter into this interesting field of speculation, because many earth changes had to take place before living organisms could inhabit even a small part of the earth. As intriguing as the origin of life upon our world may be, paleobotanists must limit themselves to a study of the actual fossil record.

Geologists subdivide earth history by time and by rock strata. The terminology applied to the major units is indicated by the following:

TIME	STRATA
Era	(No equivalent)
Period	System
Epoch	Series
Age	Stage
(No equivalent)	Zone

See also accompanying chart (page 7).

It is evident from this chart that several major divisions, each embracing a number of periods, direct attention to the broad evolutionary trends in the succession of life. The general interrelationships between biological and geological trends are likewise suggested.

The so-called geological revolutions are major changes which altered a relatively large part of the earth. The building of a great mountain system will result in the formation of formidable barriers to migration. Drainage systems will have their courses altered and their tributaries rejuvenated. Whole floras and faunas may be

TABLE 1

Subdivisions of Geologic Time

ERAS	PERIODS		MOUNTAIN-MAKING EPISODES	LIFE	YEARS AGO
CENOZOIC	QUATERNARY	RECENT		AGE OF MAN	15,000
		PLEISTOCENE			1,500,000
	TERTIARY	PLIOCENE	ALPINE-CASCADIAN	AGE OF MAMMALS AND ANGIOSPERMS	
		MIOCENE			30,000,000
		OLIGOCENE			
		EOCENE	HIMALAYAN		
MESOZOIC	CRETACEOUS		LARAMIDE	AGE OF REPTILES AND GYMNOSPERMS	
	JURASSIC		SIERRA NEVADA		180,000,000
	TRIASSIC				225,000,000
PALEOZOIC	"CARBONIFEROUS"	PERMIAN	APPALACHIAN	AGE OF FISHES AND PTERIDOPHYTES	
		PENNSYLVANIAN	HERCYNIAN		
		MISSISSIPPIAN			
	DEVONIAN				370,000,000
	SILURIAN		CALEDONIAN-ACADIAN		
	ORDOVICIAN				
	CAMBRIAN			AGE OF INVERTEBRATES AND THALLOPHYTES	
PROTEROZOIC	"PRE-CAMBRIAN"		GRAND CANYON YOUNGER LAURENTIANS		500,000,000
ARCHEOZOIC			OLDER LAURENTIANS		2,500,000,000?

isolated so that extinction is inevitable. At the same time new land may be formed for invasion by virile plants and animals, or new land-bridges pave the way for new waves or migration.

Cuvier interpreted such changes as "catastrophes." As a result of this reasoning, he believed that the life of the earth was periodically destroyed and then restored by successive creations. The first scientific compromise theorized that life was not totally destroyed by these catastrophes, but local remnant populations perpetuated their kind. This direction of compromise ultimately ended with the notion that the cataclysm, not the relict population, was local in extent. There were two fallacies in Cuvier's reasoning, that the catastrophes were almost universally violent and that transitional series of fossils do not exist. However, we cannot disregard the effects or importance of local violent changes.

The commonplace phenomena of earth processes that have just been mentioned are designated as "weathering" and "sedimentation." Sedimentation is a complex process which involves, in order, erosion, transportation, and deposition. Physical and chemical changes may take place in a sediment subsequent to its period of accumulation. The factors generally emphasized are pressure and temperature. These factors, however, are not necessarily of a great order of magnitude. This is particularly true of temperature.

Diastrophism is the major process of earth deformation or, better, earth displacement. There are a great many diastrophic phenomena, the chief being earthquakes, which usually result from fracturing and slipping in the bedrock, elevation or subsidence of the shoreline, and the folding of mountains.

Thus there are two antagonistic series of processes continuing simultaneously: gradation, which destroys the land; and diastrophism, which renews or rejuvenates the land.

The exposed sedimentary record of the earth's history is represented by approximately 70 miles of consolidated sediments. A century ago attempts were made to calculate the age of the earth by estimating the time involved in this tremendous accumulation. Computations of the age of the earth by this method vary from 100 to 300 million years. The salt in the ocean has also been considered as a clue to the length of earth history, because it is believed that the ocean was originally fresh water and that all of the salt in it has been leached from the land and carried by streams into the ocean.

These computations yield estimates not unlike those obtained by the sedimentary method. Since the discovery of radioactivity and the time involved in the decomposition of uranium, thorium, etc., is known, geochemists have estimated the age of the oldest igneous rocks to be about 2,500,000,000 years. More recently radioactive carbon (C^{14}) has been recognized as a valuable guide in age determinations of relatively modern sediments (Libby). Since many fossil structures retain carbon in varying amounts, the radioactive carbon method holds particular interest for paleobotanists. For details concerning these interesting methods, the reader is referred to the Bibliography, particularly the title by Zeuner, 1952.

The immensity of geological time is possibly the most difficult concept confronting the student, but reasonable comprehension of the idea is necessary for an understanding of organic evolution.

There are two major relationships between paleobotany and geology. The first of these is in the field of stratigraphy, which deals with the study of rock strata and attempts to determine the nature and environment of each sediment; whether the environment was fresh-water or marine, temperate or tropical, *in situ* or transported for a great distance. The second relationship is in the field of correlation, which attempts to determine the relative ages of rocks. A combination of both approaches results in data concerning paleogeography and paleoclimatology.

BIOLOGICAL ASPECTS OF PALEOBOTANY

There are four major relationships between paleobotany and biology. It is self-evident that fossils represent organisms that once lived by processes and under conditions which must have been similar to those observed by modern biologists. The physical and chemical limits within which life exists are narrow indeed.

The first relationship between botany and paleobotany is in the historical approach to the plant kingdom. It is known that there has been a gradual succession of plant types in the history of the earth. Some groups of plants have become totally extinct, while others are now more numerous and important than ever before. It is also known that there has been a gradual sequence from simple to more highly differentiated ones. This phenomenon is viewed from the standpoint of kinship. This complex sequence is the basic fact underlying the concept of biological evolution.

The second relationship between paleobotany and the botany of living plants is the "natural" classification. If all plant organisms have a common ancestry, degree of kinship may be expressed logically by a phylogenetic taxonomy. Since the time of Linnaeus, the classification of plants has undergone numerous alterations which were intended to indicate, so far as possible, lines of kinship or natural lines of descent. It is in this field of work that the study of fossil plants has made some of its most significant contributions.

The third relationship is in the field of descriptive comparative anatomy. The common organs and organ systems are homologous in all larger taxonomic groups. Since a morphological approach is used through the first half of this book, the point will not be enlarged at this time.

The fourth great relationship between fossil plants and recent plants is the perspective of time. This is an indispensable tool in the interpretation of the history of life on the earth—the time factor in organic evolution. The living flora has behind it the heritage of a billion years.

There remains for consideration a brief discussion of the plant body and its significance in classification. It is generally held by modern botanists that there are several great stages in the evolution of plants.

Life probably evolved in the sea or at least in a brackish environment. In its earliest stages the free-living and independent cell, in conventional terms the fundamental unit of structure and function, became differentiated and organized. Gradually there developed the multicellular organism, with a division of labor among its tissues. Probably the next advance was the origin of sex, with its remarkable manifestation, the alternation of generations. It was this cyclical alternation between sexual and asexual generations which made possible the invasion of land in early Paleozoic times.

The sexual generation or gametophyte in the life history of the plant is dependent upon water at least for the fertilization of the gametes. The asexual generation or sporophyte becomes increasingly able to cope with the aerial environment. Paleobotany is largely limited, by the nature of the plant body, to the study of sporophytes of the higher plants, those with woody stems or vascularized parts. There are many exceptions, but the generality is none the less true.

The plant kingdom can be briefly considered in tabular view:

THALLOPHYTA
  Algae
    Cyanophyceae
    "Chlorophyceae"
    Phaeophyceae
    Rhodophyceae
  Fungi

Cyanophyceae	Proterozoic to Recent
"Chlorophyceae"	Proterozoic to Recent
Phaeophyceae	Cambrian (?), Silurian to Recent
Rhodophyceae	Silurian to Recent
Fungi	Proterozoic to Recent

EMBRYOPHYTA
  Bryophyta

Musci	Carboniferous to Recent
Hepaticae	Carboniferous to Recent

Tracheophyta

Psilopsida, Lycopsida, Sphenopsida, Pteropsida, "Ferns" } "Pteridophyta"

Gymnospermae, Angiospermae } "Spermatophyta"

Psilopsida	Silurian-Devonian (exclusively?)
Lycopsida	Cambrian (?) to Recent
Sphenopsida	Devonian to Recent
Pteropsida	Devonian to Recent
"Ferns"	Devonian to Recent
Gymnospermae	Devonian to Recent
Angiospermae	Triassic (?), Cretaceous to Recent

The TRACHEOPHYTA, or vascular plants, include all of the conspicuous land plants and are characterized by the possession of an upright plant body which produces spores, which in turn produce gametophytes bearing sex organs which produce egg and sperm. The fertilization of gametes produces a zygote which grows through the embryo stage to the adult sporophyte.

The sporophyte in most plants is capable of terrestrial existence, sometimes under environmental conditions which are severe and unhospitable. Yet the plant body is extremely sensitive to environmental factors. In the geologic past we recognize not only individual but also mass response to environmental changes.

Bibliography

Geological Principles

Bowen, R. N. C. 1958. *The exploration of time.* George Newnes Ltd., London. An excellent synopsis of the interpretation of geologic time. Brief but quite comprehensive.

Schuchert, C. 1943. *Stratigraphy of Eastern and Central United States.* John Wiley & Sons, Inc., New York. This is a detailed and rather difficult book, but the introductory sections of the various chapters give an excellent concept of the paleogeography of sediments and their fossil content. The maps are also useful.

Twenhofel, W. H. 1932. *Treatise on Sedimentation.* 2d ed. William & Wilkins Co., Baltimore. Though now somewhat obsolete, this work is still the most usable account of the types of carbonaceous sediments and the conditions of their deposition.

Zeuner, R. E. 1952. *Dating the Past: An Introduction to Geochronology.* 3d ed. Methuen & Co., Ltd., London. The best survey of the methods and evidence used in estimating the age of sediments, particularly those of the Pleistocene.

Botanical Principles

BOLD, H. C. 1957. *Morphology of Plants*. Harper & Bros., New York.

BOWER, F. O. 1935. *Primitive Land Plants*. Macmillan & Co., Ltd., London.

FOSTER, A. S., and GIFFORD, E. M. 1959. *Comparative Morphology of Vascular Plants*. W. H. Freeman & Co., San Francisco.

SMITH, G. M. 1955. *Cryptogamic Botany*. 2 vols. 2d ed. McGraw-Hill Book Co., Inc., New York.

VERDOORN, F., *et al.* 1932. *Manual of Bryology*. Nijhoff, The Hague.

WARDLAW, C. W. 1952. *Phylogeny and Morphogenesis*. St. Martin's Press, Inc., New York.

ZIMMERMANN, W. 1930. *Die Phylogenie der Pflanzen*. Gustav Fischer, Jena.

———. 1949. *Geschichte der Pflanzen*. Gustav Fischer, Stuttgart.

Specific Reference

DORF, E. 1945. Observations on the preservation of plants in the Parícutin area, *Trans. Geophys. Un.* 26: 257-260.

2

HISTORY AND AIMS
OF PALEOBOTANY

The earliest scholars who recognized the true nature of fossils, and whose opinions are known to us, were the Greek philosophers. Xenophanes, in the sixth century B.C., observed fossil laurel leaves in the rocks of Paros. Pythagoras and Xanthus of Sardis were supposed to have held sound conceptions concerning the significance of fossil marine shells found in high mountains. Pliny (A.D. 23-79) believed that amber was engendered from trees resembling pine and compared it with resin of pines. He also noted that jet greatly resembled wood.

During the latter part of the sixteenth and the early part of the seventeenth centuries, opinions concerning fossils began to accumulate. It is altogether natural that these curiosities were interpreted according to the enlightenment of the times. The invention of printing made the Christian Bible available to those able to read. Fossils were considered to have lived prior to the time of the Noachian Flood. Martin Luther (1483-1546) expressed the view in a commentary on Genesis that petrified wood found about mines was evidence of the activity of early man, destroyed by the Deluge. The concept of a universal flood did not develop in the Renaissance, for it had in fact appeared early in Christian literature. Edwards records that De Pallio of Tertullian (A.D. c. 155-c. 222) considered fossils as remnants of the waters which covered all the earth.

The Diluvialists, however, enjoyed popularity in academical and theological circles particularly during the seventeenth and early eighteenth centuries. Scheuchzer (1672-1773) published a book devoted chiefly to fossil plants which he called the "Herbarium Diluvianum" (1709). The tender, vernal cones which he illustrated were believed to indicate that the Flood took place in the month of May. Scheuchzer also illustrated a skeleton under the name "Homo

13

Diluvii Testis," which later Cuvier correctly identified as a large amphibian. Parsons (1757) argued that the abundant "ripe" fossil fruits found at Sheppy proved that the Flood took place in the autumn. Thus Scheuchzer and Parsons attempted to date an event, however mythical, by fossil evidence.

Blumenbach in 1790 asserted that there were many different faunas and floras on the earth before the advent of man, and Erasmus Darwin (1731-1802) gave to the modern thinking world the concept of the immensity of geological time—the millions of years required for the evolution of the organic world. William Smith (1769-1839) realized that the different rock strata possessed a definite order and succession of fossils, and that different faunas and floras always characterized the different strata.

With the advent of these fundamental concepts in scientific thought, paleobotany became a geological science. The stimulation of intellectual curiosity and the search for combustible fuels for industries, developed after the so-called industrial revolution, made possible the accumulation of extensive collections of fossils. Likewise, the development of a uniform binomial classification, following Linnaeus, paved the way for the first great paleobotanists, the monographers.

Adolphe Brongniart is usually credited as the organizer of paleobotany. In 1828 there appeared the first part of his *Histoire des Végétaux Fossiles*. He divided the earth's history into four great periods of vegetation: age of cryptogams, age of ferns and conifers, age of cycads, and the age of flowering plants. Later in his career, Brongniart published a careful microscopical investigation on the structure of *Sigillaria elegans*.

Witham was probably the first investigator to study Carboniferous plants histologically. In 1833 his greatest work, published under the name *The Internal Structure of Fossil Vegetables Found in the Carboniferous and Oolitic Deposits of Great Britain*, demonstrated the unquestionable identity of tissues in fossil bodies.

The preliminary stage in the development of paleobotany was largely descriptive, that is, describing thousands of kinds of fossils, their association in floras, and their distribution in time. The more important contributions are suggested by the following sketch.

Goeppert was one of the most resourceful and ingenious paleobotanists of all times. In 1836 there appeared his *Systema*

Filicum Fossilum, and in 1841 his *Genera Plantarum.* Goeppert's works are noteworthy for their fine plates, their broad and painstaking methodology, and their diversity. In 1845 Goeppert published a study of the plants preserved in Baltic amber.

The year was an auspicious one, for two other memorable works were added to the growing literature of paleobotany: Unger's *Synopsis Plantarum Fossilium* and Corda's *Flora der Vorwelt.* Unger published a large number of taxonomic monographs chiefly on Cenozoic plants. The same may be said also of Oswald Heer, whose *Flora Fossilis Arctica* in eight volumes was one of the greatest.

Saporta and Ettingshausen likewise did fundamental work on fossil angiosperm floras. Ettingshausen published on the Cretaceous floras of Australia.

In 1869, Schimper compiled his *Traité de Paléontologie Végétale* in three volumes, which, though obsolete, is still a useful reference work in taxonomic paleobotany.

Leo Lesquereux, who was born in Switzerland and emigrated to America in 1847, became America's first recognized paleobotanist. Within a few years he had published two papers on the Carboniferous plants of Pennsylvania. These were followed by studies in Illinois and Kentucky (1866) and the *Coal Flora* (1879-1883). Lesquereux did not limit his work to the Paleozoic but wrote several comprehensive monographs on Mesozoic and Cenozoic plants. He was the first to recognize the marked similarity between American and European floras.

These illustrious men were noteworthy for their taxonomic and geological work with fossil impressions. Many of their identifications were based upon superficial resemblances, but we should not deprecate their work for this reason. However, Brongniart, Witham, and Corda did pioneering morphological research. To them must be credited the founding of microscopical paleobotany and thereby proving indisputably the former existence of great plant groups now totally extinct.

The name of W. C. Williamson will always be remembered as the outstanding morphological paleobotanist of the nineteenth century. He published, beginning in 1871, a long series of magnificently executed memoirs on coal-ball plants. Two of his British contemporaries, E. W. Binney and W. Carruthers, also made notable contributions to the morphology of Carboniferous plants.

We note, then, that by 1885 there were two great divisions of, or approaches to, the study of paleobotany; one geological and the other primarily botanical. The botanical approach was in some instances taxonomical, in others morphological. It is necessary to recognize the limitations of any narrowed approach in considering the historical literature of paleobotany.

From 1885 to 1915 paleobotany underwent its modernization chiefly because of the development of research techniques and the appearance of comprehensive textbooks and reference books.

In 1887 Solms-Laubach published a splendid botanical treatment of fossil plants under the title *Einleitung in die Paläophytologie* which was translated into English and published in 1889. In 1900 R. Zeiller published his *Eléments de Paléobotanique*. In 1912 H. Potonié wrote his *Lehrbuch der Paläobotanik*, which underwent a revision in the hands of Gothan in 1921, and by Gothan and Weyland in 1954.

No new textbooks appeared until 1939, at which time Darrah's *Principles of Paleobotany* and *Textbook of Paleobotany* were published. There followed in the next decade excellent texts by Halle (1940), Moret (1940), Walton (1940, 1953), Kryshtofovich (1941), Magdefrau (1941), Emberger (1944), Andrews (1947), and Arnold (1947). This impressive series of textbooks suggests not only the degree of current interest in paleobotany, but also the international standardization of paleobotanical knowledge.

The standard reference books are well known. D. H. Scott's obsolete *Studies in Fossil Botany,* published in three editions, is still a fundamental source of data on the morphology of Paleozoic plants. Of more extensive scope is A. C. Seward's compilation *Fossil Plants* published in four volumes (1898, 1910, 1917, 1919). Hirmer's *Handbuch der Paläobotanik*, of which only one volume was published (1927), is still indispensable.

Many other investigators have contributed to the literature of paleobotany. The student should become familiar with the names of the more important paleobotanists and the fields with which these names are associated.

One of the most useful monographic reference works, although still incomplete, commenced under the editorship of W. J. Jongmans, is *Fossilium Catalogus* (Part II: Plantae). This series is intended to collect together volumes on the smaller systemic groups of fossils. They are valuable guides to the literature.

American students particularly will find the *Bibliography of North American Geology* (United States Geological Survey) of primary necessity.

Guides to current research in paleobotany are available to institutions and serious students. The National Research Council (U.S.A.) Committee on Paleobotany has issued mimeographed annual reports covering all known research, published and in progress, in North and South America. A similar report covering European paleobotany was compiled by the Paleobotanical Department of the Swedish Museum of Natural History. The first issue reports work for the period 1939-1947; the second, 1948-1949. The Committee of British Paleobotany in January, 1953, issued the first annual report covering activity during 1952. References to work in Australia and New Zealand are included. For some years Sahni published an annual report on paleobotanical work in India, and it is to be hoped that the Birbal Sahni Institute of Paleobotany in Lucknow, established through his vision and devotion, will continue this service. The Sahni Institute publishes an official journal, *The Palaeobotanist*, the only periodical devoted exclusively to paleobotany. The first issue (1952) is a memorial volume to the late Professor Sahni.

During the Eighth International Botanical Congress (Paris, 1954), there was founded the International Organization of Paleobotany with the objective to promote international cooperation and exchange of knowledge. Reports on *World Paleobotany* are issued periodically (first, 1950-1954; second, 1955-1956).

Paleobotanists practice and enjoy a high degree of international collaboration and communicate freely information pertaining to their fields of research.

Paleobotanical collections are maintained by most of the large museums of the world, by many universities, and by the geological surveys.

A fossil plant has two points of occurrence, whereas a living plant has, in general, only one. An exact geographical locality is sufficient to place an individual of the existing flora, but a fossil plant must have a temporal locality as well as a spacial locality. The more exactly this temporal occurrence can be determined, the more valuable the fossil. For example, in southeastern Pennsylvania one can collect fossil plants of Silurian, Devonian, Mississippian, Pennsylvanian, Triassic, Cretaceous, and Pleistocene ages. At a few localities, such as Pottsville in Pennsylvania, it is possible to collect from three of these ages within a distance of one mile.

The aims of paleobotany are manifold. In the first place, it is necessary that fossils are adequately described and named taxonomically. The procedure for describing new species and genera must conform to established "International Rules of Nomenclature." These descriptive aspects are limited by the degree of preservation of the specimens. It is estimated that somewhat more than 120,000 "species" of fossil plants have been described, about one-third of this total being flowering plants. Only a small fraction of the fossil species have been described; thousands upon thousands remain undiscovered.

However, the well-known, though frequently exaggerated, fragmentary nature of fossils makes speciation both difficult and arbitrary. The paleobotanist considers the so-called species as only conveniences which are useful in designating differences and solving problems. He is the first to admit that his "species" may not satisfy the student of living plants.

The chief utility of fossil floras is in the study of geological and phytogeographical problems. Correlation of similar and dissimilar strata is based primarily upon fossils. Index-fossils are those species or genera which are known to have limited distributions either in space or time. To a certain degree fossil plants may indicate climate and environment. A palm association or a *Sequoia* forest are fairly recognizable and indicative units of vegetation.

Paleobotanists also attempt to study the history of the plant kingdom and thereby learn of the phylogenetic relationships of the plant groups.

There are six great problems which in large measure must be studied and perhaps solved by paleobotanists:

1. The nature of the early Paleozoic and pre-Paleozoic carbonaceous sediments.
2. The origin and ancestry of the Silurian and Devonian land flora.
3. The origin of the leaf.
4. The origin of the seed.
5. The origin of the angiosperms.
6. The origin of, and changes in, the existing flora.

In this survey of the field of paleobotany, attention will be directed to recent work bearing on these problems.

A phylogenetic approach has been adopted throughout this book to emphasize the kinship and unity of the plant kingdom. Because this emphasis involves assumptions and opinions which may at times be controversial, in fairness to the student the treatment is essentially conservative.

Bibliography

The titles given here need no explanation. The majority are textbooks in current use. A comparison of them will show the standardization of paleobotanical knowledge during the past thirty years.

Historical

EDWARDS, W. N. 1931. Guide to an exhibition illustrating the early history of paleontology, *Brit. Mus. Nat. Hist. Special Guide No. 8.* London.
WARD, L. 1886. The geographical distribution of fossil plants. *8th Ann. Rept. U.S. Geol. Surv.* Washington, D.C. A remarkable review of the older literature.

General Paleobotanical Works

ANDREWS, H. N. 1947. *Ancient Plants and the World They Lived In.* Comstock Publishing Co., Ithaca, N.Y.
ARNOLD, C. A. 1947. *An Introduction to Paleobotany.* McGraw-Hill Book Co., Inc., New York.
BERRY, E. W. 1923. *Tree Ancestors.* Williams & Wilkins Co., Baltimore.
BERTRAND, P. 1947. *Les végétaux vasculaires.* Masson et Cie, Paris.
DARRAH, W. C. 1939. *A Textbook of Paleobotany.* Appleton-Century-Crofts, Inc., New York.
EMBERGER, L. 1944. *Les plantes fossiles.* Masson et Cie, Paris.
HALLE, T. G. 1940. *De utdöda växterna* (Fossil Plants). In C. SKOTTSBERG, ed., *Vaxternas liv.* Vol. V. Stockholm.
HIRMER, M. 1927. *Handbuch der Paläobotanik.* Vol. I. Oldenbourg, Munich and Berlin.
HOFMANN, E. 1934. *Paläohistologie der Pflanze.* Springer-Verlag, Vienna.
KRÄUSEL, R. 1950. *Versunkene Floren. Eine Einführung in die Paläobotanik.* Kramer, Frankfurt am Main.
KRYSHTOFOVICH, A. N. 1934. (Course in paleobotany.) Leningrad. (In Russian.)
MÄGDEFRAU, K. 1951. *Vegetationsbilder der Vorzeit.* 2d ed. Fischer, Jena.
———. 1953. *Paläobiologie der Pflanzen.* 2d ed. Fischer, Jena.
MORET, L. 1949. *Manuel de paléontologie végétale.* 2d ed. Masson et Cie, Paris.
POTONIE, H., and W. GOTHAN. 1953. *Lehrbuch der Paläobotanik.* 3d ed. Borntraeger, Berlin.
SCHIMPER, W. P., A. SCHENK, and K. ZITTEL. 1890. *Handbuch der Palaeontologie.* Part 2: Palaeophytologie. Oldenbourg, Berlin and Munich.
SCOTT, D. H. 1920-1923. *Studies in Fossil Botany.* 3d ed. 2 vols. A. & C. Black, Ltd., London.
SEWARD, A. C. 1898-1919. *Fossil Plants.* 4 vols. Cambridge University Press, London.
———. 1931. *Plant Life Through the Ages.* Cambridge University Press, London.
WALTON, J. 1953. *An Introduction to the Study of Fossil Plants.* 2d ed. Macmillan & Co., Ltd., London.

3

PALEOBOTANICAL TECHNIQUES

New techniques—and improvement of old methods—have wrought a revolution in the interpretation of fossil plants. The most unpromising and controversial sedimentary rocks long disregarded by paleontologists are now being investigated with unexpected results.

THE THIN OR GROUND SECTION

We have already noted that petrifactions have structural detail preserved and that such specimens can, with suitable methods, be examined under the microscope. The earliest method devised for this purpose was the thin section. William Nicol is usually credited with the invention of this technique, although he acknowledged the prior work of another lapidary named Sanderson. As early as 1830 Witham used Nicol's method.

The thin section is prepared in the following manner. A small portion of the specimen is ground smooth on one surface. This surface is cemented to a glass slide with Canada balsam or thermoplastic resin. With the aid of a lapidary's saw or comparable equipment, as much as possible of the specimen is cut away, leaving a moderately thin slice adhering to the slide. The section is then ground down on a revolving lap with an abrasive until translucent. When sufficiently thin, the section is sealed with a cover glass and is thus permanently mounted. Automatic mechanical apparatus for grinding thin sections are available, but at considerable cost.

About 1840 Goeppert successfully removed the petrifying substance from a number of silicified and calcified specimens, recovering in these experiments organic residues of the original plant bodies. In several cases he observed the cellulose reaction with sulfuric acid.

Solms-Laubach in 1891 distinguished two types of mineral petrifaction, the first in which there is no organic residue, i.e., all appar-

20

ent structure is pseudomorphic, and the second, embedded fossils from which plant structures can be recovered by maceration. Although this distinction is today recognized as an oversimplification, the generalization is true.

For many years the thin ground section has been respected as the ideal preparation because, by its very nature, it portrays the fossil structure in unaltered condition (Fig. 1). Any technique which tampers with the matrix or modifies the plant, no matter how little, is viewed with suspicion. Some thin sections, like those of the Permian ferns of Chemnitz, Devonian Rhynie chert, and Black Hills cycadeoids, exhibit magnificent preservation. Fungal sporangia and mycelia, rhizoids, stomata, and even cell contents can be recognized. Yet silica petrifactions are often disappointing. Many fossil woods from the Triassic of Arizona and the Cretaceous of Wyoming preserve nothing of botanical interest, indicating scarcely any features except gross form, growth rings, and scattered cell masses. Such petrifactions are little more than pseudomorphs.

The older opinion, which even now persists, assumes that petrifaction is molecular mineral replacement. The insignificant carbon content (as determined by chemical analysis) is interpreted as proof of the disappearance of the original plant body. That this is not generally true can be demonstrated easily: Marie Stopes in 1918 completely demineralized a specimen of Cretaceous silicified wood and recovered tissues which were excellently preserved. Since that time hundreds of experiments with silicified, calcified, and pyritized specimens have given similar results.

We observe, then, that fossils with preserved structure can be investigated by thin section and by maceration. Since 1920 many new techniques suggested by and developed from earlier discoveries have enriched the methodology of paleobotany.

THE FILM OR PEEL TECHNIQUE

The so-called film or peel technique is a method by which serial sections can be taken from a petrified specimen. The term "peel" is unfortunate because it has become associated with the primitive experiments which depended upon unstandardized cellulose acetates and nitrates which became brittle and discolored with age. The basic technique was developed by Koopmans and Walton, whose inspiration came from an accidental observation by Nathorst (ca. 1908) that a dried film of collodion would peel off a little carbonace-

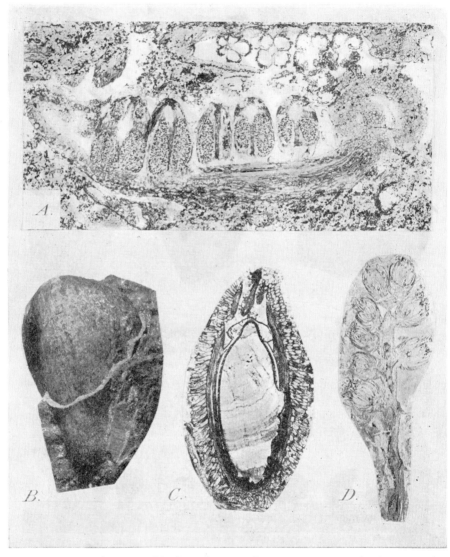

Fig. 1. Petrifactions. Fossils with internal structure preserved. A series of specimens showing types of organs and tissues commonly found in petrified condition. (A) A fern, *Cyathotrachus altissimus,* peel preparation, illustrating sporangia and spores with parent pinnules (Carboniferous: Iowa). (B) An entire pteridosperm seed, *Codonospermum,* isolated from a coal-ball (Carboniferous: Iowa). (C) *Physostoma elegans,* a pteridosperm seed from an English coal-ball, ground section showing endocarp and integumentary tissues. (D) A peel preparation of a compound strobilus of a cordaite, *Cordaianthus shuleri* (Carboniferous: Iowa).

ous material from a compression. Within recent years the method has become highly perfected, particularly in the United States.

Two distinct problems are involved in this technique: (1) selective maceration ("etching") of the surface to be peeled, and (2) compounding of a plastic colloidal mixture which upon setting will give an exact transfer of the structure of he fossil. Etching may be accomplished by various mineral acids, though for silicified specimens hydrofluoric acid is necessary. Since the film cannot transfer any more detail than is exposed by etching, the objective is to prepare the surface and follow the procedure with extreme care.

The solution can be compounded from various constituents. There is no universal or ideal mixture; the purpose determines the most suitable formula. A mixture with a wide range of application may be prepared as follows:

Nitrocellulose (Pyroxylon grade, 12-13% nitrogen) . .	115 grams
Butyl acetate	1000 ml
Amyl alcohol	200 ml
Toluol	10 ml
Dehydrated castor oil	5 ml

This mixture, which must be aged for approximately two weeks before use, will dry slowly without the inclusion of air bubbles. It may be thinned if desired by the addition of butyl acetate without addition of the other ingredients. Inasmuch as the solvent serves only as a vehicle for the nitrocellulose, a more dilute solution results in a thinner film. The highest purity Pyroxylon is recommended. The film should have the best possible optical properties and be free from foreign inclusions. Ready-prepared commercial "dopes" dry too rapidly and are undependable. If these precautions are heeded, an excellent product will be obtained. Some paleobotanists prefer a cellulose acetate mixture because of lesser inflammability, lower cost, and better availability.

The procedure may be indicated briefly by the following schedule:

1. Grind and smooth (not polish) the surface to be studied.
2. Etch the surface with a suitable mineral acid (commonly hydrochloric or hydrofluoric).
3. Wash gently with running water, using care not to touch or agitate the etched surface.
4. Air-dry the etched surface.

5. Cover, usually by pouring, the etched surface with a solution of nitrocellulose.
6. Allow film to dry at least 8 hours.
7. Peel film from matrix.

The resulting film is actually a thin transfer. Sections as thin as 0.5-1.0 micron have been measured. Thickness, of course, refers to the fossil structure, not the embedding nitrocellulose. The translucence of such preparations is far superior to that of ground thin sections, a quality enhanced by the removal of soluble minerals and insoluble clay particles. To obtain maximum permanence and optical clarity, the film should be mounted in balsam or dammar on a standard "noncorrosive" glass slide. Mounting in plastic media should not be attempted until the compatibility of all solvents used has been determined.

The film transfer method is not limited to the investigation of petrified specimens. It has been used with excellent results on compressions partially mineralized with calcite, bituminous and anthracite coals, and fine-grained sediments.

A rapid modification of the film transfer method has been devised by Joy, Willis, and Lacey (1956). In place of the nitrocellulose solution, commercial cellulose acetate film is used for the transfer. The smooth and etched surface of the specimen is moistened with acetone, and a small strip of film, cut to desired size, is applied to the surface. Such preparations dry in 10 to 20 minutes. The two chief advantages are speed and uniform thinness of film. The chief difficulty, which can be largely overcome by practice, is the trapping of minute air bubbles which may interfere with microscopic examination under high power or oil immersion objectives.

MACERATION TECHNIQUES

Maceration techniques are also used to study a wide variety of fossil structures. Following Goeppert's early work, Schultz (1855) devised a mixture of mineral acids to macerate bituminous coals. Subsequent alkalization was accomplished with sodium hydroxide, which, however, tended to cause separation of cell masses. Gümbel minimized this disintegration by more gentle alkalization with ethyl alcohol.

The Schultz mixture, hydrochloric and nitric acids, to which potassium chlorate crystals are added, quickly demineralizes a soft-rank coal and nitrifies certain organic substances in the coal. From the resulting sludge, which is usually separated by centrifuging or differential filtering, a host of identifiable fragments can be recovered: spores, pollens, cuticles, mycelia, tissues, etc. The process of coalification, like petrifaction, has proved to be extremely complicated, but results in remarkably little damage to many types of plant materials.

The adaptation of this method to "coalified" compressions was a logical refinement of technique. One of the earliest attempts to recover spores and pollens from so-called impressions was by Sellards (1903). Since then similar studies have been made on countless specimens of fructifications.

The most spectacular development which has grown from the maceration technique is the field of spore and pollen analysis. This specialized methodology is now known as palynology. Whereas in 1930 pollen analysis was largely confined to the study of postglacial deposits, today it embraces the study of living and fossil pollens and spores of every geological age and of every continent. Only a brief mention of this popular and promising approach can be made here, although further considerations appear later in this book. By this approach, Pre-Cambrian and Lower Paleozoic sediments have for the first time yielded significant paleobotanic data.

TRANSFER TECHNIQUES

Transfer techniques are simply methods developed from experience with maceration. It has been assumed generally that cutinized or resinoid structures like the exospores of spores and pollens, cuticles, and heavily lignified xylem elements are so resistant to chemical attack by mineral and organic acids that their abundance and fidelity of preservation are greater than other types of tissues. Although this is relatively true, the assumption tends to obscure the prevalence of the more delicate structures of fossils. The possibility that a whole mount or "transfer" of a bleached or cleared specimen might provide much more information than macerated residues was first ingeniously explored by Walton about 1925.

The Walton technique involves four basic steps:

1. Cementing the specimen with balsam to a glass slide.
2. Coating the exposed area of the glass with wax.
3. Macerating the matrix with mineral acids to remove the associated rock.
4. Washing the specimen thoroughly.

By way of final preparation the specimen is dehydrated, covered with balsam, and protected permanently by a cover glass. Thus the specimen is "transferred" from the rock to a glass slide or plate.

There are two limitations to this method: the specimen is generally dense and opaque, and further manipulation is difficult if not impossible. Leclercq demonstrated that the limitation due to opacity may be overcome to some extent by photographing with infrared light.

The transfer technique was a notable contribution to the methodology of paleobotany because it demonstrated, beyond dispute, that the so-called carbonized impression was in many cases a compression of the original plant body. Of equal significance was the proof that in compression, lateral distortion is negligible. Thus freed from such prejudices, it was possible to turn to still greater refinements in technique.

In view of the achievements by maceration and transfer techniques, the recovery of mummified compressions by an intermediate transfer process is not a very great departure. Darrah has devised methods by which the bituminous impregnating substances can be dissolved and the specimen manipulated with minimum destruction.

Various procedures more or less similar have proved to be successful. The following schedule is typical.

1. Slowly macerate the specimen in a solution of equal parts of nitric acid, hydrochloric acid, and water. Maceration should continue from 3 to 7 days. Some types of matrix require longer periods and a change of fresh solution.
2. Wash the specimen gently in running water for 4 hours, or immerse in water for 6 hours with at least four changes of water.
3. At this stage the matrix should be tested for softness by means of a fine needle. If it has become soft or somewhat mushy and the specimen has loosened along the edges, it should be possible to lift the specimen gradually by prying gently around the periphery, working a little at a time. If, on the other hand, the specimen does not yield, further maceration is desirable.
4. When the acid maceration and rinsing have been accomplished, the specimen is placed in a 3 per cent solution of sodium hydroxide or a 5 per cent solution of ammonium hydroxide. Gradual dissolution of the "humic" constituents occurs with concomitant clearing. Experience will indicate how long alkalization should

be continued. Two to 10 minutes is usually sufficient, but in some cases 8 hours is not excessive.

5. The specimen is then transferred, manually by forceps or lifter, to a shallow watch crystal, washed repeatedly with water, and then covered with a 50 per cent solution of ethyl alcohol. After 5 minutes in the 50 per cent solution, the specimen is dehydrated gradually by successive changes of 70 per cent, 85 per cent, 90 per cent, 95 per cent, and absolute alcohol.

6. Following immersion in xylol for 1 minute, the specimen is placed on a microscope slide, wetted with a drop of xylol, covered with balsam or dammar dissolved in xylol, and permanently sealed with a cover glass.

Most tissues investigated by this method show surprising mechanical strength and can be manipulated, with reasonable care, without difficulty. Translucency can be increased by a rinse in benzene between steps 5 and 6 described above. Many organic solvents may be used to remove selectively the impregnating bituminous compounds. Mention of three solvents—benzene, pyridine, and aniline —will suggest the nature of their action.

MICROTOME METHODS

Once the presence of recognizable, albeit collapsed, tissues was demonstrated, the compression type of preservation assumed new meaning. If tissues could be recovered by transfer or flotation subsequent to maceration, then they could be embedded and sectioned by established microtome technique. Experiment, indeed we may say practice, has proved this to be true. Two distinct embedding methods are practicable: (1) the celloidin method of Jeffrey originally devised for sectioning xyloid lignites and other woody structures, and (2) a paraffine method devised by Halle.

In either method, it is necessary first to demineralize the specimen completely because the presence of crystallites will damage the cutting edge of the microtome knife and tear the section. Foreign particles such as quartz or feldspar are particularly detrimental.

Unlike the methods discussed previously, the celloidin and paraffine embedding techniques involve rather costly supplementary equipment, however, such as is available in many biological laboratories. The celloidin method requires a sliding microtome of the Jung or Jeffrey-Thompson type while the paraffine procedure utilizes a rotary microtome. Freehand sectioning, although possible, is extremely difficult because of the toughness of some materials and the friability of others. The materials are manipulated in accordance with standard laboratory practice, with the exception of staining which, in most specimens, would be superfluous.

Microtome sectioning of fossil tissues has not gained its deserved general recognition, probably because of the prolonged and complicated processing involved in demineralizing and embedding. However, the remarkable preparations of Jeffrey, Halle, and others, justify much wider application.

X-RAY RADIOGRAPHY

The question naturally arises, "In what condition do plant tissues occur in the fossil specimen?" Ground thin sections, of course, exhibit the undisturbed structure, but because of inherent limitations they cannot show thick or large features. In 1948, Darrah commenced experiments with x-ray photography in an attempt to identify structure in certain calcified seeds removed from coal-balls. The ultimate objective was to orient promising specimens so that in subsequent cutting and peeling, critical structures would not be destroyed or bypassed. A very considerable amount of detail was observed in these experiments. The position of the seed spore, sometimes collapsed, boundaries between tissue and mineral matrix, and vascular traces could be recognized. Some radiographs portray the structure "in the round."

A few of the problems encountered in the application of radiography to fossil plants will be discussed briefly. A radiograph is simply a shadow picture recorded by a sensitized film. The object is photographed by x-rays, differences in density being recorded by corresponding differences in shadow effects. The radiograph, being a shadow formation, is subject to distortion, particularly in magnification, which varies directly as the distance of the object from the sensitized film. The clarity or contrast of the image depends upon many factors, of which two are critical: radiographic energy and focus. The amount of radiation energy (Re) which strikes the object may be expressed by the empirical formula:

$$\text{Re} = \frac{\text{Voltage}^x \times \text{Current} \times \text{Time}}{\text{Distance}^2}$$

where, Voltage = kilovolts (Kv), Current = milliamperes (ma), Time = seconds, and Distance = inches or millimeters.

The exponent x is a variable which for a given set of conditions may be taken as 1. The values found to be most generally satisfactory for calcified and silicified specimens with thickness varying between 5 and 15 mm were:

$$\text{Re} = \frac{5 \text{ kv} \times 5 \text{ ma} \times 6 \text{ sec}}{12^2 \text{ in.}} = 1.0^+$$

Equipment capable of large focus was used for most of the investigation despite the fact that good radiographs were obtained with fine focus equipment of the type commonly used in dentistry. It was possible to make adequate exposures using Cobalt-60 as the source of radiation with a simple lead dark box.

It is not necessary to enter into a discussion of radiology. The many applications of x-radiation and radiology in industry, medicine, and dentistry and the diversity of commercially available equipment have made detailed information readily accessible.

ELECTRON MICROSCOPY

At least one experiment with the electron microscope has been performed on the xylem of a fossil plant (*Lepidodendron*). Although these preparations revealed cellulose and lignin components of the cell wall, the complicated equipment and the intricate procedure involved have limited the usefulness of the technique. The method has not proved practical (see Wesley and Kuyper, 1951).

CHEMICAL METHODS

These provide still another source of information concerning fossil plants. The techniques described thus far have as their purpose the preparation of specimens for investigation. The methods to be discussed here pertain to the identification of constituents of the plant body. The earliest important contributions are those of Fischer and Treibs, who recognized the possibilities of tracing the derivatives of chlorophyll and hemoglobin in bituminous coal, asphalt, petroleum, and other carbonaceous sediments. Using spectroscopic methods chiefly, Treibs obtained well-defined porphyrins in 88 selected samples of these varied materials—with negative results on some, including anthracites and the Swedish Kolm. Recognizable porphyrins were more abundant in the Cenozoic and

Mesozoic sediments, but were well represented in the Carboniferous materials examined.

More recently Lederer has demonstrated the presence of carotinoids in lacustrine muds from post-Pleistocene lakes near Moscow. In this connection it is worthy to note that Fox found carotene A and B and xanthophyll in marine muds collected at a depth of 2000 meters. These substances recognized by Treibs, Lederer, and Fox are primarily decomposition products of chlorophyll. Conant has suggested that it would appear that plant bodies have contributed more to the origin of Paleozoic petroleums than animals.

The Carbon-14 or radiocarbon method, as its name implies, is the application of mass spectrography to paleobotanical materials. The world-wide distribution of radiocarbon and its calculated half-life value make it possible to determine, within relatively narrow limits of error, the ages of plant materials. Arnold and Libby, and other teams, have published long series of "radiocarbon dates" determined by this method. The lists thus far compiled include chiefly archeological materials such as those from a Kentucky Indian mound (about 1200 years), Egyptian artifacts (approximately 2000 years), Chincha Island guano (19,000 years), wood from frozen muck near Fairbanks, Alaska (more than 20,000 years), and wood from the Bronson Interglacial of Minnesota (more than 19,000 years). While this method of dating postglacial events, including the activities of early man, is attractive, the possibility of dating older sediments is still more intriguing.

Attempts have been made to date more ancient materials by carbon isotopes. Comparison of the early paper by Nier and Gulbranson (1937) and a summary by Libby (1955) will suggest the trend of recent studies of this type. In determining the relative abundance of carbon isotopes in carbonaceous rocks of various geological age, they proved the applicability of the isotope method not only in dating ancient sediments but also in indicating the nature of the coalification process.

Fossils are therefore something more than "evidence of former life"; in many cases they are the organisms which inhabited the earth in ages past. Though the body has decomposed, oftentimes recognizable tissues remain and these by suitable techniques may reveal intimate details concerning structure, composition, function, and environment.

Claude Bernard once said that the progress of a science depends upon the invention of new techniques. Paleobotany looks forward with more promising tools than ever before to a broader interpretation of fossil plants.

Bibliography

ARNOLD, J. R., and W. F. LIBBY. 1951. Radiocarbon dates, *Science* 113: 111-120. A considerable number of lists of radiocarbon determinations have been published in the last decade, but no critical integrated summary has been attempted. See also Libby, 1955, below.

DARRAH, W. C. 1936. The peel method in paleobotany, *Bot. Mus. Leaf. Harv. Univ.* 4, pp. 69-83.

———. 1941. Changing views of petrification, *Pan. Amer. Geol.* 76: 13-26.

———. 1952. The materials and methods of paleobotany, *Paleobotanist* 1: 145-153. Much of this paper has been incorporated in this chapter.

GOEPPERT, H. R. 1864. *Die fossile Flora der permischen Formation.* Cassel.

HALLE, T. G. 1933. The structure of certain fossil spore-bearing organs believed to belong to the pteridosperms, *Kungl. Svensk Vetensk. Handl.* 12: 5-13.

JEFFREY, E. C. 1916. Methods of studying coal, *Sci. Conspectus* 6: 71-76.

———. 1928. Technical contributions, *Bot. Gaz.* 86: 456-487.

KRÄUSEL, R. 1929. *Die paläobotanischen Untersuchungsmethoden.* Springer-Verlag, Jena.

LANG, W. H. 1926. A cellulose-film transfer method in the study of fossil plants, *Ann. Bot.* 40: 710-711.

LECLERCQ, S. 1933. Application de la lumière infra-rouge à l'étude microscopique des végétaux fossiles, *Ann. Soc. Géol. Belg.* 56: 351-356.

LIBBY, W. F. 1955. *Radiocarbon dating.* 2d ed. University of Chicago Press, Chicago. The standard work in this field of research.

SITHOLEY, R. V. 1946. Microfossils from a kerogen shale of the saline series in the Khewra Gorge, Salt Range, *Proc. Nat. Acad. Sci. India* 16: 220-225.

SOLMS-LAUBACH, H. 1891. *Fossil Botany.* Clarendon Press, Oxford.

VOIGHT, E. 1935. Die Erhaltung von Epithelzellen mit Zellkernen von Chromatophoren und Corium in fossiler Froschhaut ..., *Nov. Act. Leopold,* n.f. 3: 339-360.

WALTON, J. 1923. On a new method of investigating fossil plant impressions or incrustations, *Ann. Bot.* 37: 379-391.

———. 1928. Recent developments in paleobotanical technique, *C. R. Congr. Avanc. Études strat. Carb.,* Heerlen 1927, pp. 740-754 (Liege).

———. 1936. On factors which influence external form of fossil plants, *Roy. Soc. Lond. Phil. Trans.* B 226: 219-225.

WESLEY, A., and B. KUYPER. 1951. Electron-microscopic observations on the xylem elements of a fossil plant, *Nature* 168: 137-140.

4

EARLY PLANT RECORDS:
THALLOPHYTES

So little is known concerning the life and environment of the Proterozoic and early Paleozoic eras that geologists figuratively leave no stone unturned in seeking clues to the problem. There are in ancient sediments many peculiar structures which appear to be of organic origin. Some of these structures have been given generic and specific names, often upon questionable grounds frankly admitted by the investigators who named them. Thus much of the knowledge of the earliest plant records is based upon indirect evidence and must be considered in this light. Nevertheless, with each passing year new forms are recognized and convincing direct evidence supplants more dubious opinion.

It is self-evident that the evolution of the animal kingdom in Pre-Cambrian times indicates or presupposes a comparable development of the plant kingdom. The existence of bacteria, plankton, and photosynthetic thallophytes must be assumed without serious question. Although the actual record is meager, each of these forms of plant life has left undoubted remains. The possible prevalence of these groups is suggested by the description of nearly a thousand new species of fossil algae since 1930; most of these, however, are from the more recent geological periods. In this summary only the larger taxa will be considered.

SCHIZOMYCETES (Bacteria and Blue-Green Algae)

Bacteria. Gruner described a number of supposed bacteria and blue-green algae from the Proterozoic iron ores and associated cherts from Michigan. These bacteria have a marked resemblance to *Chlamydothrix*. Walcott observed structures in Proterozoic limestones of Montana which he interpreted as bacteria (*Micrococcus*). In both instances these may be mineral and not organic forms. A variety of bacteria have been recognized in thin sections of silicified plants, coals, and in coprolites of reptiles and fishes. Since bacteria are the principal organisms of decay, we may assume their abundance in ancient times.

CYANOPHYCEAE (Blue-Green Algae)

The discovery of recognizable micro-organisms in nonferruginous cherts in the Proterozoic (mid-Huronian) of southern Ontario (Tyler and Barghoorn, 1954) provided substantial evidence for both algae and fungi 1,500,000,000 to 2,000,000,000 years ago. The algae include unicellular calcareous flagellates and filamentous forms comparable to *Rivularia* and *Oscillatoria*. The fungi include branched hyphae and spores probably referable to the phycomycetes. That many similar occurrences await discovery is most probable.

Marpolia described by Walcott from the mid-Cambrian of British Columbia is another member of this group. This form resembles *Schizothrix*. The Devonian *Archaeothrix* from Scotland is also referable to the OSCILLATORIACEAE. *Girvanella* also referred to this family has an impressive history from the Cambrian to the Cretaceous. *Gloeocapsomorpha* is a remarkable colonial alga which constitutes the bulk of the Ordovician kuckersite, a kerosene shale from Estonia.

"CHLOROPHYCEAE" (Green Algae s. lat.)

The green algae are properly subdivided into a number of major classes, but for convenience are here considered as a single complex. The flagellates have left few undoubted remains in the Proterozoic and Paleozoic, although typical representatives occur in the Cretaceous and Tertiary. Undoubted diatoms likewise appear in the Mesozoic (Triassic). Several questioned forms have been reported from the Carboniferous. The silicious test of the diatom, despite fragility, resists chemical destruction and is abundantly preserved, sometimes in great accumulations of "diatomaceous earth." Because of the nature of the shells and their abundance as microfossils, the exploration for petroleum by drill-core analysis relies heavily on diatoms.

Just as *Gloeocapsomorpha* occurs in the combustible kuckersite, so do other algal forms make up the so-called boghead coals and kerosene shales. *Pila* and *Reinschia* (BOTRYOCOCCACEAE) have been the subject of long-standing controversy. C. E. Bertrand and

Renault first pointed out the affinity with *Botryococcus braunii*, but their opinion was contested by contemporaries who interpreted these structures as deformed spores or congealed resinoid masses, a position maintained by Jeffrey. Bogheads and kerosene shales occur in many parts of the world from the Cambrian to the present: kolm (Cambrian) Gotland, kuckersite (Ordovician) Estonia, torbanite (Carboniferous) Scotland, boghead (Permian) France, coorongite (Recent) Australia. The algal origin of these sediments, long advocated by D. White and Thiessen, is now generally accepted.

Other green algae are well-known as fossils. The CODIACEAE are represented in the Paleozoic by such genera as *Dimorphosiphon* and *Palaeoporella*. *Halimeda*, another member of this group, appears in the Cretaceous.

Dimorphosiphon rectanulare Høeg from the Ordovician of Norway is probably the oldest known member of the CODIACEAE. It is a calcified form built up of branched tubular cells without cross-walls. Høeg also found in Norway (Silurian) an uncalcified siphoneous alga, *Chaetocladus*.

The DASYCLADACEAE of the Paleozoic include *Rhabdoporella* (Silurian), *Vermiporella* (Ordovician to Permian), *Dasyporella* (Ordovician), *Anthracoporella* (Carboniferous), *Cyclocrinus* (Ordovician), *Callithamniopsis* (Ordovician), and *Primicorallina* (Ordovician) (Fig. 2). The DIPLOPORACEAE are first recognized in the Upper Permian.

Before leaving the chlorophycean complex, attention is called to a discovery by Baschnagel of remarkable microfossils from the Onondaga chert (Devonian) of central New York, including many algae of the green complex: ULOTRICHALES (cf. *Geminella*), CHLOROCOCCALES, and PERIDINIALES (*Ceratium*). All these forms are characteristic of fresh-water plankton.

PHAEOPHYCEAE

The brown algae are not nearly so abundantly represented in the fossil record as paleobotanists once believed. Many so-called fucoids, of strap-like or superficially thalloid appearance, were interpreted as algae. Most of them are indeterminable. Indeed the best-known forms occur in the Jurassic Solenhofen lithographic stone. *Thamnocladus* (Fig. 2) from the Devonian of New York is believed to be fucoid or dictyotan.

Fig. 2. Early Paleozoic algae. Restoration of a marine habitat with typical representatives of the algae. These forms are not contemporaries. They are illustrated together to compare growth forms. On bottom, from left to right are: *Cryptozoon* (Cambrian and Ordovician), *Primicorallina* (Ordovician), *Delesserites* (Silurian), and *Thamnocladus* (Devonian). (Courtesy of the Brooklyn Botanic Garden.)

RHODOPHYCEAE

The red algae are somewhat better known than the brown algae, partly, of course, because of the calcareous nature of many of them. Ruedemann described *Delesserites salicifolia* (Fig. 2) from the Silurian of New York, but the reference of this form is open to question. *Solenopora* occurs in the Silurian and has been reported from the Cambrian. *Lithothamnion* and other coralline algae are abundant in the Mesozoic and Tertiary.

CHAROPHYTA

The charophytes are an isolated group of fresh-water algae characterized by an erect nodal branched thallus and ornately sculptured oospores. Literally hundreds of species of fossil oospores have been described, chiefly from Mesozoic and Cenozoic deposits. Kidston and Lang found *Palaeonitella* in the Devonian Rhynie chert. This species, somewhat doubtfully referable to the charophytes, is based upon thalloid remains. The most abundant Devonian and Carboniferous forms are known as *Trochiliscus*. *Gyrogonites* extends from the Carboniferous to Pliocene, while *Clavator* and *Primneste* have been recognized in the Jurassic. The oospores of charophytes are abundant fossils, indeed being found in fresh-water shales and limestones almost whenever a persistent search is made for them.

UNCERTAIN ALGAL GROUPS

In addition to these well-established records representing the principal groups of algae, paleobotanists have described a great number of questionable forms. These are of unequal merit, some being undoubted algae of uncertain systematic position, others are at best unconvincing. Nevertheless, it would be prejudicial to ignore their possible significance.

Cryptozoon (Cryptophycus) proliferum named by James Hall in 1833, are large concentric structures, up to 2 feet in diameter, which formed reeflike masses in Cambrian limestone at Saratoga, New York (Fig. 2). Since this discovery, similar structures have been collected in Pre-Cambrian rocks at many localities such as Ontario, the Gobi Desert, northern Greenland, and Rhodesia. *Cryptozoon* and related problematical algae are usually classed together as stromatolites.

Stromatolites (sometimes called spongiostromes) are nodular, laminar, and vesicular. They are calcareous or dolomitic, have a definite mode of occurrence, a constant structure, and a limited geological distribution. The many forms are referred to the genera *Collenia, Newlandia,* and *Camasia.* Fenton and Fenton believe that many stromatolites were built by symbiotic aggregations of red algae and blue-green algae. Algologists are gradually accepting the "species" of *Collenia* as biological entities and thus see the record of fossil plants penetrate the Archean (Nash Formation Late Keewatin), in other words an age estimated to be more than 1,400,-000,000 years. Stromatolites are most abundant in the late Proterozoic, declining in the early Paleozoic, but persisting throughout the Mesozoic and Cenozoic, with certain types occurring in modern seas.

For further information on these and other algal fossils, the reader is referred to the Bibliography, especially titles by Fenton, Peck, and Pia. Pia contributed the section of THALLOPHYTA in Hirmer's *Handbuch der Paläobotanik* (1927), but it is now considerably out of date.

This cursory survey of algae and supposed algae from the Proterozoic and Paleozoic rocks with comments on notable post-Paleozoic records suggests that the sum-total of our knowledge of fossil algae must be expressed in cautious terms. Certainly it may be said that the great evolutionary trends among the algae were already well established before the Cambrian: blue-greens, green complex, browns, and reds. The green complex was perhaps diversified as much as at present. Of course those forms which secrete or are associated with the deposition of calcium carbonate are most abundant, but this does not imply any real preponderance. The greatest discoveries in the future await investigations of the earlier silicified sedimentary rocks, such as Cambrian and Ordovician cherts.

FOSSIL FUNGI

Many petrifactions contain hyphae, sporangia, and spores of fungi. Both septate and nonseptate hyphae have been recognized in Paleozoic plant tissues; thus, presumably phycomycetes and ascomycetes were present. The Proterozoic has yielded at least two forms: one with many-branched nonseptate hyphae and sessile lateral spores, and another matted hyphae with associated spores, both probably phycomycetes. Cretaceous and Cenozoic leaves frequently show characteristic disease areas, and Straus has described several score of pathogenic and epiphytic fungi remarkably similar to existing ascomycetes and basidiomycetes.

Among the numerous fossils of Silurian and Devonian age we encounter certain strange forms which cannot readily be interpreted. In some respects they present algal features, yet at the same time they show unmistakable approaches to terrestrial habit.

Nematophyton, the largest of these plants, was long considered to be a brown alga (*"Nematophycus"*) while Dawson referred it to the conifers (*"Prototaxites"*). It occurs commonly in Silurian marine sediments; however, specimens have been found in the Rhynie chert (terrestrial, Devonian). *Nematophyton* had a "stem" nearly 2 feet in diameter, constructed of small, elongate, intermingled "tubes," some large in diameter and others smaller, but with no tissue differentiation. The larger tubes are oriented vertically while the smaller tubes form matted masses filling the spaces between the larger tubes. No reproductive organs have been found attached to *Nematophyton* which, superficially at least, has a resemblance to the stipe of a large kelp. Chiarugi was the first to recognize the unique algal affinities of these large plant structures and to propose a major systematic position for them.

More recently Lang described *Nematothallus* from the Upper Silurian of England and Wales. The structures appear to be thin, flat, leaflike or thalloid expansions composed of a system of interlacing tubes, often with a pseudocellular pattern, producing small cuticularized spores of varying size in tetrads. These spores are imbedded in the tubes and are not produced in a differentiated sporangium. Lang, independently of Chiarugi, proposed a new phylum NEMATOPHYTA to accommodate these plants, which seem to be intermediate between algae and tracheophytes. In the absence of more complete data, this group is usually given the ordinal rank NEMATOPHYTALES. It is possible that *Foerstia* (= *Protosalvinia* Dawson in part; *Sporocarpon*) and *Parka*, the former from the Devonian of Ohio, the latter from the upper Silurian and Devonian of England and Wales, should also be referred to this group. *Foerstia* is a small bifid thalloid plant or plant fragment of pseudocellular parenchymatous construction producing large cuticularized spores in tetrads (which were once erroneously described as the eggs of an alga). *Parka* differs in two respects: the flat thallus is circular in outline and is covered by flattened discs about 2 mm in diameter which bear numerous cuticularized spores. There is no evidence that these were produced in tetrads.

The nematophytes, using the term to include all four of these form genera, approach in varying degree the vascular plants, compressions of which appear suddenly but contemporaneously in the upper Silurian.

BRYOPHYTES

The bryophytes have left a surprisingly meager fossil record, but the number of forms recognized are of such diversity that they cover most of the major taxa living today. Liverworts have been found in the middle Carboniferous of England, while mosses have been described from the late Carboniferous of France.

Both groups seem to have developed during the Mesozoic. Harris described several hepatics from the Rhaetic of Greenland. In the early Cretaceous, forms referred to *Marchantites* are almost indistinguishable from the existing genus. *Sphagnites* and *Jungermannites* occur in the upper Cretaceous. By Miocene times forms resembling such mosses as *Hypnum, Plagiopus,* and *Polytrichum* have been described. These, however, are not sufficiently preserved to permit inclusion in the existing genera, but the resemblances to them are striking.

Probably the most remarkable fossil bryophyte is *Naiadita lanceolata,* from the Triassic of England, ingeniously investigated by Harris. The plant body consists of sparsely branched axes with sparse spirally disposed leaves. Some branches bear sessile archegonia which are surrounded by a perianth of four lobes. The sporangia are produced on short stalks. Terminal gemmae cups have also been found. *Naiadita* is thus the most completely known bryophyte, but its systematic position is uncertain. Harris has suggested a relationship with the *Sphaerocarpales* in the HEPATICAE.

To summarize, the bryophytes seem to have been differentiated into the HEPATICAE and MUSCI prior to the Carboniferous. No fossil representative thus far recognized suggests that ancient bryophytes were very different from living forms. There is no paleobotanical evidence, despite the great antiquity of the group, that the bryophytes were in any manner the ancestors of the vascular land plants known to exist today.

Bibliography

No adequate summary of fossil algae has been published. A brief and incomplete review is available in the following:

JOHNSON, J. H. 1951. Fossil algae, Chap. 10 in *Manual of Phycology*. G. M. SMITH (ed.). A Chronica Botanica Publication. The Ronald Press Co., New York.

Specific References

BASCHNAGEL, R. A. 1942. Some microfossils from the Onondaga chert of central New York. *Bull. Buffalo Soc. Nat. Hist.* 17: 1-8.

DARRAH, W. C. 1937. Spores of Cambrian plants, *Science* 86: 154-155.

——. 1940. The position of the NEMATOPHYTALES, *Chron. Bot.* 6: 52-53.

FENTON, C. L. 1946. Algae of the Pre-Cambrian and Early Paleozoic, *Amer. Midl. Nat.* 36.

FENTON, C. L., and M. A. FENTON. 1936. Walcott's Pre-Cambrian Algonkian algal flora and associated animals, *Bull. Geol. Soc. Amer.* 47: 609-620.

GHOSH, A. K., and A. BOSE. 1952. Spores and tracheids from the Cambrian of Kashmir, *Nature* 169: 1056.

HANNA, G. D., and W. M. GRANT. 1926. Miocene marine diatoms from Maria Madre Island, Mexico. *Proc. Cal. Acad. Sci.,* IV, 15: 115-193.

HARDER, E. C. 1919. Iron-depositing bacteria and their geologic relations. *U. S. Geol. Surv. Prof. Pap.,* p. 112.

HARRIS, T. M. 1939. *Naiadita,* a fossil bryophyte with reproductive organs, *Ann. Bryol.* 12: 57-70.

JOHNSON, J. H. 1943. Geologic importance of coralline algae with annotated bibliography, *Quart. Colo. School Mines* 38: 1-102.

LANG, W. H. 1937. On the plant remains from the Downtonian of England and Wales. *Roy. Soc. Long. Phil. Trans.* B 227: 245-291.

MAMAY, S. H. 1959. *Litostroma,* a new genus of problematical algae from the Pennsylvanian of Illinois. *Amer. Jour. Bot.* 46: 283-292.

PECK, R. E. 1934. Late Paleozoic and Early Mesozoic Charophyta, *Amer. Jour. Sci.* 27: 44-55.

——. 1941. Lower Cretaceous Rocky Mountain non-marine microfossils, *Jour. Paleont.* 15: 285-304.

PIA, J. 1927. In M. HIRMER, *Handbuch der Paläobotanik.* Vol. 1, pp. 1-146. Oldenbourg, Munich and Berlin.

——. 1936. Algen als Leitfossilien, *Prob. Palaeont.* 1: 11-34.

RASKY, R. 1945. *Fossile Charophyten-Früchte aus Ungarn.* Ungar. Naturwiss. Mus., Budapest.

STEERE, W. C. 1946. Cenozoic and Mesozoic Bryophytes of North America, *Amer. Midl. Nat.* 36: 298-324.

5

THE PSILOPSIDA

THE EARLIEST LAND PLANTS

Fossil plants were recognized in Devonian rocks early in the nineteenth century, but their fragmentary nature and apparently uninteresting aspect discouraged serious study. In 1859 Sir William Dawson described a peculiar, naked, dichotomously branched plant with small sporangia at the tips of the ultimate branches, giving it the name *Psilophyton*. Botanists were not prepared to admit this "monstrosity" and Dawson's interpretation was ignored and ridiculed. For all practical purposes it remained in limbo until the spectacular discovery and description of a diminutive flora in the mid-Devonian chert of Rhynie, Scotland in 1920.

So simple in organization were the petrified Rhynie plants that paleobotanists at once sensed far-reaching significance. It has been widely believed that these forms typify the ancestral stage of all vascular plants. The old morphological concepts of "stem," "root," and "leaf"—to say nothing of their derivatives—became meaningless.

More recently, still older vascular plants have been found in the Cambrian of Russia and the Silurian rocks of Australia. Some of these plants are more complex than the Rhynie genera. The fact remains, however, that even though the RHYNIALES are the most simple vascular plants known to us, there is a growing skepticism that they are an ancestral group. A perspective may be established by considering the sequence of discoveries.

The several Rhynie forms have much in common with *Psilophyton*, a fact which was immediately recognized. Furthermore, because Dawson's interpretation was essentially correct, we can visualize the plant body.

Psilophyton was a land plant. It had a rhizome, out of which grew an erect dichotomous axis up to a meter in height with circinately coiled tips in young plants. This axis was vascular, an

41

assertion which Dawson had made on very meager evidence but subsequently proved by Halle, who showed that the xylem elements were scalariform. Although without true leaves, the shoots were provided with stomata. In mature plants there were spinelike emergences at the base. These have been considered leaves by some botanists. The sporangia were borne terminally on the tips of the shoots. They were 3 to 10 mm long, oval, often borne in pairs on the slender, naked branches. Several species of *Psilophyton* have been distinguished.

Dawson in 1871 described a second Devonian genus *Arthrostigma* (= *Drepanophycus*). Since the recognition of this type, further discoveries in rocks of similar age in Scotland, Canada, Norway, and Belgium have referred to the genus. The plant resembles a large *Psilophyton*, with a stout axis sometimes over 25 mm thick, lateral branches, and with the stalks having longitudinal ribs as well as very large stout spines. As in *Psilophyton*, it is not certain whether these emergences are true leaves. In this genus, however, there is commonly found a distinct vein in the spine; this vein has been interpreted as a vascular strand. Halle has demonstrated the presence of a protostele in *Arthrostigma*.

Nathorst in 1915 described still another form of interest, *Thursophyton*. This type was based upon fragments long known as *Lycopodites milleri*. *Thursophyton* is a dichotomously branched plant resembling a club-moss to a remarkable degree. The stalks are of nearly uniform thickness, with little taper. They are covered with small, scalelike "leaves" (which may again be considered merely "emergences") about 7 mm long; these were spirally arranged and were lanceolate, directed upward. Small structures in the axils of some of the leaves have been interpreted as sporangia, but no spores have been detected in them.

All these forms remained suspect and enigmatic until the discovery and investigation of the Rhynie chert (Kidston and Lang).

THE RHYNIE FLORA

In the Rhynie chert have been found four well-preserved and remarkable vascular plants: *Rhynia gwynne-vaughani*, *R. major*, *Horneophyton lignieri*,[*] and *Asteroxylon mackiei* (Fig. 3). In

---

[*] *Hornea* Kidston and Lang, 1920, is preoccupied by *Hornea* Baker, 1877 (= SAPINDACEAE). The name *Horneophyton* Barghoorn and Darrah is to be preferred (*Bot. Mus. Leafl. Harvard Univ.*, vol. 6, No. 7, 1938).

order to recognize the characteristics of these Devonian land plants and the reasons for assuming the psilopsids as ancestral to the higher tracheophytes, it is necessary to describe these types in some detail.

Rhynia gwynne-vaughani. This was the first of the Rhynie chert psilopsids to be considered by Kidston and Lang. Like its relatives *R. major* and *Horneophyton lignieri*, it was a small leafless plant, branching dichotomously, and with terminal sporangia (Fig. 4). The slender stem, particularly in compression specimens, superficially resembles a thallus. The stem attained a maximum length of 20 cm and varied in diameter from 0.1 to 6 mm. The stem, which gradually tapers upward, was not smooth in life, but bore at its base numerous hemispherical protuberances which possibly may be interpreted as leaves. These were not distributed according to any apparent phyllotaxy. Some of the bulges had rhizoid-like hairs growing out from the epidermis, but in nearly all cases these hairs were on the bottom of the plant, near the rhizome-stem transitional region.

The stem, observed transversely, consisted of the following tissues: xylem, phloem, inner and outer cortex, and epidermis. There was a thick cuticle over the epidermis. The xylem is composed of annular tracheids.

Sporangia have been found in actual continuity with stems, although it is not known whether they occurred on the main or only on lateral stems. In some specimens the sporangium itself is bifurcated. Well-preserved spores have been recovered from many sporangia. They vary considerably in size, but average 40 microns in diameter. The sporangia have an average length of 3 mm and are attached to axes about 0.2 mm in diameter. The sporangial wall is very thick with a dense cuticle. The outer wall is constructed of long narrow cells and the tapetum is of small, rounded cells. No dehiscence mechanism has been recognized.

The spores bore the typical tetrad scar. They are seen, *in situ*, both in tetrads and singly according to the age of the sporangium and the state of its preservation.

Sometimes the sporangium did not differentiate into definite tapetum and outer wall, but the spores formed in the undifferentiated tip of the stem. This supports the suggestion that the sporangium is the modified tip of an ordinary stem. It is of interest to find this type of sporangium coexistent in the same species with a more specialized type, provided with a tapetal layer and a specially constructed and thickened epidermal layer.

Fig. 3. (See next page for caption.)

Rhynia major. This psilopsid (Fig. 4) is very closely allied to *R. gwynne-vaughani*. In habit it is the same; the stem and rhizome differ in proportion only. The sporangium as well as the spores are similar. It differs, however, in that the spherical projections are absent. It is literally a leafless plant. There is no definite evidence to show the height of the plant, but it is apparently taller and more robust than *R. gwynne-vaughani*. The stems vary in thickness from 1.5 to 6 mm. The spores are about 65 microns in thickness. The sporangium varies from 3 to 4 mm in thickness, and from 5 to 12 mm in length.

Horneophyton lignieri. The third of the vascular Rhynie chert plants is *Horneophyton lignieri*. In general it is similar to *Rhynia*, but differs in several important respects. There is a large tuberous underground stem without a vascular strand, rather than smooth branching rhizomes. It also has a columellate sporangium recalling that of a bryophyte. The stems are smooth, with no hemispherical projections nor lateral branches, varying from 1 to 2 mm in diameter. Many of the branches bear terminal sporangia, others are sterile at the tips (Fig. 5).

The tuberous rhizome is unlike that of *Rhynia* in that it is bulbous and possesses no vascular system. It is made up of a parenchymatous mass in which the stele of the stem ends blindly. Rhizoids, probably absorbent, grew out from the base of the rhizome. The parenchyma connecting the stele with the rhizome is a funnel-shaped mass which has been compared with the protocorm of a lycopod. The stele resembles that of *Rhynia* in general construction. The phloem is composed of long, thin cells and the solid xylem of tracheids. One distinguishing feature of *Horneophyton*

Fig. 3. Devonian plants. An idealized artist's conception of a landscape showing the principal Devonian genera. The illustration includes both early and late Devonian plants, which do not occur together. However, a fair comparison of habits and sizes is presented. A group of *Rhynia* (1) is shown in the center foreground. A *Psilophyton* (greatly enlarged out of proportion) appears at the extreme lower left (2). The bizarre branched plant near it is *Cladoxylon* (3). The fern at the lower right is *Archaeopteris* (4). The sphenopsid *Calamophyton* (5) is shown to the left of *Rhynia*. *Hyenia* (6) appears at the extreme right. The larger plants at the left include the columnar *Archaeosigillaria* (7) and, on both sides of it, examples of *Aneurophyton* (8). Several other forms are indicated, chiefly fernlike genera. (By permission from *Verdwenen Werelden*, by Hubrecht. Copyright, by Uitgeverij Oisterwijk.)

xylem is the constant difference in size between the narrow central and the larger outer tracheids. In the central xylem, there appear to be transverse breaks, while the outer xylem seems to be continuous.

Fig. 4. *Rhynia*, the simplest vascular plant thus far recognized. The naked axis branches dichotomously and bears single terminal sporangia. Left, *Rhynia gwynne-vaughani;* right, *R. major.* Devonian. (From Kidston and Lang.)

The sporangium of *Horneophyton* is made up of a thick outer wall and a column of sterile tissue running up into the cavity. As already noted, it bears a resemblance to the bryophytic columella. The cutinized spores are numerous. The sporangium evidently arose by transformation of the tips of certain branches of the plant. When the apex is simple, there is but one sporangium; if the axis is dichotomizing, the sporangium itself forks and forms a partly separated sporangium. The columella itself may fork. The columella, being an apex of a branch, would normally follow a dichotomy.

The size of the sporangium is proportionate to the size of the stem bearing it, a fact which accounts for the great variability in size. The wall is very thick. The middle zone of several layers is more frequently preserved than in *Rhynia;* and a characteristic tapetum is always present. The outer wall is more noticeable than the stem epidermis, and there are no indications of dehiscence. The spores, which attain a diameter of 70 microns, are borne in conspicuous tetrads.

The bryophytic columellate sporangium recalls another fossil sporangium, *Sporogonites,* found by Halle in the Lower Devonian of Roragen, Norway. This obovate stalked sporangium measures 6-9 × 3-4 mm and is 50 mm long. In the capsule six large longitudinal furrows alternate with an equal number of small ones. The lower part is sterile, while the upper portion consists of three zones—a many-layered wall, a sporogenous tract, and a sterile columella, as in *Horneophyton.* The globular spores are tetrahedral, measuring 20-25 mm in diameter. This fructification is more moss-like than that of *Horneophyton.*

Asteroxylon. Two well-defined species of *Asteroxylon* are known: *A. Mackiei* Kidston and Lang from the Rhynie chert, and *A. elberfeldense* Kräusel and Weyland from Elberfeld, Germany (Fig. 6). Several other species have been attributed to the genus.

Asteroxylon Mackiei is a more complicated plant than either *Rhynia* or *Horneophyton* in general appearance, and indeed in anatomical detail. Superficially at least it resembles a club-moss (Fig. 5). The plant is larger than the other Rhynie plants, the diameter of the main stem often exceeding 25 mm. The aerial stem is branched—both monopodially and dichotomously. The axis arises from an underground rhizome which is smooth, but which, unlike that of *Rhynia* and *Horneophyton,* is apparently devoid of absorbent hairs. The axis is closely packed with spirally arranged "leaves," but the sporangia are believed to have been borne on naked sporangiophores. The sporangia were dehiscent.

The rhizomes are profusely branched and are provided with a root system, as can be observed in *in situ* preservations of *Aster-*

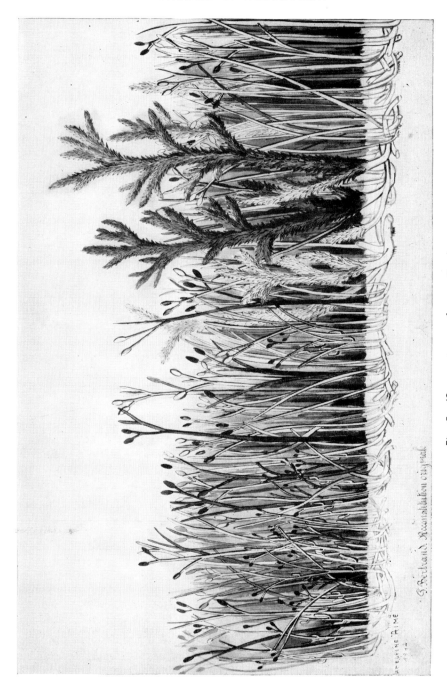

Fig. 5. (See next page for caption.)

oxylon rhizomes penetrating decaying *Rhynia* and *Horneophyton* material in the silicified peat. No hairs are found on the epidermis. The internal anatomy of the rhizome is remarkably like that of *Rhynia* stems, and *Asteroxylon* rhizomes have been mistaken for the former. The epidermis is followed inwardly by the outer cortex, the inner cortex, the phloem, and the solid xylem strand.

There is a region of transition from the smooth rhizome to the leafy stem. The epidermis thickens, the xylem gradually becomes stellate, small scaly leaves appear, and leaf traces run out into the leaf bases as the transition becomes more pronounced and complete.

The diameter of the leafy shoot varies from 1 to 30 mm. The leaves at the base of the aerial shoot are small, hardly more than spines; sometimes their bases are not apparently provided with a strand of vascular tissue. The higher regions of the stem have large, lanceolate leaves with a vascular supply to every leaf base.

The internal stem anatomy is not as simple as that of *Rhynia*. The epidermis with its cuticle is followed inwardly by the narrow outer cortex, a broad three-zoned inner cortex, phloem, and solid stellate xylem composed of annular and spiral tracheids. The phloem completely covers the ends of the xylem rays and fills in the bays between them, the stele being cylindrical. *Asteroxylon* has no true roots, and the leaves have no vascular systems beyond the leaf base.

It is believed that the sporangia were borne on naked branches which forked laterally and dichotomously from the leafy shoots. These have not been found in actual connection with the shoots of *Asteroxylon Mackiei*, but in intimate association. The shoots have a protostele and a smooth epidermis, like *Rhynia*. They were at first assumed to be *Asteroxylon* rhizomes. The sporangia borne on these are pear-shaped, with a definite terminal dehiscence, unlike

Fig. 5. The Rhynie Flora. A representation of the principal genera of the Rhynie flora, suggesting the dense creeping habit. *Rhynia,* with a naked dichotomously branched axis and terminal sporangia, is indicated by the two species *R. major* (in the background) and *R. gwynne-vaughani* (lower left). *Horneophyton* (lower right) is similar, except for the bulbous base, which is not clearly shown in the reconstruction. *Asteroxylon,* though characterized by a simple dichotomously branched axis, is clothed with small leaflike emergences. (Original reconstruction by Paul Bertrand. By permission from Mme. P. Bertrand and Masson et Cie, Paris.)

Rhynia or *Horneophyton.* The spores, produced in tetrads, averaged about 64 microns in diameter. The cuticle is extremely thick, frequently retaining a yellow color.

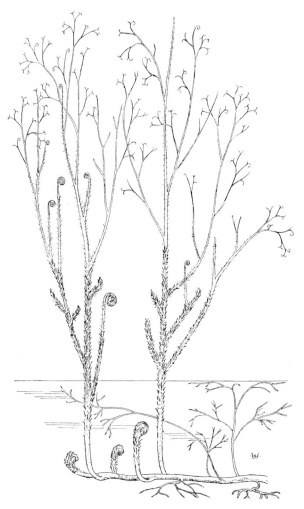

Fig. 6. *Asteroxylon elberfeldense.* The dichotomously branched body shows considerable differentiation, particularly with respect to appendages. Devonian. (Courtesy of R. Kräusel and H. Weyland.)

Asteroxylon elberfeldense, Fig. 6, occurs in the Middle Devonian of western Germany, Bohemia, Scotland, and Norway. The lower, leaf-clad portions of this *Asteroxylon* were formerly known as *Thursophyton,* and the naked sporangia-bearing shoots as

are vast unexplored expanses of the Ordovician and Silurian that invite pioneering spirits. Recent recoveries of lycopsids and cutinized spores from Cambrian sediments have opened wide this vista. Kryshtofovich has described *Aldanophyton antiquissimum* from the mid-Cambrian of Aldan, U.S.S.R., which through approaching *Drepanophycus* and *Baragwanathia* in habit, is referred to an uncertain lycopsid group.

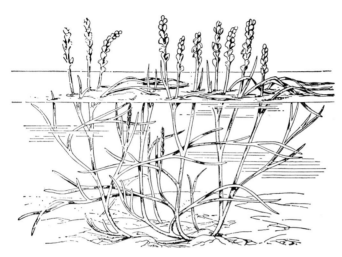

Fig. 7. *Zosterophyllum rhenanum;* a restoration indicating branching, aggregations of sporangia, and supposed aquatic habitat. Devonian. (Courtesy of R. Kräusel and H. Weyland.)

Thus far, we have been considering plants which are characteristic of the Upper Silurian and Lower Devonian. Despite considerable diversity, they possess various features in common. Almost contemporary with them are other plants not so easily interpreted.

During mid-Devonian times, plant forms increase in variety, complexity, and geographic distribution. Extensive floras have been collected in Scotland, Spitsbergen, western Norway, Bohemia, France, Germany, Canada, the United States, and China. Many groups of plants are represented in them.

At Elberfeld, Germany, Kräusel and Weyland discovered a number of striking new forms at the base of the upper mid-Devonian, among them *Asteroxylon elberfeldense*, *Aneurophyton germanicum*, *Hyenia elegans*, *Calamophyton primaevum*, *Cladoxylon scoparium*, and *Protopteridum*. *Asteroxylon elberfeldense* has already been discussed. *Aneurophyton germanicum* possesses massive secondary wood which agrees in pitting with that of the Scotch Devonian *Paleopitys milleri*.

In encountering such complex structures we have entered a new stage of plant evolution with portentous suggestion of things to come. We pause then to recapitulate the chief characteristics of the *Psilophyton–Rhynia* group which in its broadest sense is usually circumscribed as the PSILOPSIDA.

CHIEF FEATURES OF THE PSILOPSIDA

The PSILOPSIDA are composed of plants which have simple thalloid, dichotomously branched axes, without differentiation into stem, leaf, and root, and with terminal sporangia. The axis is generally protostelic, but a pith is present in a few forms. These ancient plants cannot be referred to any existing group, although some botanists regard the isolated living genera *Psilotum* and *Tmesipteris* to be distantly related descendants.

In *Drepanophycus* there are densely arranged leaflike appendages, sometimes with sporangia placed in the axils of these structures. In a few species the "leaves" are arranged spirally and in other cases whorled. In this characteristic, this arrangement foreshadows the LYCOPSIDA, and even the SPHENOPSIDA, which will be discussed in later chapters.

In other types, such as the dichotomously branched thalloid plant bearing terminal sporangia and known as *Protopteridium*, we find the essential features of the PTEROPSIDA.

Among the plants of the Upper Silurian and Lower Devonian, we find no such structures as roots, strobili, or seeds. Indeed most of the plants lack true leaves. The plant body is little more than a simple photosynthetic axis bearing terminal sporangia in which isospores are developed. These are the barest essentials of a land plant; there are few embellishments. One must forget that any other structures really exist; in point of time they have not yet evolved.

This simple basic plant is comparably simple in internal organization. The central stele is composed of thickened xylem cells surrounded by phloem. Next follows a cortex of comparatively large extent around which is the epidermis and cuticle. The epidermis is provided with stomata.

From this simply organized plant we shall trace the evolution and development of two main structures: the leaf and the branch. Together they enter into the formation of the strobilus and all of its modifications.

This is the so-called "new morphology" of H. Hamshaw-Thomas, Lam, and many others. Our morphology is not new; we begin at the natural beginning, rather than from the vantage of existing plants, which proceeds backward along circuitous and misleading routes.

The reader will observe that this attitude seems to assume that the RHYNIACEAE are the ancestral stock from which all vascular plants have been derived. This is not necessarily true; indeed, most botanists are convinced that the RHYNIALES are not the ancestors of higher plant groups. Nevertheless, the Rhynie flora, because of its extreme simplicity, fulfills all the specifications of a fundamental complex, and we consider it only as an illustration of a very simple stock.

It is possible that the simplicity is secondary; i.e., in part due to the peculiar ecological conditions under which they lived. This suggestion, proposed many years ago by Jennings, has been revived recently by Leclercq.

Bibliography

DAWSON, J. W. 1859. On fossil plants from the Devonian rocks of Canada, *Quart. Jour. Geol. Soc. Lond.* 15: 477-488. Every student of paleobotany should examine this famous paper in which *Psilophyton* was described. Despite the fragmentary nature of the specimens, Dawson's shrewd and critical judgment made possible a correct interpretation.

KIDSTON, R., and W. H. LANG. 1920-21. Old red sandstone plants showing structure, from the Rhynie chert, Aberdeenshire, parts I-V, *Roy. Soc. Edinb. Trans.* 51: 761-784; 52: 643-680, 831-902. Probably the greatest classic in paleobotany combining, as it does, painstaking detail in description of material with far-reaching influence.

LECLERCQ, S. 1954. Are the psilophytales a starting or a resulting point? *Svensk Bot. Tidsk.* 48: 301-315. This interesting contribution reviews the limitations of the evidence on which the ancestral nature of the psilophytes has been based. Professor Leclercq calls attention to the possibility that they are parallel to, not ancestral to, the other groups of vascular plants. This is an example of the skepticism, or rather dissatisfaction, with present phylogenetic concepts.

All of the references which follow are technical papers describing Devonian plants. They illustrate methods of investigation and the concepts of comparative morphology used to interpret totally extinct plants.

COOKSON, I. C. 1935. On plant remains from the Silurian of Victoria, Australia, that extend and connect floras hitherto described, *Roy. Soc. Lond. Phil. Trans.* B 225: 127-148.

COOKSON, I. C. 1949. Yeringian (lower Devonian) plant remains from Lilydale, Victoria, with notes on a collection from a new locality, in the Siluro-Devonian sequence, *Mem. Nat. Mus. Melbourne* 16: 117-131.

CROFT, W. N., and W. H. LANG. 1942. The lower Devonian flora of the Senni Beds of Monmouthshire and Breconshire, *Roy. Soc. Lond. Phil. Trans.* B 231: 131-163.

DORF, E. 1933. A new occurrence of the oldest known vegetation from Beartooth Butte, Wyoming, *Bot. Gaz.* 95: 240-257.

KRÄUSEL, R. 1930. Die Flora des deutschen Unterdevons, *Abh. Preuss. Geol. Landesanst.* n.f. 131: 1-92.

LANG, W. H. 1931. On the spines, sporangia, and spores of *Psilophyton princeps* Dawson shown in specimens from Gaspe, *Roy. Soc. Lond. Phil. Trans.* B 219: 421-442.

LANG, W. H. and I. C. COOKSON. 1930. Some fossil plants of early Devonian type from the Walhalla Series, Victoria, Australia, *Roy. Soc. Lond. Phil. Trans.* B 219: 133-163.

———. 1935. On a flora including *Monograptus* in rocks of Silurian age from Victoria, Australia, *Roy. Soc. Lond. Phil. Trans.* B 224: 421-449.

STOCKMANS, F. 1940. Végétaux éodévoniens de la Belgique, *Mém. Mus. Roy. Hist. Nat. Belg.* 93: 1-90.

6

OTHER DEVONIAN PLANTS

The PSILOPSIDA in a broad sense are the abundant and characteristic plants of the lower half of the Devonian. We have seen in what manner they appear to be simple and undifferentiated, and for what reason they have been looked upon as an ancestral stock from which the higher tracheophytes may have evolved.

Within the past thirty years many larger plants have been described from localities in nearly all parts of the world. The majority of these mid- and upper Devonian plants do not belong to the PSILOPSIDA. There is an increasing tendency to consider the psilopsid group as a purely artificial complex which represents a level of development.

A SEQUENCE OF DEVONIAN FLORAS

The following chronological sequence of floras will give some idea of the development of the higher plant groups.

1. The Upper Silurian (or Lower Devonian) flora from Victoria, Australia.
2. Lower Devonian floras from Gaspé (Canada), England, Scotland, Wales, Germany, Belgium, Wyoming, China, and Australia.
3. The Rhynie flora, which is of lower mid-Devonian age.
4. The mid-Devonian floras from Germany, Belgium, France, Bohemia, Scotland, and lesser ones from Great Britain, Spitsbergen, Norway, South Africa, Queensland (Australia), and North America.
5. Upper Devonian floras, notably from Germany, New York, Belgium, Russia, Bear Island, and Spitsbergen (Fig. 32).

There are many others, but this list indicates the principal occurrences.

We have already considered in some detail the upper Silurian flora from Victoria. The age has been determined on the basis of the occurrence of the graptolite *Monograptus* in the same strata as the plants. It is possible that the flora is of lower Devonian age because the genus *Monograptus*, although characteristic of late Silurian

57

times, has been found in the Lower Devonian of New York. In any event, the *Yarravia-Hedeia-Baragwanathia* flora from Australia is the oldest well-preserved land flora concerning which we have information.

Probably the next oldest well-developed flora is known from Beartooth Butte, Wyoming. Dorf described the following genera found in this association: *Psilophyton, Bucheria, Hostimella,* and *Broggeria* —all of them referable to the Psilophytales. *Bucheria* is of particular interest because of its close affinity with *Zosterophyllum.*

The Rhynie flora follows in sequence and the chief genera have already been discussed.

The richest mid-Devonian floras have been found in Bohemia, Germany, and Belgium. The celebrated flora from the vicinity of Elberfeld has yielded a remarkable number of plants, which have been investigated brilliantly by Kräusel and Weyland. The chief forms are *Protopteridium, Duisbergia, Barrandeina, Pseudosporochnus, Hyenia, Calamophyton, Asteroxylon,* and *Zosterophyllum.* This assemblage has proved to be of widespread occurrence in rocks of similar age and sedimentation environment.

It should be self-evident that by mid-Devonian times the plant world was conspicuously different from that of the lower Devonian. In order to place these plants in perspective, they will be grouped first chronologically and then compared systematically. The enumeration of a long list of generic names is unavoidable because these forms will be referred to, time and again, in later chapters.

The early Devonian is characterized by such forms as *Nematophyton, Pachytheca, Zosterophyllum, Psilophyton, Drepanophycus,* and *Protolepidodendron.* Some of these persist into the late Devonian.

The general aspect of the mid-Devonian is indicated by such genera as *Calamophyton, Hyenia, Protopteridium, Aneurophyton,* and *Pseudosporochnus.*

The Upper Devonian floras include a very large and varied number of plants, among which the following are typical: *Archaeosigillaria, Cyclostigma, Clepsydropsis, Dimeripteris, Archaeopteris,* and *Callixylon.* One example must suffice to suggest the richness of the late Devonian floras.

The New Albany shale of Kentucky and Indiana has yielded more than 40 species, all based upon structurally preserved material. There is a mixture of such plants as *Nematophyton, Foerstia*

(*Protosalvinia*) and possibly *Asteroxylon*, with precursors of later types: *Lepidodendron*, *Callixylon*, *Cladoxylon*, and *Clepsydropsis*. The ferns (and supposed seed-ferns) are particularly well represented. In other words, the diversification of vascular plants had proceeded to the extent that the major groups were fully differentiated. A selection of these types will be described briefly to indicate along what lines development had progressed, but most of them will be considered with the systematic groups to which they belong.

Drepanophycus Goeppert (= *Arthrostigma* Dawson), from the lower Devonian of Canada, Scotland, Norway, Germany, China, and Australia, usually has a very characteristic appearance, with thick stems up to 3.5 cm in diameter, sometimes with thick branches, which at first were horizontal and then suddenly turned upward; in other cases the axis divided dichotomously. There is a thin central vascular strand composed of annular tracheids. Stomata are also known. The spines were remarkable, being large but of varying size, broad and triangular at the base. They contained a strand, connected with the central strand by a "leaf-trace." The thinner axes are difficult to distinguish from *Psilophyton*. The sporangia were rounded bodies, each attached by means of a short stalk to the upper surface of a spine.

Protolepidodendron (Fig. 9). The structure of the middle Devonian *P. scharyanum* has been investigated by Kräusel and Weyland on German and Bohemian material. This species occurs also in Scotland and probably in Australia. The plant recalls the habit of a modern *Lycopodium*, except that it was somewhat larger; the axes measured several centimeters in diameter and contained a triangular protostele. They were densely clad with leaves, which differ from those of *Lycopodium* in being forked near the tip. On the fertile axes the leaves were more distant and bore a sporangium on the upper surface.

Hyenia (see Fig. 18) has been found in Norway, Spitsbergen, Germany, Belgium, and the United States. The plant body was a horizontal rhizome bearing aerial shoots which were sparingly branched. Smaller shoots were sometimes unbranched. The leaves were small and divided dichotomously into filiform segments. They were arranged in a semi-verticillate manner, the whorls in some parts of the plant being quite regular, in other parts the segments are spiral. The upper portions of ultimate branches were fertile,

Fig. 8. (See next page for caption.)

dividing dichotomously a few times at short intervals and bearing a single sporangium on each tip. The fertile region had a verticillate arrangement.

Pseudosporochnus from the Middle Devonian of Bohemia, Scotland, and possibly Norway, is one of the largest known psilopsids, attaining a height of more than a meter. The erect, stout stem divides by repeated dichotomy into a number of main branches which through further ramification form a great number of ultimate divisions, bearing, in some places, small sporangia containing minute spores.

Aneurophyton (Fig. 8) had the habit of a tree-fern, with a stout main axis, the anatomy of which is almost completely known. There was no pith, but there was a central strand of primary xylem of trilobed outline, with protoxylem situated in the ends of the lobes. This strand was surrounded by secondary xylem consisting of radial rows of pitted tracheids and uniseriate wood rays of considerable height (60 cells or more). The foliar organs resembled large fern leaves, but the vascular bundle was built like that of the axis, consequently the branching seems to have taken place in three directions, not in one plane only. There was no lamina, but the ultimate ramifications were simple, linear, recurved, apparently without vascular bundles. The sporangia were borne in dense clusters on fertile "leaves" resembling the sterile ones; they were oval and dehisced longitudinally without any elaborate opening mechanism. Spores were tetrahedral, with spines ending in grapnel-like hooks. Kräusel and Weyland have suggested the possibility that there might have been two kinds of sporangia, of which the microsporangia alone are well known.

Aneurophyton was an abundant type. There is a tendency among present paleobotanists to refer many specimens to this genus. *Eospermatopteris*, formerly believed to be a pteridosperm, is referable to the fern *Aneurophyton*.

Fig. 8. The Middle Devonian Forest of Gilboa, New York. The celebrated habitat group in the New York State Museum. The habit of *Aneurophyton* is shown in the background; sandstone casts of the basal portions of the trunks are placed in the foreground. The plant was originally interpreted as a seed-fern ("*Eospermatopteris*") but has since been recognized as a representative of the widely distributed Devonian fern *Aneurophyton*. Restoration by Henri Marchand and sons, Georges and Paul, under the supervision of Winifred Goldring. (By permission from the New York State Museum and J. A. Glenn.)

Protopteridium comprises a number of species from Bohemia, Belgium, Germany, Scotland, and eastern United States. The habit of the entire plant and the morphology of its branch-systems are not yet fully known. But it is certain that it had *Hostimella*-like axes, bearing lateral branches alternately in one plane. Some of the latter divided repeatedly, at least in the first divisions by dichotomy, so as to form subpinnate branch systems of a frondlike appearance. Young branch systems and the upper part of older ones were incurved. Other branches of the same type bore numerous elongate sporangia containing, in *P. thompsonii,* large spores surrounded by a broad wing.

There is still another series of forms which do not readily admit reference to any of the known groups of plants. For convenience they may be considered as a family, the PLATYPHYLLACEAE, though it is questionable whether they comprise a natural group or even whether they are closely related. The genera *Platyphyllum, Psygmophyllum, Ginkgophyllum, Germanophyton,* and perhaps the remarkable *Enigmophyton* may be referred to this group.

Platyphyllum is a form-genus accommodating fan-shaped leaves with parallel bifurcating venation. The xylem in the veins of this and certain other form-genera (the Devonian *Psygmophyllum* and *Ginkgophyllum*) is composed of tracheids, annular in *Platyphyllum* and pitted in *Psygmophyllum.*

Germanophyton Høeg was originally described as *Prototaxites psygmophylloides* Kräusel and Weyland. The axis contains tubes of the *Nematophyton* type but attained considerable size and bore flabellate leaves with bifurcating veins.

Enigmophyton Høeg was a plant which reached a height of a meter or more with stems of uniform breadth dividing dichotomously and bearing lateral branches. The leaves are large, flabellate, and inserted at the points of bifurcation. The veins are parallel, bifurcating and not anastomosing. The only known species, *Enigmophyton superbum* Høeg, is from the mid-Devonian of Spitsbergen. A spiked heterosporous fructification found associated with the vegetative remains may belong to this plant.

In none of these interesting forms do we have definite knowledge of the fructification, nor, except in the case of *Germanophyton,* which is difficult to interpret, do we have details of the internal structure of the axis. Any attempt to assign them to a particular class of plants would be premature and unwarranted.

A SYNOPSIS OF DEVONIAN PLANT TYPES

If the various Devonian plants are compared with one another, such as in Table 2 below, certain features appear to be held in common while others are localized in one or two forms.

The chief similarities are : (1) absence of roots, (2) the dichotomous mode of branching which, though complicated by digitate or sympodial branching of the main axis, persists in the ultimate ramifications, and (3) single sporangia (except in *Yarravia*) and the complete absence of strobili. The chief characteristics of the various groups are given in the accompanying table.

The features which divide these groups into two or three major natural series are: (1) naked and spinous axes, (2) terminal or lateral sporangia, and (3) microphyllous or laminar foliar organs.

Few of these plants can be included in the PSILOPSIDA, nor can they be regarded, in all cases, as natural groups.

The merging of characteristics, which we associate with definite classes of existing vascular plants, in these Devonian groups has been interpreted as sufficient reason for regarding the tracheophytes as a monophyletic group. The major divisions, LYCOPSIDA, SPHENOPSIDA, and PTEROPSIDA, appear to have developed from a common ancestral stock. *Drepanophycus* and *Baragwanathia* are hardly admitted to membership in the PSILOPSIDA, yet their affinities with *Thursophyton*, *Psilophyton*, and *Asteroxylon* on one hand and with *Protolepidodendron* on the other seems clear. The situation is even more convincing with *Hyenia* and *Calamophyton*, which bridge the gap between the psilopsid complex and the SPHENOPSIDA. The PTEROPSIDA also find beginnings among the psilopsids. Such genera as *Pseudosporochnus*, *Rhacophyton*, *Protopteridium*, and *Aneurophyton* scarcely admit any other interpretation.

Yet a measure of caution is necessary. Classification of the PSILOPSIDA is very difficult; most of the Devonian plants are not thoroughly known. It is easy to assume simplicity on superficial evidence. The occurrence of the synangial *Yarravia* and the leafy *Baragwanathia* in the Silurian is another cause for caution. The exposition of the PSILOPSIDA has inspired the Telome theory of plant morphology.

The Telome Theory. This theory enjoys considerable popularity, partly because it avoids equivocal terms which have been used and misused by several generations of morphologists and partly

TABLE 2
Tabular Synopsis of Devonian Plants

Family	Body	Leaves	Sporangia	Representative Genera
RHYNIACEAE	Cylindrical rhizome with rhizoids and dichotomous aerial shoots	None	Terminal	*Rhynia* *Cooksonia*
HORNEOPHYTACEAE	Lobed rhizome with rhizoids and dichotomous aerial shoots	None	Terminal, columellate	*Horneophyton* *Sporogonites*
PSILOPHYTACEAE	Similar to RHYNIACEAE, but larger	Emergences, with vascular strand	Terminal	*Psilophyton* *Dawsonites* *Loganella*
ZOSTEROPHYLLACEAE	Rhizome, profusely branched, with aerial shoots	None	Terminal on short side branches, clustered, racemose	*Zosterophyllum* *Bucheria*
YARRAVIACEAE	Similar to RHYNIACEAE so far as known	None	Not solitary but synangial, terminal	*Yarravia*
ASTEROXYLACEAE	Cylindrical branched rhizome bearing dichotomous aerial shoots	Small leaves	Terminal	*Asteroxylon* *Schizopodium*
DREPANOPHYCACEAE	Branching rhizome with dichotomous aerial shoots	Spinous	Lateral, clustered bifurcated sporophyll	*Drepanophycus (Arthrostigma)* *Baragwanathia*
PROTOLEPIDODENDRACEAE	Rhizome bearing dichotomously branched axis	Small bifurcated leaves	Borne on upper surface of some leaves; not strobilar	*Protolepidodendron*
HYENIACEAE	Rhizome, axis with digitate branching	Small leaves whorled	Terminal on recurved sporophyll	*Hyenia*
CALAMOPHYTACEAE	Rhizome, axis with digitate branching noded axes	Small leaves whorled	Terminal on recurved sporophyll	*Calamophyton*
PSEUDOSPOROCHNACEAE	Rhizome bearing upright axis digitately branched ultimate ramifications, dichotomous	Filiform ultimate branches	Terminal	*Pseudosporochnus*
PROTOPTERIDACEAE	Rhizome bearing sympodially branched axes, ultimate branches dichotomous	Small foliar organs, dichotomous lobes and venation	Terminal on small branches	*Protopteridium* *Aneurophyton* *Rhacophyton?*
PLATYPHYLLACEAE	Where known—dichotomous ultimate branches	Large foliar organs, dichotomous lobes and venation	Not definitely known	*Platyphyllum* *Psygmophyllum* *Germanophyton (Enigmophyton?)* *Ginkgophyllum*

because it is a unifying principle. The theory holds that the plant body is a branched axis and that each ultimate ramification of the axis is a telome. This is quite different from the concept that the plant is composed of three fundamental parts: stem, root, and leaves. The leaf is a telome or combination of sterile telomes; a sporangiophore may be either a single fertile telome or several fused telomes. Thus the ultimate division of a *Rhynia* axis is a telome. The prevalence of simple dichotomy among Devonian plants is interpreted as evidence of telomic origin of leaves and sporangiophores. Indeed, true dichotomy persists in many plant groups, including the angiosperms (Van der Hammen). It is possible that morphologists will work the theory to death, but meanwhile it is a useful means of interpreting not only ancient plants which do not fit into conventional classifications, but also the unexplained complex structures of many existing plants. It is in this sense that the Devonian plants in general and the PSILOPSIDA in particular have profoundly influenced botanical thought.

SUMMARY

These brief considerations of directions of advancement among the early tracheophytes bring out the fact that there is a basic kinship among the LYCOPSIDA, SPHENOPSIDA, and PTEROPSIDA. In each group the earliest members were dichotomous protostelic plants with single terminal sporangia. Thus such organ systems as the secondary body and the strobilus have developed independently in each group.

In spite of certain pitfalls, we have for this survey accepted the Devonian RHYNIACEAE as representative of the earliest stage in the evolution of the vascular plants. Although this concept is prevalent among botanists familiar with the fossil record, the story is not so simple. Even if the Silurian flora from Australia were to be disregarded, there are land plants older than the PSILOPHYTALES—as, for example, the NEMATOPHYTALES. And these plants are much more "primitive" in organization.

Paleobotanists are in virtual agreement that the bryophytes have had no direct relationship with the vascular plants, despite obvious embryological and sporogenetic similarities. This belief has been strengthened by recent discoveries among the nematophytes. The origin of the PSILOPSIDA remains a mystery. To be sure it was from the algal complex—but from what group or what stock? There is not yet a hint. Bertrand hypothesized the "PRORHYNIALES," which might have mothered both the bryophytes and tracheophytes. Inviting as this fancy may appear, it is without substance.

Bibliography

The papers cited below represent a sampling of studies on Devonian plants from many parts of the world, indicating gross similarities and regional differences. Many of references in the bibliography to Chapter 5 also apply to the present chapter.

ARNOLD, C. A. 1931. On *Callixylon newberryi* (Dawson) Elkins and Wieland, *Contr. Mus. Paleont. Univ. Michigan* 3: 207-232.

———. 1936-1939. Observations of fossil plants from Devonian of eastern North America, Parts I-IV, *Contr. Mus. Paleont. Univ. Michigan* 5: 37-56, 75-78, 271-314.

BROWNE, I. M. P. 1935. Some views on the morphology and phylogeny of the leafy sporophyte, *Bot. Rev.* 1: 383-404, 427-447.

DAWSON, J. W. 1859. On fossil plants of the Devonian rocks of Canada, *Quart. Jour. Geol. Soc. Lond.* 15: 447-488.

———. 1871. The fossil plants of the Devonian and upper Silurian formations of Canada, *Geol. Surv. Canada* (Montreal).

DORF, E., and J. R. COOPER. 1943. Early Devonian plants from Newfoundland, *Jour. Paleont.* 17: 264-270.

HØEG, O. A. 1937. The Devonian floras and their bearing upon the origin of vascular plants, *Bot. Rev.* 3: 563-592.

———. 1942. The Downtonian and Devonian flora of Spitzbergen, *Norges Svalberg- og Ishous-undersokelser*, 83 (Oslo).

HSU, J. 1947. Plant fragments from Devonian beds in Central Yunnan, China, *Jour. Ind. Bot. Soc., Iyengar Mem. Vol.* (1946) 1947: 339-360.

KRÄUSEL, R. 1941. Pflanzenreste aus dem Devon von Nord-Amerika *Palaeontographica* 86 (B): 1-78.

KRÄUSEL, R., and H. WEYLAND. 1923-1929. Pflanzenreste aus dem Devon, I-X, *Senckenbergiana* 14, 16, 17 and 19.

———. 1935. Neue Pflanzenfunde im rheinischen Unterdevon, *Palaeontographica* 80 (B): 171-190.

LECLERCQ, S. 1940. Contribution à l'étude de la flore du Dévonian de Belgique, *Mém. Acad. Roy. de Belg.* Vol. 12, No. 3.

———. 1942. Quelques plantes fossiles receillies dans le Dévonien inférieur des environs de Nonceveaux, *Ann. Soc. Géol. Belg.* 45: 193-211.

NATHORST, A. G. 1902. Zur Oberdevonischen Flora der Bareninsel, *Kung. Svensk Vetensk. Handl.* Vol. 36, No. 3.

POTONIÉ, H., and C. BERNARD. 1904. *Flore dévonienne de l'étage H. de Barrande*, Leipzig.

READ, C., and CAMPBELL. 1939. Preliminary account of the New Albany Shale flora, *Amer. Midl. Nat.* 21: 435-453.

7

THE LYCOPSIDA

The living Lycopsida comprise an inconspicuous group of small, spore-bearing vascular plants. They are characterized by a differentiated sporophyte with microphyllous leaves (generally disposed spirally) and single sporangia borne upon the adaxial surface of the sporophylls. The group includes only four living genera: *Lycopodium* (about 180 species), *Phylloglossum* (one species), *Selaginella* (about 800 species), and *Isoëtes* (60 species). With the exception of *Phylloglossum,* which occurs in Australia, New Zealand, and Tasmania, these genera are distributed over the earth. *Selaginella* is most abundant in the tropics. The ancient lycopsids were a rich and varied group which enjoyed far greater dominance in past geological ages. This dominance is not only shown by numerical abundance but also by morphological diversification. Whereas existing lycopsids are mostly creeping or herbaceous forms, many extinct members of this group attained tree size and developed complicated sporangial mechanisms approaching the seed habit.

The earliest lycopsids, as has already been noted, trace their beginnings among the psilophyte complex. *Protolepidodendron* (Fig. 9) and *Baragwanathia* are not psilopsids. Their possession of microphyllous leaves and adaxial sporangia place them among primitive lycopsids. Yet the retention of the dichotomous habit and poorly defined phyllotaxy clearly distinguish them from other lycopsids.

Our chief interests in the Lycopsida are:

(1) the arborescent habit and how it was attained,
(2) the strobilus, and
(3) heterospory,

which in some members approximates the seed habit. Before entering into a discussion of these points, reference should be made to Table 3 summarizing representative families.

TABLE 3

Comparison of Representative Lycopsid Families

Family	Habit	Sporangial Mechanism	Typical Genera	Geological Distribution
DREPANOPHYCACEAE	Plant small, branching rhizome with dichotomously branched aerial shoots, crowded spinelike or elongate leaves	Solitary sporangia borne upon bifurcated sporophylls, sporophylls sometimes clustered	*Baragwanathia* *Drepanophycus*	Silurian-Devonian Devonian
PROTOLEPIDO-DENDRACEAE	Similar, with small bifurcated leaves	Borne upon upper surface of some leaves, not strobilar	*Protolepido-dendron* *Archaeo-sigillaria* *Colpodexylon* (leaves trifurcate)	Devonian
LEPIDODENDRACEAE	Arborescent; axis branching dichotomously, large linear leaves (except on young branches), large rhizophore	Heterosporous, strobilar	*Lepidodendron*	Devonian to Permian
SIGILLARIACEAE	Similar, but trunk rarely branched, crown composed of large grass-like leaves	Heterosporous, strobilar	*Sigillaria*	Devonian to Permian

68

Family	Description	Reproductive characteristics	Genera	Geologic range
BOTHRODENDRACEAE	Similar, trunk sparsely branched	Heterosporous, strobilar, endosporous gametophyte	*Bothrodendron*	Devonian and Carboniferous
PLEUROMEIACEAE	Small plants to 2 meters high, stem unbranched, lobed base	Round scalelike sporophylls, single sporangium	*Pleuromeia* *Nathorstiana*	Triassic and Jurassic Cretaceous
ISOËTACEAE	Cormlike stem, not differentiated into axis and rhizophore, 5 to 50 cm tall	Nonstrobilar	*Isoëtites* *Isoëtes*	Cretaceous to Pliocene, Recent
LEPIDOCARPACEAE	Similar to LEPIDODENDRACEAE (all evidence points to *Lepidophloios* as parent plant)	Strobilar, heterosporous, sporangium enveloped by sporophyll, endosporal gametophyte	*Lepidocarpon*	Carboniferous
MIADESMACEAE	Similar to SIGILLARIACEAE	Strobilar, heterosporous	*Miadesmia*	Carboniferous
SELAGINELLACEAE	Small, herbaceous, leaves microphyllous, rhizophoric	Heterosporous	*Selaginellites* *Selaginella*	Carboniferous to Recent
LYCOPODIACEAE	Small herbaceous or shrubby plants, leaves microphyllous, eligulate	Homosporous, well developed strobilus in some, fertile zones in others	*Spencerites*(?) *Lycopodites* *Lycopodium* *Phylloglossum*	Carboniferous Carboniferous to Recent Recent Recent

69

Fig. 9. (See next page for caption.)

THE CARBONIFEROUS LEPIDODENDRIDS

The LEPIDODENDRACEAE and SIGILLARIACEAE are in many respects the most conspicuous elements in the Carboniferous flora (Fig. 9). The chief genera *Lepidodendron* and *Sigillaria* grew to great size, oftentimes 40 to 50 meters high. Only under most unusual circumstances are individual plants preserved where they lived; generally our knowledge is based upon fragments transported for lesser or greater distances, mixed with remains of other types of plants, frequently in great profusion and confusion, and finally buried beneath sediment.

A brief digression concerning this fragmentary nature of fossil plants is pertinent, although this problem may be exaggerated or overemphasized. A large plant, as, for example, a *Lepidodendron,* lived for many years. During life it shed leaves and spores which fell to the ground, perhaps at some distance from the parent plant. Branches and strobili were broken off, and these too littered the forest floor. Finally in old age the trunk itself toppled to the ground. Even assuming that the *Lepidodendron* was preserved where it fell, it would be found in detached parts. Remembering then that fossils are rarely preserved *in situ,* we can appreciate some of the difficulties involved in correlating fragments, piecing together information, and reconstructing the habit of the plant.

Actually our knowledge of some species of *Lepidodendron* is surprisingly complete. There are many *in situ* "forests" of stumps, the most famous of these being the Fossil Grove at Victoria Park, Glasgow, Scotland. Besides, the study of countless specimens has made it possible to correlate leaves with branches, strobili with

---

Fig. 9. Paleozoic Lepidodendrids. Representative genera showing the habits found among the larger Devonian and Carboniferous lycopsids. The small Devonian *Protolepidodendron* with recurved branches is shown on the left. The stately *Bothrodendron* (Devonian and Carboniferous) with fertile branches near the trunk dichotomies appears in the left center. *Lepidodendron,* with spirally disposed rhomboid leaf bases and terminal strobili, is shown in the right center (Carboniferous and Permian). *Sigillaria,* with rigid acicular leaves and vertical rows of leaf base scars on the trunk, is represented by several species on the right (Carboniferous and Permian). The prostrate trunk of *Sigillaria* on the extreme lower right shows the *Stigmaria* "root" system (a rhizophore). Stigmarian structure is typical for all lepidodendrid rhizophores so far as is known. (By permission of the Brooklyn Botanic Garden.)

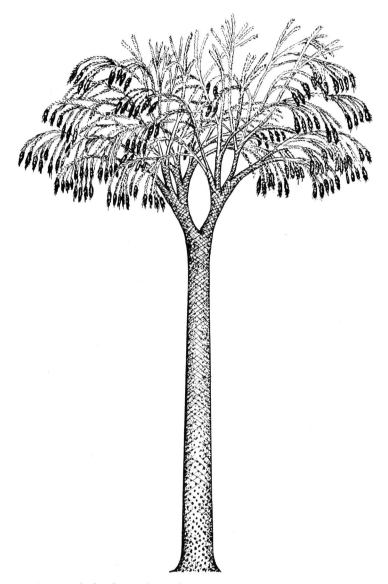

Fig. 10. *Lepidodendron,* the arborescent sporophyte, showing columnar trunk, leaf bases on trunk, dichotomous branching, and strobili. (Drawn by G. W. Dillon.)

branches, isolated sporangia with known strobili, and so on. This fragmentary nature of fossils necessitates the creation of "form genera" to accommodate isolated parts. The result might appear to be awkward: the leaf of the plant is referred to one genus, the strobilus to another, and the branch to a third. The paleobotanist is well aware of the complications of this scheme, but he must reckon with detached fragments and can only hope that new material will provide needed "connecting links." In practice this empirical system works satisfactorily. Certain adaptations of the International Rules of Botanical Nomenclature have been agreed upon to minimize duplication of names and to establish standard procedures.

Some idea of the relationships of form genera will be evident from the following:

Trunks and branches:	*Lepidodendron, Lepidophloios*
Decorticated trunks :	*Knorria, Bergeria, Aspidiaria*
Rhizophore :	*Stigmaria, Stigmariopsis*
Leaves :	*Lepidophyllum*
Strobilus :	*Lepidostrobus*
Sporophylls :	*Lepidostrobophyllum*
Spores :	*Triletes*, with many subgenera

Thus a *Lepidodendron* has a *Stigmaria* base, a *Lepidodendron* trunk bore *Lepidostrobus* with *Triletes* spores (which in all probability means two "species"—one for the microspores, the other for the megaspores).

The *Lepidodendron* sporophyte, Fig. 10, consists of a large straight columnar trunk, one to two, occasionally 4 meters in diameter, which tapers very gradually until it branches by repeated dichotomies to give a spreading crown. Some trunks reached a length of 30 meters before branching. The young branches are covered with slender needle-like leaves, in some species up to 20 cm long. The base of the trunk forks dichotomously, producing an extensive shallow subterranean system commonly known as *Stigmaria*, Fig. 11.

The stigmarian system was a rhizophore, that is, an underground root-bearing stem. The so-called stigmarian appendages ("rootlets") are true roots. The rhizophore produced a large cylinder of secondary wood composed of scalariform tracheids. There was a well-developed middle cortex and a thick periderm. The appendages are spirally disposed, a feature which led some morphologists to misinterpret them as modified leaves. This is negated by the fact that the outer cortex of the appendage is continuous with that of the main axis.

The leaves were attached for their whole base and when shed left a projecting scar (generally more or less trapezoidal in outline). These leaf cushions, which are spirally disposed, were persistent even in old trunks. The shape and configuration of these cushions varies with different species.

The internal structure of several species of *Lepidodendron* is known in great detail. Two of these will be discussed here, *L. selaginoides* (= *vasculare*) and *L. johnsonii*. The former is abun-

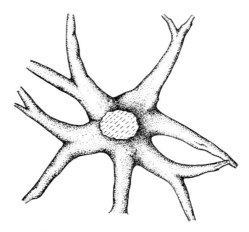

Fig. 11. *Stigmaria*, the rhizophore system of *Lepidodendron* and *Sigillaria*. Top view, suggesting dichotomous branching of the subterranean portion of the axis. (Drawn by G. W. Dillon.)

dant in the mid-Carboniferous of England and Belgium, the other from the mid-Carboniferous (lower Pennsylvanian) of Colorado.

Lepidodendron johnsonii Arnold had a trunk with a diameter exceeding 0.5 meter. The stele or vascular system was composed of a central pith (3-4 cm) surrounded by a narrow cylinder of primary xylem (1-5 mm) and a fairly extensive secondary xylem (3 cm or more) produced by a cambium. The tracheids are scalariform. Rays, one to 20 (usually less than 10) cells high, occur in the secondary xylem. Leaf traces leave the primary cylinder at a steep angle but soon bend outward. The siphonostele obviously was inadequate to provide mechanical support for the great size of the trunk. The chief support was by a secondary periderm of complex structure, which reached a thickness of 20 cm.

Lepidodendron selaginoides had also a small stele, in this species composed of a solid primary cylinder mixed with parenchyma. Secondary thickening occurred even in small twigs of 1 cm diameter. The secondary tissues consisted of xylem, phloem, and periderm. The periderm developed from a zone of cells of the outer cortex and produced extensive cortical tissue.

HETEROSPORY AND SEEDLIKE STRUCTURES AMONG THE LYCOPSIDS

The strobili of lepidodendrids were generally large, though they varied in size from 20 mm to 40 cm in length and 10 mm to 75 or 80 mm in diameter. The axis bears crowded, spirally disposed sporophylls, each of which bears a single sporangium on the upper surface. In *Lepidostrobus oldhamius* only minute spores (20 microns) are known, although it was presumably heterosporous. *Lepidostrobus veltheimianus* bears both microspores (20 microns) and megaspores (800 microns) in the same strobilus. There were only 8 or 16 megaspores in each sporangium. In *Lepidostrobus foliaceus* there are but four megaspores per sporangium.

The gametophytes of a number of lycopsids have been found. All of these are endosporally developed. In *Lepidostrobus veltheimianus* the cellular prothallus fills the megaspore. Archegonia of typical construction have been recognized. Further details on the gametophyte will be discussed under *Lepidocarpon*. In *Bothrodendron* (Fig. 9) the gametophyte protrudes from the megaspore (Fig. 12).

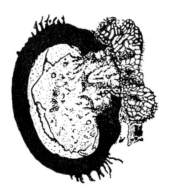

Fig. 12. *Bothrodendron mundum.* Megaspore with gametophyte. Archegonia are formed in the protruding prothallus. Carboniferous. (Redrawn from McLean.)

We have already noted that there occurs among lepidophytes the state of heterospory. It is a remarkable fact that this tendency is advanced to the attainment of the seed habit in at least three forms of the Carboniferous period: *Lepidocarpon, Mazocarpon,* and *Miadesmia.*

Mazocarpon Benson is a highly complex heterosporous cone attributed to *Sigillaria* (*Sigillariopsis sulcata* Scott). Benson regarded *Mazocarpon* as a *Sigillariostrobus* with structure preserved, but there is no basis for assuming that all, or many, species of *Sigillariostrobus* had a *Mazocarpon* structure. The best known species are *Mazocarpon shorense* Benson and *M. oedipternum* Schopf. The fructification is a strobilus with a slender, almost hexagonal axis, with a narrow band of centripetal xylem, and with numerous leaf-traces which lead out, one to each sporophyll. Each sporophyll bears a single sporangium upon the upper surface of the pedicel. There are several thick layers of tissue in the sporangial wall, and an enormous central pad of tissue fills the middle part of the sporangium. From four to eight large megaspores are arranged in a single series around the pad. These extraordinarily large spores attain a diameter greater than 2 mm. The megasporangium—for such it is, was shed detached from the cone, but frequently a single megaspore was attached to a remnant of the bract. The microsporangia are known to bear spores 75 microns in diameter. The presence of several megaspores in the sporangium is, of course, a feature not found in true seeds.

Lepidocarpon lomaxi Scott is a strobilus form closely resembling the ordinary *Lepidostrobus,* but each megasporangium contains only one mature, or fully developed megaspore, often, however, with three abortive spores. Part of the sporophyll enveloped the megasporangium, leaving a "micropyle." Scott called attention to the fact that this micropylar opening is a narrow slit rather than a tube. This condition approximates the seed habit, particularly because these seedlike structures had heavy integuments, a micropyle, an embryo sac, and became detached after attaining great size. It is interesting to observe that these "seeds" were known to paleobotanists for many years under the name *Cardiocarpon anomalum,* presumably seeds of an unknown gymnosperm.

The third type which demonstrates this tendency is known as *Miadesmia membranacea* Benson. This slender plant is presumed to have been a herbaceous sigillarian. As in *Lepidocarpon,* the mega-sporangium is enclosed in an integument which has a micropylar opening. The integument is also provided with delicate, long tentacles which are believed to have aided in "pollination." Only one megaspore is developed, but no abortive sister spores have been observed. There is less sterile tissue in *Miadesmia* than in *Lepidocarpon,* especially in the development of the sporangial wall. It is possible that *Miadesmia* is a winged seed.

These three lycopsid fructifications provided a method of accomplishing reproduction with far greater probability for success than the mere production of a prodigious number of spores. There is an evolutionary sequence exhibited here: an original state of homospory; then heterospory, with the production of a large number of microspores; finally the development of the fertilized egg, the new sporophyte, not only within the megaspore, but also with the megasporangium.

Lepidocarpon, Mazocarpon, and *Miadesmia* are not true seeds because the entire sporophyll formed part of the seedlike organ and was shed with it. On the other hand, the single megaspore and the nucellus are homologous with features of true seeds.

The gametophyte has been recognized in a number of lepidodendrids. Scott described the gametophytes of *Lepidocarpon lomaxi* and *L. wildianum* as parenchymatous tissue nearly filling the sporangium. Andrews, 1942, found in *L. magnificum* a somewhat smaller gametophyte with several archegonia (Fig. 13). In *Lepidocystis glabrum,* a naked sporangium with endosporal development, there is an extensive gametophyte with several archegonia. In this form the embryo is preserved. The youngest sporophyte measures about 2 mm in length and superficially at least resembles *Isoëtes* (Darrah, 1949). The embryo shows two apices (Darrah, 1952) and thus gives no clue to earlier embryogeny. Larger embryos are vascularized and show leaf primordia. Considerable controversy has developed over this form. Because the "seed" has vascular tissue, Andrews has questioned whether *L. glabrum* is a lycopsid, but the evidence is strongly in favor of its reference to this group. Vascularization of the sporangium is a property occurring in many Paleozoic groups.

Contemporaneously with these arborescent lepidodendrids typified by striking sporangial mechanism, there lived other lycopsids of more diminutive size. There were undoubtedly herbaceous forms in the Carboniferous. Certain species of *Lycopodites* are too delicate to be regarded as ultimate branches of larger plants, although they may be juvenile sporophytes. Other forms are referred to *Selaginellites* (because of anisophylly and presence of a ligule). *Selaginellites amesiana* from the Carboniferous of Illinois is known from a well-preserved strobilus with endosporal gametophytes.

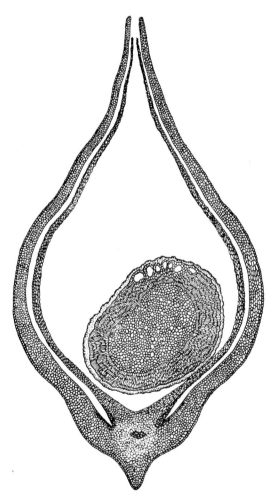

Fig. 13. *Lepidocarpon magnificum.* A well-preserved lepidocarp with endosporal gametophyte and archegonia. Carboniferous. (Redrawn from Andrews.)

GEOLOGICAL DISTRIBUTION OF THE LYCOPSIDA

The LYCOPSIDA were prominent members of the Upper Devonian floras, becoming dominant floral elements in the Carboniferous, and diminishing in importance gradually to the present time. *Archaeosigillaria*, one of the oldest genera, is interesting because it exhibits characters of both *Lepidodendron* and *Sigillaria*. The leaf scars are arranged vertically near the base and spirally in the upper portions. *Archaeosigillaria* was a sparsely branched plant attaining a height of 5 meters. There was no stigmarian structure, the rootlets being attached directly to the swollen base of the trunk. The leaves were small.

Lepidodendropsis, a Lower Carboniferous representative, also attained a height of 4 to 5 meters. On smaller branches the leaf scars are crowded and contiguous, more or less round, and without distinct leaf bases. Older branches have the scars slightly enlarged and separated. The leaves were usually straight and rigid, and measured 40 to 50 mm in length. The sporangia (*Lepidocystis* form) appear to have been borne nakedly on the sporophylls.

Pinakodendron which occurred in the Upper Devonian and Lower Carboniferous attained considerable height, perhaps 10 meters. It is remarkable because the sporophylls were borne in zones along the stem, much as in the living *Lycopodium lucidulum*.

The typical Carboniferous lycopsids were of course *Lepidodendron, Sigillaria, Lepidocarpon*, and *Lepidophloios*. The group reached its maximum diversification and abundance in the Carboniferous.

In the early Mesozoic there are a few survivors of the lepidodendrids. However, *Pleuromeia* (Triassic) and *Nathorstiana* (Cretaceous), which represent a distinct phyletic line, are typical. This series exhibits marked reduction and may give a clue to the ancestry of the ISOËTALES.

Pleuromeia, Fig. 14, a small plant with an unbranched stem, attained a height of 2 meters. The maximum diameter of the stem was approximately 10 cm. The base was divided into four fleshy lobes recalling somewhat those of *Isoëtes*. Many rootlets were borne upon the lobes, in a manner recalling both *Stigmaria* and *Isoëtes*. The leaves were linear, with a broad expanded base and a double mid-vein. The sporophylls were reniform or oval in shape and compactly clustered on the axis. The plant was heterosporous.

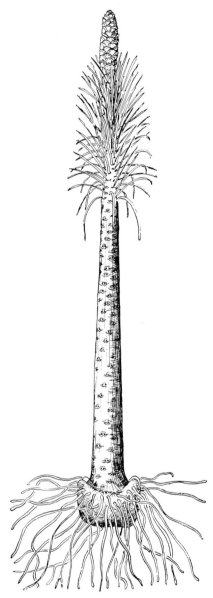

Fig. 14. *Pleuromeia,* showing the terminal aggregation of sporangia, the swollen base, and rhizoids. A Mesozoic lycopsid believed to have affinities with the Isoëtales. (Redrawn from Hirmer.)

Nathorstiana, which was even smaller, attaining a height of only 10 or 12 cm, had a swollen base with a number of ridgelike lobes, bifurcated rootlets, and a crown of leaves resembling *Isoëtes.*

From the Cretaceous to the Present, the only recognized lycopsids are referable to *Lycopodites, Selaginellites,* and *Isoëtites,* of modern aspect.

RELATIONSHIPS OF THE LYCOPSIDA

The Devonian *Protolepidodendron* and *Drepanophycus* show unmistakable affinities with the psilopsid complex, but in cognizance of their more complex organization may be regarded as progenitors of the lycopsids.

The relationships within the LYCOPSIDA are fairly clear: both the ligulate and eligulate lines are distinct in the Carboniferous. Side by side throughout the Carboniferous were arborescent and herbaceous members of both lines.

Retention of the megaspore and the gametophyte seems to have been a common tendency, culminating in the lepidocarps.

Unquestionably the LYCOPSIDA were a diverse group which experimented (to speak teleologically) with various structures—most notably the root, strobilus, and megaspore. Despite great successes they gave rise to no "new" major groups.

Bibliography

ANDREWS, H. N. 1949. *Nucellangium,* a new genus of fossil seeds previously assigned to *Lepidocarpon, Ann. Mo. Bot. Gard.* 36: 479-500.

ANDREWS, H. N., and E. PANNELL. 1942. Contributions to our knowledge of American Carboniferous floras, II. *Lepidocarpon, Ann. Mo. Bot. Gard.* 29: 19-35.

ARNOLD, C. A. 1940. *Lepidodendron Johnsonii* sp. nov. from the lower Pennsylvanian of central Colorado, *Contrib. Univ. Mich. Mus. Paleont.* 6: 21-52.

BOCHENSKI, T. 1936. Ueber Sporophyllstande (Bluten) einiger Lepidophyten aus dem produktiven Karbon Polens, *Ann. Soc. Geol. Pol.* 12: 193-240.

CALDER, M. G. 1934. Notes on the Kidston collection of fossil plant slides, V and VI. Structure of lepidodendroid stems, *Trans. Roy. Soc. Edinb.* 58: 113-124.

DARRAH, W. C. 1938. A remarkable fossil *Selaginella* with preserved female gametophytes, *Bot. Mus. Leafl. Harv. Univ.* 6: 113-136.

———. 1949. Paleozoic lepidodendroid embryos, *Paleobotanical Notices* 2: 1-60.

———. 1952. Materials and methods of paleobotany, *Paleobotanist* 1: 153, pl. 2.

GORDON, W. T. 1910. Note on the prothallus of *Lepidodendron, Ann. Bot.* 24: 821-822.

GRAHAM, R. 1935. An anatomical study of the leaves of the Carboniferous arborescent lycopods, *Ann. Bot.* 49: 587-608.

LECLERCQ, A. 1930. A monograph of *Stigmaria bacupensis, Ann. Bot.* 44: 32-54.

LUNDBLAD, B. 1948. A selaginelloid strobilus from East Greenland (Triassic), *Medd. Dansk Geol. Foren.* 11: 351-363.

McLEAN, R. C. 1912. Two fossil prothalli from the lower coal measures, *New Phyt.* 11: 305-318.

SCHOPF, J. M. 1941. *Mazocarpon oedipternum* sp. nov. and *Sigillaria* relationships, *Ill. St. Geol. Surv. Rept. Invest.* 75.

———. 1941. Notes on the LEPIDOCARPACEAE, *Amer. Midl. Nat.* 25: 548-563.

STEWART, W. N. 1947. A comparative study of stigmarian appendages and stigmarian roots, *Amer. Jour. Bot.* 34: 315-324.

WALTON, J. 1935. Scottish lower Carboniferous plants. The fossil hollow trees of Arran and their branches (*Lepidophloios wunschianus*), *Trans. Roy. Soc. Edinb.* 58: 313-337.

8

THE SPHENOPSIDA

The SPHENOPSIDA, like the LYCOPSIDA, are spore-bearing plants, with apparently microphyllous leaves, without leaf and branch gaps, but they differ in having jointed stems. The name ARTICULATAE is sometimes applied to them. The group has three main divisions: calamarians, equisetaleans, and sphenophylls.

Jeffrey originally included the EQUISETALES in the LYCOPSIDA because they were microphyllous and bore their sporangia in strobili. Scott separated the SPHENOPSIDA chiefly because the stem is divided into nodes and internodes, the leaves are whorled instead of spiral, and because there is some evidence that the sphenopsid leaf is reduced rather than truly microphyllous.

In contrast with the LYCOPSIDA, which includes a thousand surviving species among several families, the SPHENOPSIDA includes a single genus *Equisetum*, with only 24 or 25 species. The existing species are widely distributed and some species, like *E. arvense*, are almost cosmopolitan. The largest living species is *E. giganteum,* which attains a height of 10 meters.

Hirmer and Zimmermann agree essentially in their classifications of the SPHENOPSIDA, although Hirmer treats the various subdivisions as suborders while Zimmermann treats them as orders. A conventional summary is given in the following table.

SPHENOPSIDA (= ARTICULATAE)

1. HYENIALES
   a. CALAMOPHYTACEAE   Devonian
   b. HYENIACEAE   Devonian

2. PSEUDOBORNIALES
   a. PSEUDOBORNIACEAE   Devonian

3. SPHENOPHYLLALES
   a. SPHENOPHYLLACEAE   Devonian to Triassic

4. CHEIROSTROBALES
   a. CHEIROSTROBACEAE   Carboniferous

5. EQUISETALES
   a. ASTEROCALAMITACEAE   Devonian and Lower Carboniferous
   b. CALAMITACEAE   Carboniferous and Permian
   c. EQUISETACEAE   Carboniferous to Recent

It is apparent that this group enjoyed its maximum development in the Paleozoic and in the Devonian exhibited a great diversification.

We have already considered the Devonian *Calamophyton* and *Hyenia* and noted that these forms possess bifurcated leaves and pendulous or recurved sporangia. Such primitive features recall the psilopsids and at the same time show how much the early sphenopsids differed from the typical equisetalean plant.

THE CARBONIFEROUS CALAMITES

The outstanding representative of the SPHENOPSIDA is the Carboniferous *Calamites* (Fig. 15). This genus has many marked affinities with *Equisetum* but at the same time retains numerous features of a more primitive nature.

Many of the CALAMITACEAE attained tree size. There has been found in Lancashire, England, a medullary cast of a calamite 10 meters long, with the diameter of the pith amounting to 12 cm in the thickest part. The writer has seen pith casts from Nova Scotia nearly 20 cm in diameter. Grand'Eury estimated the height of the stem in many of the Calamarians at from 20 to 30 meters.

The most common mode of preservation of *Calamites* is in the form of casts of the medullary cavity. The ribs which they show do not correspond to any features of the external surface but to the print of the inner surface of the wood. The superficial resemblance of these specimens to the ribbed stem of an *Equisetum* is fallacious, except that in both cases the marks on the surface are related to the course of the vascular bundles.

Petrified specimens of the various parts of plants belonging to calamites are common in coal-balls of the Carboniferous of England and Iowa and among the silicious remains in the Upper Carboniferous and Permian of France. The anatomical structure of all the organs has thus become rather well known. We are

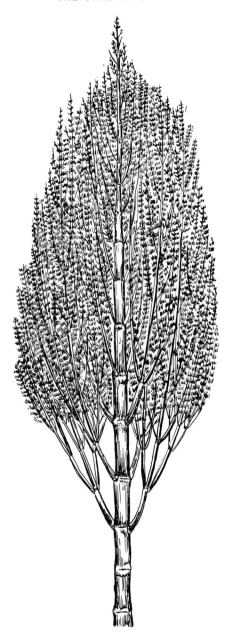

Fig. 15. *Calamites,* an arborescent sphenopsid. Reconstruction by Hirmer, indicating the articulation of the axis and the whorled branching. Carbonifer·ous. (Redrawn from Hirmer.)

obligated chiefly to Williamson, Weiss, Grand'Eury, Browne, Jongmans, and Andrews for our knowledge concerning the calamarians.

In a typical *Calamites* with well-preserved structure, we find the following characters: a central pith, usually hollow in mature stems; surrounding the pith is a ring of collateral vascular bundles; a considerable mass of secondary tissue has usually been formed, so that each of the bundles has assumed a more or less regular wedge-like form; and the inner limit is marked by a definite canal so that the whole appearance is very like that of a living *Equisetum*. The cortex consists of two zones, the inner formed of thin-walled tissue, and the outer of smaller thick-walled cells. One well-preserved stem from Iowa measures 70 mm in diameter, of which 22 mm is stele and 48 mm cortex.

The young stem of a calamite is in all essentials similar to that of an *Equisetum* stem. Surrounding the pith, interrupted at every node by a persistent diaphragm, there is a ring of collateral vascular bundles, with centrifugally developed wood; at the inner border of each is a canal containing the tracheids of the protoxylem. Thus the calamite resembles an *Equisetum* with secondary thickening. *Calamites* branched freely, and each branch developed immediately above the node.

There is no evidence that any calamarian was without secondary growth. The *Calamites* supposed to be without this feature have proved to be medullary casts from which the surrounding tissues have been destroyed. The specimens with cellular structure preserved invariably possess secondary tissues—the only exceptions being very young twigs, and even these often show the commencement of the cambial growth.

Another type of calamarian stem is represented by *Protocalamites pettycurensis*. It is interesting that this Lower Carboniferous species should be the only calamite so far observed which has centripetal wood. The protoxylem is in the usual position, but in this case the development of the primary xylem proceeded in both the inward and outward directions.

The leaves of the calamarians, Fig. 16, were arranged in whorls and were usually of a simple acicular or lanceolate form, though in the several Devonian genera, including *Archaeocalamites*, they were forked. The whorl of leaves was evidently united into a continuous sheath at the base. The detached leaves are given names of form-genera, such as *Asterophyllites, Annularia,* and *Calamocla-dus* (Abbott).

In leaves referred to *Calamocladus (Asterophyllites) charaeformis,* Thomas found the following structure: in the center is a small bundle, the xylem surrounded by a thin-walled tissue, probably phloem; outside the bundle is a sheath, consisting of rather large cells with black contents; beyond the sheath is a very well-developed palisade layer consisting of radiating columnar cells with large inter-

Fig. 16. *Annularia,* a common foliage form of *Calamites.* These leaf whorls are commonly found isolated. (Redrawn from Bertrand.)

cellular spaces. This is immediately surrounded by the epidermis, which has a thicker cuticle on the abaxial surface. Stomata are limited to the flatter adaxial surface. The cell walls of the guard cells are transversely striated, as in a modern *Equisetum.*

Little is known of the structure of the flat leaves of *Annularia,* or of the comparatively large leaves found on some calamarian stems.

The roots of calamarians were referred by Williamson to his genus *Astromyelon* in 1871. The chief characters of *Astromyelon* are a persistent pith (though, in the larger specimens, it may have become fistular), surrounded by a ring of bundles, and in most cases a thick zone of secondary wood is present.

These details give a fair picture of the vegetative anatomy of *Calamites*. There are five main types of strobili which belong to the Calamarians: *Calamostachys, Palaeostachya, Macrostachya, Cingularia,* and *Archaeocalamites*.

Calamostachys is the best known and most widely distributed type. It is characterized by alternate and equidistant whorls of bracts and sporangiophores. In *C. binneyana* there are six or eight sporangiophores to a whorl, and these produce a large number of spores up to 90 microns in diameter. There is occasional abortion of one or more members of the tetrad. The mature spores show the triradiate scar. *Calamostachys binneyana* was apparently homosporous, but in *C. casheana* heterospory certainly occurs. The axis of the strobilus has a persistent pith, surrounded by three or four vascular bundles, which usually appear double. There is usually some secondary development. Some forms of *Calamostachys* have no pith in the axis.

Macrostachya Schimper is a generic name applied to strobili of extraordinarily large size. *Macrostachya thompsonii* exceeds 20 cm in length and has more than 50 whorls of bracts, with 30-36 bracts in each whorl. The species is homosporous with enormous spores. The sporangiophores are arranged as in *Calamostachys*. Another species, *M. heterosporoides*, somewhat smaller than *M. thompsonii*, is heterosporous with a spore diameter ratio approximately 4:1. *Macrostachya* is included by many taxonomists, in *Calamostachys*, but the giant size, woody bracts, and compact construction warrant separation.

Palaeostachya Weiss is closely similar to *Calamostachys*, but the sporangiophores are placed in the axils of the bracts instead of being inserted midway between the whorls of bracts. In both genera, the peltate sporangiophore bears four sporangia upon the lower surface. Most species of *Palaeostachya* are homosporous, though heterospory has been demonstrated in at least one species.

Cingularia Weiss is a genus based upon small strobili in which the sporangiophores are inserted immediately below the bracts instead of above them. Thus far only one carbonized species, *C. typica*, has been adequately described. The most curious feature of this fructification is the strap-shaped sporangiophore which divides into two lobes as it approaches the periphery of the whorl. Each sporangiophore bears four sporangia on the lower surface. The genus occurs in western Europe and in eastern United States.

The fifth type is the Devonian and lower Carboniferous *Archaeocalamites* in which the sporangiophores are without bracts, or rarely, with bracts at infrequent intervals. There are 8-10 sporangiophores in each whorl, having the usual peltate form, each bearing four sporangia upon the lower surface. The leaves of *Archaeocalamites* were forked instead of simple.

It is not yet possible to correlate, with confidence, the various strobilar types with foliage or stems. *Calamostachys*, at least in some species, belongs with *Annularia*. The relationship of *Archaeocalamites* is well established.

We return now to further consideration of the earliest sphenopsids.

THE EARLIEST SPHENOPSIDS

Calamophyton (Fig. 17) was a plant of moderate size, with the larger shoots attaining a diameter of 2 cm. The ultimate bifurcations were as small as 2 mm. The plant body was divided into nodes, more or less scattered in the lower region of the stem. The forked leaves were 8 to 10 mm long, and in some cases were wedge-shaped. The fertile branches bore two rather oblong pendant sporangia. The plant was presumably homosporous. The anatomy is very incompletely known, but there is some evidence that *Calamophyton* possessed secondary thickening.

Hyenia, Fig. 18, was smaller than *Calamophyton*, and it is possible that the specimens represent upper portions of a larger plant. The leaves are several times forked. They have a length of 1-2.5 cm. The sporangia are placed pendulously as in *Calamophyton*, but there are two or three sporangia on each limb of the bifurcated sporangiophore. The detailed anatomy is unknown.

This condition of leaf dichotomy suggests the possibility that the sphenopsids are not truly microphyllous but that they have become apparently microphyllous by reduction from ramified, lateral, thalloid axes.

In the peculiar Upper Devonian *Pseudobornia ursina* Nathorst the leaves are much broader and longer than in *Hyenia*. This remarkable plant from Bear Island in the Arctic Ocean is known only in the form of impressions. The main stems, which were probably creeping, attain a diameter of about 10 cm. The stem is articulated and branched, the smaller branches bearing whorled leaves, which appear to be four per verticil. The leaves are compound, dividing by repeated dichotomy into several leaflets, each of which is deeply pinnatifid. The isolated leaves were formerly supposed to belong to a fern.

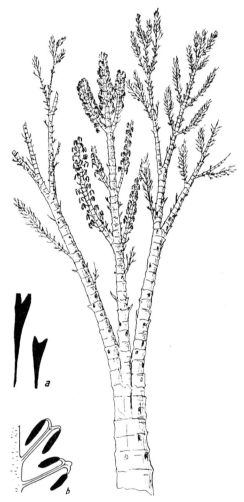

Fig. 17. *Calamophyton primaevum.* Portion of a sporophyte showing articulated axis, leaves (a) and "sporophylls" (b). Devonian. (Courtesy of R. Kräusel and H. Weyland.)

The fructification is in the form of long, lax spikes, bearing whorled sporangiophores which resemble reduced vegetative leaves. Nathorst considered this plant the type of a distinct class, the PSEUDOBORNIALES, showing affinity with the SPHENOPHYLLALES, as well as with ARCHAEOCALAMITES.

Fig. 18. *Hyenia elegans.* Portion of a sporophyte, with details of leaf (a) and "sporophylls" (b). Devonian. (Courtesy of R. Kräusel and H. Weyland.)

THE SPHENOPHYLLS

The order SPHENOPHYLLALES includes only one well-defined family, with *Sphenophyllum* (Fig. 19) the best-known genus. They occur from the Upper Devonian to early Triassic and attain maximum development during the late Carboniferous and early Permian. Several other genera are hesitatingly appended to the family.

The sphenophylls appear to have been herbaceous creeping plants. The slender stems were articulated and bore whorls of wedge-shaped leaves, usually six in number. The stems were branched, the branches springing from immediately above the nodes. In the middle of the stem there is a solid strand of primary wood with pith. This strand is either triarch or hexarch and is always centripetally developed. The structure of the leaf has been studied by Renault, but it is not particularly unusual. It is noteworthy, however, that its strong mechanical construction indicates that the sphenophylls were not floating plants, as has sometimes been suggested.

Fig. 19. *Sphenophyllum.* Portion of a plant indicating leaf dimorphism and strobili. (Redrawn from Hirmer.)

The chief interest in the sphenophylls lies in their strobili, which show several remarkable features.

The fructification of *Sphenophyllum,* usually called *Sphenophyllostachys* (= *Bowmanites*) shows considerable variety in different species. The first of these is *Sphenophyllostachys dawsonii* (Williamson), which includes two forms, the larger of which is probably identical, as Zeiller believed, with S. *cuneifolium*, while the smaller (form B) represents the fructification of S. *plurifoliatum*. We will consider only the larger, better-known form.

The cones reach a length of 12 cm with a diameter 1 cm or more, and in gross features are similar to the calamarian fructification. The cone has an axis 2-3 mm in diameter, bearing at intervals numerous whorls of leaflike bracts; the bracts of each whorl are fused for half their length, forming a cup around the axis. The free portions of the bracts overlap the whorls immediately above. Each of the sporangiophores, which are more numerous than the bracts, bears a single erect sporangium.

The sculptured spores were numerous in each sporangium and were all of one kind, though rather variable in size. Their average diameter is about 90 microns.

So many specimens of S. *dawsoni*, all showing spores of the same kind, have now been investigated that there remains little doubt that these cones were homosporous.

Sphenophyllum fertile Scott, a well-preserved fructification from the British Lower coal measures, has peltate, bisporangiate sporangiophores. The strobile is composed of two kinds of appendages, fertile pedicels bearing two sporangia each and sterile unbranched stalks.

Sphenostrobus thompsonii Levittan and Barghoorn from the Carboniferous of Iowa, of uncertain taxonomic position, is undoubtedly a sphenophyll. The stele is tetrach instead of triarch, but for this feature the fructification is quite conventional. The sporophylls are fused in whorls and the organization of the strobilus and spores resemble closely *Sphenophyllostachys*.

Cheirostrobus. This unusual strobilus will be described in some detail because of its extremely complex structure. All specimens thus far found occur at Pettycur, on the Firth of Forth, into the Calciferous sandstone series, at the base of the Carboniferous. Nothing is known as to the vegetative organs on which it was borne. The cone was large—from 3.5 cm to 4 cm in diameter, and exceeding 10 cm in length. The axis, about 8 mm thick, bore numerous crowded verticils of modified leaves or sporophylls, of which there were twelve in each whorl, the number apparently diminishing toward the apex. The sporophylls were compound, each sporophyll being subdivided in two planes. Above its base it branched into an inferior and a superior lobe, while at the same time both lobes subdivided, in a palmate manner, into segments. The total number of segments was usually six, three of which belonged to the lower lobe and three to the upper. The sporophyll attained a length of 1.5 cm. The segments of each sporophyll were of two kinds, the one set fertile, the other sterile; the three superior segments were the fertile sporangiophores, while the three inferior members were sterile bracts.

The fertile segments or sporangiophores had each a thick peltate lamina, much like that of an *Equisetum* or *Calamostachys*, bearing four sporangia on its inner side. The complete sporophyll consisted of three lower sterile segments and three sporangiophores above them, each of which bore four sporangia, so that the sporophyll as a whole produced twelve sporangia. Since there were twelve such sporophylls in a verticil, and the verticils were numerous, the total production of sporangia by a cone of *Cheirostrobus* must have been considerable. In each sporangium there were produced a large number of spores with a diameter of 65 microns which, so far as is known, were all of one kind.

Scott once remarked that the cone of *Cheirostrobus pettycurensis* "is perhaps the most complex cryptogamic fructification at present known to us." *Cheirostrobus* shows the most marked affinities with the SPHENOPHYLLACEAE, as indicated by the arrangement of the appendages in verticils. It has more in common with *Sphenophyllum* than with any other known group of plants.

MINOR SPHENOPSID GROUPS

There are several other fossil groups which are conventionally classed with the sphenopsids.

The Permian and Triassic *Phyllotheca* and the Triassic *Schizoneura* are interesting but rather unimportant members of the EQUISETALES. More doubtful are the NOEGGERATHIALES, of which *Tingia* is the most widely distributed (Permocarboniferous).

Among the more recently discovered forms worthy of note are two Lower Devonian plants, *Climaciophyton* Kräusel and Weyland and *Sphondylophyton* Schultes and Dorf. These are described as the oldest members of the sphenopsids, but since there are no fructifications nor articulation, the evidence cannot be accepted as conclusive despite the fact that the sessile leaves are borne in whorls.

The various groups of the SPHENOPSIDA are characterized in Table 4.

TABLE 4

Comparison of Representative Sphenopsid Families

Family	Habit	Sporangial Mechanism	Representative Genera	Geological Distribution
CALAMOPHYTACEAE	Moderate size, noded; digitate branching of main axis, otherwise dichotomous; whorled, bifurcate leaves	Pendulous naked sporangia, nonstrobilar	*Calamophyton*	Devonian
HYENIACEAE	Similar but smaller; leaves bifurcated several times; not noded	Two or 3 sporangia on each limb of the bifurcated sporangiophore, nonstrobilar	*Hyenia*	Devonian
PSEUDOBORNIACEAE	Axis articulated and branched; creeping (?); compound leaves, verticillated	Long, lax spikes of whorled sporangiophores resemble reduced sterile leaves	*Pseudobornia*	Devonian
SPHENOPHYLLACEAE	Herbaceous, creeping, semi-aquatic; slender, noded stems bearing whorls of 6 or more leaves	Compact strobili; whorled strobili of considerable complexity, homosporous	*Sphenophyllum*	Devonian to Triassic
CHEIROSTROBACEAE	Unknown	Large, extremely complex strobilus, each whorl having 12 sporophylls, each of which has 3 sterile and 3 fertile segments, homosporous	*Cheirostrobus*	Carboniferous
ASTERO-CALAMITACEAE	Moderate size; noded leaves bifurcated several times	Whorls of peltate sporangiophores, with few sterile bracts (in some forms none)	*Asterocalamites*	Devonian and Lower Carboniferous
CALAMITACEAE	Attained great size (up to 30 m) articulated throughout body; whorled leaves; secondary growth	Compact strobili; generally homosporous, heterospory in some forms	*Calamites*	Carboniferous to Triassic
EQUISETACEAE	Noded body, small leaves; no secondary growth	No whorls of sterile bracts in strobili	*Equisetites* *Equisetum*	Carboniferous (?) to Recent

95

There is a marked decline of the sphenopsids during the Mesozoic. By the beginning of the Cenozoic one family survives, probably one genus, *Equisetum* (though the fossil forms are cautiously called *Equisetites*). Thus we see that *Lycopodium* and *Selaginella* among the lycopsids and *Equisetum* among sphenopsids remind us of venerable plant groups which enjoyed dominance in ages long past.

Bibliography

ABBOTT, M. L. 1959. American species of *Asterophyllites, Annularia* and *Sphenophyllum, Bull. Amer. Paleont.* 39, No. 174.

BROWNE, I. M. P. 1925. Notes on the cones of the *Calamostachys*-type in the Renault and Roche collections, *Ann. Bot.* 39: 313-358.

———. 1927. A new theory of the morphology of the Calamarian cone, *Ann. Bot.* 41: 301-315.

DARRAH, W. C. 1936. A new *Macrostachya* from the Carboniferous of Illinois, *Bot. Mus. Leafl. Harvard Univ.* 4: 52-63.

———. 1936. The occurrence of the genus *Tingia* in Texas, *Bot. Mus. Leafl. Harvard Univ.* 5: 173-188.

HARTUNG, W. 1933. Die Sporenverhältnisse der Calamariaceen, *Arb. Inst. f. Palaeobot. u. Petrogr. Brennsteine* 3: 95-194.

HOSKINS, J. H., and A. T. CROSS. 1943. Monograph of the Paleozoic cone genus *Bowmanites* (SPHENOPHYLLALES), *Amer. Midl. Nat.* 30: 113-163.

KIDSTON, R., and W. J. JONGMANS. 1917. A monograph of the *Calamites* of western Europe, *Meded. van de Rijksops. van Delfstoffen*, No. 7.

KON'NO, E. 1929. On genera *Tingia* and *Tingiostachya* from the Permian beds in northern Korea, *Jour. Geol. and Geogr.* 6: 113-147.

LECLERCQ, S. 1935-1936. Sur un épi fructifère de Sphenophyllales, *Ann. Soc. Géol. Belg.* 58: 182-194; 59: 222-248.

LEVITTAN, E. D., and E. S. BARGHOORN. 1948. *Sphenostrobus thompsonii*—a new genus of the SPHENOPHYLLALES? *Amer. Jour. Bot.* 35: 350-357.

SELLING, O. 1944. Studies on calamitean cone compressions by means of serial sections, *Svensk. Bot. Tids.* 38: 295-330.

THOMAS, H. H. 1911. On the leaves of *Calamites, Phil. Trans. Roy. Soc. Lond.* B 202: 51-70.

9

PTEROPSIDA: FERNS

The third great division of vascular plants which differentiated from the psilopsid complex was the PTEROPSIDA, characterized by large leaves and with leaf and branch gaps interrupting the vascular cylinder. All higher plants—ferns, gymnosperms, and angiosperms —are pteropsids in body form. In this sense, and with the discovery of pteridosperms, the "pteridophyte-spermatophyte" classification became obsolete.

The ferns have left a magnificent fossil record extending from the mid-Devonian to the present. Our knowledge of Paleozoic representatives, both structurally preserved and compressions, is constantly increasing. Yet there is considerable confusion in interpretation of the older ferns. The Paleozoic members for the most part belong to extinct families which do not fit into the conventional subdivisions of existing ferns. Furthermore, there is a dual terminology resulting from the independent studies of petrified and compression forms. It was believed for many years that the ferns were the most abundant plants of the Carboniferous. Then with the recognition of the pteridosperms, opinion verged in that direction until suspicion was cast upon all but a few genera. Gradually, appreciation of the importance of the true ferns has been restored. For these reasons, however, it has not been possible to establish a fully satisfactory classification of the ferns.

DEVONIAN FERNS

Among Devonian plants there are several types which certainly belong to the ferns in a broad sense. Although knowledge of these genera is incomplete, some known solely from compressions, others only from fragmentary petrified remains, there is sufficient information to characterize their main features.

Protopteridium, from the middle and upper Devonian, retains many features of the psilopsid body, but it is advanced in hav-

97

ing sympodially branched axes with the branches divided dichotomously. Some of the ultimate divisions are flattened. The sporangia are terminal. There are six or eight well-defined species occurring in western Europe, eastern North America, and eastern Asia.

Rhacophyton, another upper Devonian form, has been known for many years, but its importance became evident only recently (Leclercq). A remarkable species, *R. zygopteroides*, Fig. 20, found in Belgium, permits a synthesis of a whole series of scattered observations. The vegetative fronds are borne in an alternate or spiral manner while the fertile fronds are modified pairs of pinnae, coalescent at the base, sterile in the basal region, and fertile in the upper portion. This modified frond is dichotomized many times, forming a graceful "head," bearing great numbers of symmetrically disposed fusiform sporangia. The form *Cephalopteris* from Spitsbergen is in all probability the fructification of a *Rhacophyton*.

Until now no structural remains of *Protopteridium* or *Rhacophyton* have been recognized. Whether their structure will prove similar to that observed in the contemporary IRIDOPTERIDALES discussed later remains to be determined.

THE COENOPTERIDS

The great majority of Paleozoic ferns are grouped more or less naturally into a single order COENOPTERIDALES, which may be divided into two suborders (or orders): PHYLLOPHORALES and INVERSICATENALES.

The PHYLLOPHORALES (the ordinal rank being used here for convenience) include plants with a main stalk ("phyllophore") which is intermediate in position and structure between a stem and petiole. The phyllophore is axially, not bilaterally, symmetrical and bears subdivisions in two or four rows.

The INVERSICATENALES include plants with slender stems, repeatedly branched, and bearing spirally arranged fronds.

There are several other small groups of Paleozoic ferns which are clearly distinguishable yet cannot be referred to these two orders without hesitation. The CLADOXYLALES are somewhat related to both but are distinct in being polystelic and developing considerable secondary growth. There are three or four genera, of which *Cladoxylon* with about a dozen species is typical. Usually the CLADOXYLALES are placed with or near the INVERSICATENALES

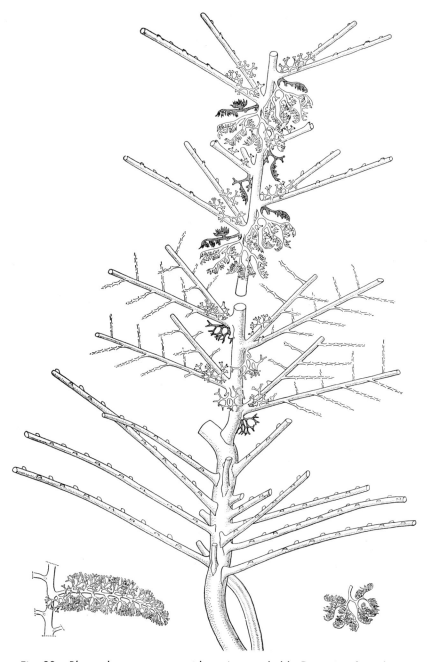

Fig. 20. *Rhacophyton zygopteroides*. A remarkable Devonian fern showing zygopteroid branching, leaves, and pendulous fertile branches. (Courtesy of Prof. Suzanne Leclercq.)

because of the characteristic petiolar trace. Another small group of mid-Devonian age, the IRIDOPTERIDALES, contains several genera which exhibit a body plan reminiscent of the psilopsids. The stele is actinostelic and one of the genera, *Arachnoxylon*, is believed to be leafless. *Iridopteris*, from which the group receives its name, bears small, spirally arranged leaf traces and approaches the INVERSICATENALES. If the IRIDOPTERIDALES are a natural group, that is to say, if further study does not exclude *Arachnoxylon* from it, then they are the most ancient and primitive ferns. If, on the other hand, *Arachnoxylon* is ultimately segregated, the remaining members are probably referable to the INVERSICATENALES.

The PHYLLOPHORALES include several families, of which the ZYGOPTERIDACEAE is the most important. It embraces a homogeneous series of well-known genera: *Asteropteris, Stauropteris, Etapteris, Ankyropteris, Clepsydropsis, Metaclepsydropsis,* and *Diplolabis.*

The INVERSICATENALES include several genera which by some workers are placed in monotypic families. *Botryopteris* and *Anachoropteris* are the best known.

None of the groups of Paleozoic ferns discussed thus far can be accommodated by the two-fold classification of existing ferns, EUSPORANGIATAE and LEPTOSPORANGIATAE. In the EUSPORANGIATAE the sporangia are borne upon fertile spikes (outgrowths from the leaf blade) or in sori on the abaxial surface of a leaf. The sporangium has a jacket layer of more than one cell in thickness, and produces a large number of spores. In the LEPTOSPORANGIATAE the sporangia are generally borne in sori either marginally or upon the abaxial surface of the leaf. The sporangial jacket is one cell thick. There are no vegetative features which serve to distinguish the LEPTOSPORANGIATES from the other ferns. Among fossil ferns the gametophytic generation and embryologic development are virtually unknown, thus the criteria of greatest value in distinguishing existing ferns cannot be applied.

Among coenopterid ferns, which are obviously a heterogeneous group, we find differences in position of the sporangia. Some forms have the sporangium borne singly at the apex of a dichotomy, in others in massive clusters, and in some on the lamina. The jacket is more than one cell thick, and there is a terminal slit or pore through which the spores escaped. This condition is more primitive than that observed in the EUSPORANGIATAE, but the difference is in degree only. As suggested earlier, the fundamental differences appear in the vegetative features of the coenopterids. A few examples will show how striking these really are.

Stauropteris, Fig. 21, is abundantly represented in the Carboniferous by two species, S. *oldhamia* Binney and S. *burntislandica* Bertrand. *Stauropteris* was bushlike in habit, almost radially symmetrical, with highly compound, i.e., repeatedly branched, fronds but without differentiated laminae. The sporangia were borne

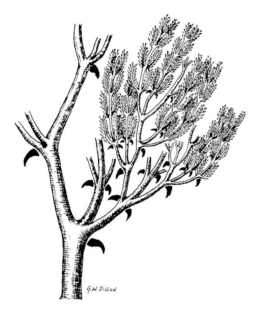

Fig. 21. *Stauropteris.* Portion of the sporophyte, showing characteristic mode of branching. Carboniferous. (Redrawn from Hirmer.)

terminally upon the ultimate branches. The stele appears square in transverse section, with cruciform xylem and phloem filling the spaces between the xylem arms. The branches developed in pairs, with succeeding pairs arising on opposite sides of the rachis. The two pinnae of a pair were united at the base and thus appear to be members of a dichotomy. The strand of each secondary rachis repeats the structural form of the strand of the primary rachis. In S. *oldhamia* the terminal sporangia were nearly spherical with a diameter of 0.7 mm and had a sporangial wall several cells thick. There was no annulus, but a stomium through which the spore escaped was present. Numerous spores, 32 to 40 microns in diameter were produced in each sporangium. Well-preserved germinating spores have been observed. S. *burntislandica* has been shown to be heterosporous, a condition which distinguishes these ancient ferns from modern primitive ferns. The megasporangia (*"Bensonites"*) contain 2-6 large spores. Heterospory is known in several coenopterid genera.

A somewhat different aspect is presented by *Botryopteris*, the most varied and abundant genus of structurally preserved Carboniferous ferns. The stem axis has a remarkably simple structure, the stele consisting of a solid strand of tracheids surrounded by phloem. The relatively large petioles, borne spirally, contain a single bundle, which in most species resembles the letter omega in transverse section.

The characteristics of the vegetative organs are in all respects those of a simple type of fern. The fructifications, although confirming a filicinean affinity, differ from any existing ferns. The sporangia, densely grouped in tufts on the naked rachis of a modified frond, reached 1.5 to 2 mm in length in several species, though smaller in others. In *B. globosa* Darrah, there were thousands of sporangia occurring in a great compact terminal "head." The sporangium had a broad annulus, forming a longitudinal band many cells in width, running the whole length of the sporangium on one side. There is no close analogy to this structure among recent ferns, though the areola of the osmundaceous sporangium has been regarded as a shortened multiseriate annulus. There are approximately twenty known species of *Botryopteris*, half based upon structurally preserved petioles, the remainder on sporangia.

Ankyropteris (*Zygopteris*) is a much more advanced type than either *Stauropteris* or *Botryopteris*. The stele may be stellate; the xylem is of complex structure, the larger elements forming a broad external zone, while the interior is occupied by a system of smaller tracheids intermingled with parenchyma. The petiolar trace usually appears as a double anchor in transverse section. In *A. corrugata*, branching was essentially dichotomous. The pyriform sporangia are borne on a fertile modified frond. A broad multiseriate annulus is present. It is believed the *Corynepteris*, based upon fertile fronds of sphenopteroid habit, is referable to *Zygopteris*. The synangium of *Corynepteris* approaches the MARATTIACEAE.

PALEOZOIC FERNLIKE LEAVES (Pteridophylls)

Compressions of fernlike foliage are among the most abundant late Paleozoic fossils—so preponderant that paleobotanists once referred to the Carboniferous as the "age of ferns." The puzzling fact that most of these supposed ferns were invariably sterile was explained in many devious ways, and not until the discovery of the pteridosperms was it realized that many, perhaps a majority of the foliar form-genera, were not ferns. The reference of a given species based upon foliar remains to the ferns or to the pteridosperms is rarely possible. A brief synopsis of the more abundant "pteridophylls," however, is of interest.

Brongniart, in his great *Histoire des Végétaux Fossiles* in 1828, published the system of nomenclature which in modified form is still in use today. Nearly all of the form-genera he recognized were diagnosed on the basis of sterile fronds, with the result that some of these genera are so artificial that plants belonging to diverse orders sometimes fall into a single genus.

Key to the Carboniferous "Fern" Form-Genera

1. Fronds with entire pinnules.
    2. Secondary veins forming a network.
        3. Pinnules attached by whole breadth of base .... *Lonchopteris.*
        3. Pinnules attached at a single point .... *Linopteris.*

    2. Secondary veins not forming a network.
        4. Pinnules with a distinct midrib.
            5. Pinnules small, attached by whole base. .... *Pecopteris.*
            5. Pinnules large.
                6. Decurrent at base .... *Alethopteris.*
                6. Constricted at base .... *Taeniopteris.*

    4. Pinnules without, or with an indistinct, midrib.
        7. Pinnules attached by whole base .... *Odontopteris.*
        7. Pinnules attached at a point .... *Neuropteris.*

1. Fronds with pinnules lobed, or dissected; rarely with rounded pinnules.
    8. Pinnules small, veins radiate fanlike from base of pinnule *Sphenopteris.*
    8. Pinnules large, basal pinnule decurrent .... *Mariopteris.*

The more common pteridophyll forms are shown in Figs. 22 and 23.

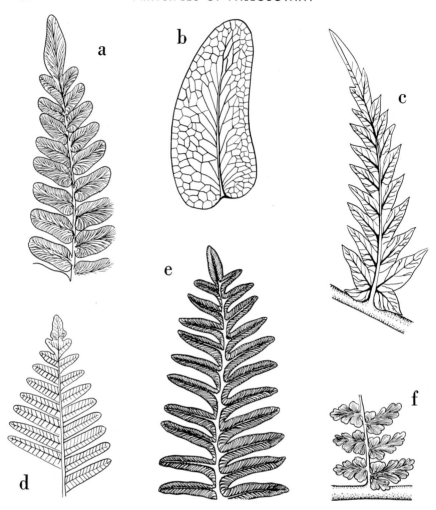

Fig. 22. The common form-genera of Carboniferous pteridophylls. The great majority of fernlike compressions are assigned to these genera. a. *Neuropteris;* b. *Linopteris;* c. *Mariopteris;* d. *Pecopteris;* e. *Alethopteris;* f. *Sphenopteris.* (Drawn by G. W. Dillon.)

PALEOZOIC MARATTIACEAE

Next to the coenopterid ferns—which unquestionably include many distantly related, if not unrelated, forms—the most abundant group of Paleozoic ferns was the MARATTIACEAE. Although the evidence is somewhat equivocal, there is a strong case for the occurrence of MARATTIACEAE in the Carboniferous.

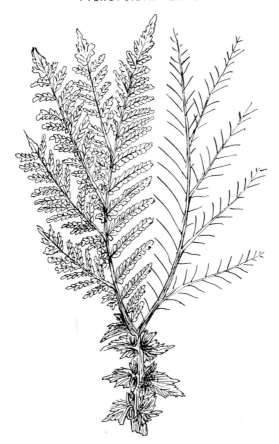

Fig. 23. A frond of *Mariopteris* showing characteristic branching and the aphlebian pinnules along the "petiole." (Redrawn from Bertrand.)

The form-genera *Ptychocarpus, Asterotheca, Acitheca, Scolecopteris, Cyathotrachus,* and *Eoangiopteris,* all based upon synangial fructifications, are usually referred to this family.

There is considerable confusion of generic designations largely because the original descriptions were based upon single, or at best, few specimens. The complications increased when better-preserved material was attributed to new genera instead of amplifying knowledge of previously described forms. Hence *Asterotheca,* the most abundant fructification among pecopterids, is being by-passed while the scope of *Scolecopteris* increases. Actually they are one and the same. Similarly, *Cyathotrachus* is nothing more than *Ptychocarpus,* which was based on meager data.

In *Ptychocarpus*, which bears a resemblance to the living *Kaulfussia*, the sporangia, usually six to eight in number, are grouped together in a circular sorus. The sporangia are united to each other and to a central column. The whole sorus is embedded in tissue. The individual exannulate sporangium possesses a tapetal wall and produces a large number of small spores (18-20 mu); the best known species, *P. unitus*, occurs in western Europe and eastern United States. *Cyathotrachus altissimus* (Fig. 1) is probably the most fully described species attributed to this genus.

In *Ptychocarpus* and *Cyathotrachus* there is a synangial sheath, while in *Asterotheca* and *Scolecopteris* a sheath is absent. All these synangial types represent a closely allied series of forms, and the parent foliage, where known, is always *Pecopteris*.

Pecopteris is known to have been borne upon peculiar, large cauline stems called *Psaronius*, Fig. 24. Whether all species of *Pecopteris* belong to *Psaronius*, or vice versa, is of course not known. As is so often the case with fossil plants, many different names have been applied to parts of the plant body under different conditions of preservation.

The name *Psaronius* applies to structurally preserved stems. External casts or impressions are loosely described as *Megaphyton* and *Caulopteris* (Fig. 25). The *Psaronius* trunk viewed in transverse section is divided into a relatively small vascular portion surrounded by a much larger sheath of cortical or adventitious roots. Superficially, this sheath resembles the cortical root mantle observed in *Angiopteris*. The nature of these "rootlets" is still disputed, with present opinion tending toward their adventitious or extracortical origin. The vascular portion of the trunk is a complex dictyostele. The large leaf traces are crescent or horseshoe-shaped, which in detached petioles are identified as *Stipitopteris*. A zone of sclerenchyma surrounds the stele but is broken at points of departure of the traces.

Psaronius is subdivided into three groups: *Distichi*, in which the leaf traces occur in two series; *Tetrastichi*, which have four series of leaf traces; and *Polystichi*, in which the traces are spirally disposed. The *Distichi* are coextensive or congeneric with *Megaphyton* while the *Tetrastichi* and *Polystichi* are referable to *Caulopteris*. There are other compression stem genera, but they do not invalidate the generalization here stated.

Fig. 24. *Psaronius* (group *Polystichi*) bearing large fronds of the *Pecopteris* type. Carboniferous. (Drawn by G. W. Dillon.)

It is of interest to note in passing that a century ago large numbers of silicified trunks of *Psaronius* were collected in the vicinity of Athens, Ohio. The largest collection, amounting to hundreds of specimens, some measuring from two to three meters in length and

Fig. 25. (See next page for caption.)

more than 33 cm in diameter, was sent to Harvard University in 1866. Alas, in ignorance of their value, but a few score remain; the larger pieces were used for fill when the Biological Laboratories building was constructed. Some future paleobotanist may unearth this intrusive burial.

The Paleozoic MARATTIACEAE show several significant relationships with the coenopterids. The synangial sheath found in *Cyathotrachus*, *Ptychocarpus*, etc., resembles that found in *Chorionopteris* and is somewhat reminiscent of a modified cluster of *Etapteris* sporangia (Fig. 25). *Corynepteris* (*Zygopteris*) also approaches the MARATTIACEAE. Certain petiolar types, particularly *Anachoropteris*, bear striking similarity to some of the smaller forms of *Stipitopteris*. It should be borne in mind, however, that some of the forms we are accepting as coenopterids may be excluded from this group. It is a simple feat to set up or demolish imagined phylogenetic series.

QUESTIONABLE PALEOZOIC GROUPS

Before leaving the Paleozoic ferns some notice must be given to several small groups of Devonian ferns which cannot be referred to any of the categories thus far considered. Probably further study will show them to be members of known groups and their systematic isolation due merely to insufficient information. The groups to be considered briefly are: *Archaeopteris*, *Aneurophyton*, and *Cladoxylon*.

Archaeopteris (Fig. 30), a form-genus based primarily on frond compressions, has been regarded for some time as a probable pteridosperm. Recently, however, Arnold has demonstrated heterospory in *A. latifolia*, with a spore size ratio of approximately 10:1. The megaspores, which measure about 300 microns in diameter, are produced eight to sixteen per sporangium, while the microspores are produced in great numbers. The internal structure of the

Fig. 25. Carboniferous Ferns. A reconstruction indicating typical growth forms. (1) (Lower left) *Mariopteris*, type *M. muricata*, a slender, low, creeping form. (2) (Extreme lower right) *Zygopteris*, a low erect form. (3) (Left center) *Megaphyton*, a large tree-fern. (4) (Center) *Hagiophyton* and (5) (right) *Caulopteris* are also tree-ferns. *Megaphyton*, *Hagiophyton*, and *Caulopteris* have stems with internal structure known as *Psaronius* and fronds of the *Pecopteris* type. They are considered to belong to the Marattiaceae. Reconstruction by Paul Bertrand. (By permission from Mme. P. Bertrand and Masson et Cie, Paris.)

petiole or stem of *Archaeopteris* has not been recognized but undoubtedly will prove to be of a known type. *Archaeopteris* is an abundant, indeed, the most characteristic component of upper Devonian floras. There is evidence that some species of *Archaeopteris* were borne upon *Cladoxylon* petioles.

Aneurophyton presents a puzzling combination of features. The general aspect is that of a large psilopsid but having monopodial rather than dichotomous branching. The leaves are small (3 to 5 mm in length), apparently without a vascular trace. The terminal sporangia are produced in loose clusters. The stems, which attained a diameter of 1 meter or more near the base, had extensive compact secondary xylem. The tracheids are of the multiseriate bordered-pit type. *Eospermatopteris*, the supposed seed-fern from Gilboa, New York, is identical with *Aneurophyton*. The affinities of *Aneurophyton* are uncertain and the most definite conclusion consistent with present knowledge is that they are pteropsids which have attained the fern level of development. Although the plant body produced secondary wood, the fructification is cryptogamic. Thus in several respects the group approaches the pteridosperms.

Much the same opinion applies to *Cladoxylon*. The stem is polystelic as viewed in transverse section. Secondary wood with pitted tracheids has been observed in all species. The leaf-trace is clepsydroid and thus strongly suggests a coenopterid affinity. *Cladoxylon* ranges from the mid-Devonian to the lower Carboniferous. In this survey, no attempt will be made to refer *Archaeopteris, Aneurophyton,* or *Cladoxylon* to a system; rather, they are accepted as ancient ferns of uncertain systematic position.

Table 5 correlates various form-genera of the principal groups of fossil ferns.

EXISTING FAMILIES OF FERNS

The presence of OSMUNDACEAE in the Paleozoic is attested both by sporangia and petrified petioles. Kidston and Gwynne-Vaughan have published in great detail the descriptions of various species of OSMUNDACEAE. The Paleozoic members are usually placed in the genera *Zalesskya* and *Thamnopteris*. The later species are usually named *Osmundites*.

For the leptosporangiate ferns, which comprise most of our existing forms, we cannot trace with certainty family histories earlier

TABLE 5

Principal Fossil Fern Groups

Position	Group	Orders	Vegetative Forms	Fructification	Foliage	Distribution
COENOPTERIDINEAE	PHYLLOPHORALES Main stalk of phyllophore axially symmetrical; with 2 or 4 rows of subdivisions	IRIDOPTERIDALES (?) STAUROPTERIDALES	Iridopteris Rhacophyton Stauropteris	Unknown Cephalopteris Stauropteris	Unknown Rhodea Apparently none	Devonian Devonian Carboniferous
		ZYGOPTERIDALES	Etapteris Ankyropteris Clepsydropsis	Etapteris Corynepteris Unknown	"Sphenopteris" Alloiopteris Uncertain	Carboniferous Carboniferous Carboniferous, Permian
	INVERSICATENALES Slender stem repeatedly branched, spirally arranged fronds. No secondary growth.	BOTRYOPTERIDALES	Botryopteris Anachoropteris	Botryopteris Chorionopteris	Sphenopteris Linopteris Sphenopteris	Carboniferous
Uncertain Position		CLADOXYLALES	Cladoxylon	Unknown	Archaeopteris (?)	Devonian
		OSMUNDALES MARATTIALES	Osmundites	Osmundites	Cladophlebis Osmundites	L. Carboniferous Carboniferous to Recent
FILICINEAE	EUSPORANGIATAE	OPHIOGLOSSALES				
		FILICALES	Oligocarpia Schizaea, Gleichenia, Cyathea, Matonia, Polypodium, et al.	Oligocarpia	Sphenopteris Pecopteris	Carboniferous Triassic to Recent
	LEPTOSPORANGIATAE	SALVINIALES	Salvinia	Salvinia	Azolla Salvinia	Cretaceous to Recent

than Jurassic and Cretaceous. The HYMENOPHYLLACEAE are doubtfully recorded from the Jurassic. Undoubted GLEICHENIACEAE are present from the Cretaceous onward, with the Carboniferous *Oligocarpia* and Triassic *Mertensides* possible, but questionable, representatives. Seward has recorded the geological history of the MATONIACEAE, and both *Matonidium* and *Laccopteris* have many Mesozoic species. The CYATHEACEAE have a continuous history from the Jurassic to Recent. *Dicksonia* and *Thyrsopteris* are the earliest members of this family.

The POLYPODIACEAE have been recorded from the Jurassic of Japan (*Onychiopsis*). The three existing genera, *Aspidium*, *Adiantum*, and *Polypodium* occur from the lower Cretaceous onward.

Various specimens have been referred to SALVINIACEAE. The consensus of opinion seems to be that *Salvinia* and *Azolla* occur from the Cretaceous to the present.

The ferns are still highly successful members of the pteropsids. There is some evidence to indicate that the ferns attained their maximum during the late Paleozoic and early Mesozoic and have since begun to decline. The prominent Mesozoic representatives will be discussed in Chapter 16.

There are several important evolutionary tendencies which Bower has recognized in the development of the FILICINEAE. From the undifferentiated protostelic axis of *Stauropteris* with its terminal sporangia, we can trace several variations on the dichotomous habit of the Devonian vascular plants: persistent monostelic stems (protostelic or siphonostelic) and so-called polystelic stems. In addition, we can trace a series of changes in the position of sporangia from isolated terminal, to clustered terminal, to marginal, to superficial. Although homospory is normal for the group, heterospory developed in several "orders," including some coenopterids.

Bower pictures the archetype of the filicinean sporophyte as a simple upright shoot of radial symmetry, probably rootless, dichotomizing if branched at all, with the little distinction between axis and leaf, with a solid xylem core, and with large, thick-walled, solitary terminal sporangia. The plants most nearly approaching this type are *Stauropteris* and *Protopteridium*.

Thus we find again in the filicineans that the morphological differentiation of the pteropsid phyla, as did the lycopsids and sphenopsids, began in the psilophyte complex during Mid-Devonian times.

We have already noted in several connections that many primitive fernlike plants are not ferns at all, but seed-ferns which thus belong to the alliance of gymnosperms. In the filicineans we encounter a new type of body plan constructed on the basis of large leaves and pinnatifid branches. The gymnosperms have done well with these two new structures.

Bibliography

ANDREWS, H. N., and E. M. KERN. 1947. The Idaho Tempskyas and associated fossil plants, *Ann. Mo. Bot. Gard.* 34: 119-186.

ARNOLD, C. A. 1940. Structure and relationships of some middle Devonian plants from western New York, *Amer. Jour. Bot.* 27: 57-63.

BERTRAND, P. 1935. Contribution à l'études des cladoxylées de Saalfeld, *Palaeontographica* 80 B: 101-170.

CORSIN, P. 1948. Reconstitutions de Pecopteridées: genus *Caulopteris* Lindley and Hutton, *Megaphyton* Artis, et *Hagiophyton* nov. gen., *Ann. Soc. Géol. du Nord* 67: 6-25.

DARRAH, W. C. 1939. Fossil flora of Iowa coal balls, II. The fructification of *Botryopteris*, *Bot. Mus. Leafl. Harv. Univ.* 7: 157-180.

————. 1941. The coenopterid ferns in American coal balls, *Amer. Midl. Nat.* 25: 233-269.

KIDSTON, R., and D. T. GWYNNE-VAUGHAN. 1907-1914. On the fossil OSMUNDACEAE, *Trans. Linn. Soc. Lond.* 45, 46, 47, and 50.

LECLERCQ, S. 1951. Étude Morphologique et anatomique d'une fougère du Dévonien supérieur, *Ann. Soc. Géol. Belg. Mém.* 9: Liége.

MAMAY, S. H. 1950. Some American Carboniferous fern fructifications, *Ann. Mo. Bot. Gard.* 37: 409-459.

READ, C. B., and R. W. BROWN. 1937. American Cretaceous ferns of the genus *Tempskya*, *U.S. Geol. Surv. Prof. Pap.* 186: 105-131.

SAHNI, B. 1941. Indian silicified plants, I. *Azolla intertrappea*, *Proc. Ind. Acad. Sci.* 14: 489-501.

SINNOTT, E. W. 1914. Some Jurassic OSMUNDACEAE from New Zealand, *Ann. Bot.* 28: 471-479.

STIPANICIC, P. N., and C. A. MENENDEZ. 1949. Contribución al conocimiento de la flora fósil de Barreal, I. DIPTERIDACEAE, *Bol. Inform. Petrol.* 291: 44-73.

10

THE PTERIDOSPERMS

The pteridosperms or seed-ferns more than any other group of
fossil plants have suffered by the whims of speculation. Brongniart
called the Carboniferous the "age of ferns" because of the numerical
preponderance of impressions of fernlike foliage. The scarcity of
fruiting specimens did not disturb anyone in particular until 1883
when Stur suggested that at least some of these fernlike fossils might
not be ferns.

DISCOVERY OF THE SEED-FERNS

Shortly thereafter Potonié created a new systematic group
("CYCADOFILICES") to accommodate structurally preserved stems
exhibiting characteristics intermediate between those of ferns and
cycads. About the same time Oliver and Scott (1903) demonstrated the seed habit of *Lyginopteris*, and Sellards (1905) isolated
pollen grains from a peculiar campanulate fructification (*Codonotheca*) found associated with *Neuropteris* in Illinois. It soon became
apparent that the CYCADOFILICALES [*sic*] and PTERIDOSPERMAE were
coextensive groups.

Paleobotanists now found seeds everywhere; as a result, suspicion
was cast upon nearly all the types of fernlike foliage known from
the Devonian to Triassic. Such Devonian plants as *Archaeopteris*,
Eospermatopteris, and *Aneurophyton* were widely considered as
pteridosperms, but they are now generally accepted as ferns. On the
other hand, within the past twenty years recognition of a number
of Mesozoic (Triassic and Jurassic) pteridosperms shows that the
limits of the groups are far from established.

GENERAL FEATURES OF THE PTERIDOSPERMS

The group may be defined as plants of fern habit, with bi-, tri-, or
quadripinnatifid fronds, bearing seeds and synangial microsporangia
producing true pollen.

The seed is generally, but not always, radially symmetrical and characterized by a peculiar pollen chamber formed at the apex of the nucellus (megasporangium) by the separation of the inner and outer layers. Pollen grains are commonly found in the chamber, and it is assumed that some contrivance such as is found among living gymnosperms drew the pollen into the cavity. In many, but not all, pteridosperms, the orthrotropic seed was produced singly in a cupule. The nature of the cupule, which is most completely known in *Lyginopteris* (Fig. 26), is not understood, although some investigators (e.g., Halle) consider the campanulate microsporangiate mechanism strictly homologous with the cupule.

The mature gametophyte (prothallus) of *Lagenostoma* has been preserved in a number of specimens, including such structures as archegonia and egg cells, as pointed out by Long in his paper on the prothallus of this species (1944).

The microsporangia are usually produced in pendulous clusters, sometimes with the pollen sacs separated for most of their length (*Codonotheca, Crossotheca*, Fig. 27); in other forms, they are completely fused superficially, resembling a seedlike body (*Aulacotheca*), with all intergrades (*Dolerotheca, Whittleseya*, Fig. 28, *Boulaya*). *Crossotheca* as presently defined is an unnatural formgenus including supposed ferns as well as seed-ferns.

In the *Crossotheca* group the microspores are filicoid, while in the *Dolerotheca* group they are oval, nearly bilaterally symmetrical. The pollen grains have a multicellular gametophyte, with 12, 24, or more cells (*Dolerotheca*). Pollen grains in *Boulaya fertilis* and *Crossotheca hughesiana* seem to have cells inside the spore and may have been hollow, producing free nuclei within it, according to Florin.

The stems may be protostelic (*Tetrastichia, Heterangium, Lyginopteris*) or polystelic (*Medullosa*). *Lyginopteris* and *Medullosa* produced extensive secondary wood.

The better-known Paleozoic pteridosperms are summarized in Table 6.

There are many distinct types of detached, well-preserved seeds of unknown parentage. *Physostoma, Conostoma, Stephanospermum, Rotodontiospermum, Codonospermum* (Fig. 1B), and *Gnetopsis* are but a few of them. The first two are probably lyginopterid, the next two medullosan; the last two are entirely unknown.

Fig. 26. (See next page for caption.)

TABLE 6

Correlation of Representative Form-Genera of Paleozoic Pteridosperms

	Stem	Rachis	Foliage	Seed	Micro-sporangia
LYGINOPTERI-DACEAE ...	Heterangium Lyginopteris	Lyginorachis Tetrastichia	Sphenopteris Sphenopteris	Sphaerostoma Lagenostoma*	Telangium Crossotheca (pars)
MEDULLOSACEAE	Medullosa	Myeloxylon	Neuropteris, Alethopteris	Trigonocarpus, Pachytesta, Neuropterocarpus	Potoniea, Dolerotheca, Whittleseya, Aulacotheca, Codonotheca
	Sutcliffia Colpoxylon	Myeloxylon			

* The cupulate branches from which the seeds have been shed are known as Calymmatotheca.

COMMON STEM TYPES OF PTERIDOSPERMS

Heterangium. This type is believed to represent one of the most primitive seed-ferns because it has a protostele resembling that of the living *Gleichenia*. The strand is mesarch and the centrifugal tracheids have spiral or scalariform markings. The centripetal tracheids are pitted.

Fig. 26. Carboniferous Pteridosperms. Reconstruction indicating the general habit of the principal pteridosperms. (1) (Center) *Sphenopteris* (lyginopterid) with dissected pinnules. (2) (Left) *Neuropteris*, type *N. heterophylla*, (medullosan) with large pinnules and very large aphleboid pinnules along the rachis. (3) (Right) *Odontopteris*, type *O. reichi*, (medullosan) with laciniate aphleboid leaves. Original reconstruction by Paul Bertrand. (By permission from Mme. Bertrand and Masson et Cie, Paris.)

Fig. 27. *Crossotheca*, a form-genus of epaulette-like organs bearing sporangia or pollen sacs. Known attached to both *Pecopteris* and *Sphenopteris* foliage. Carboniferous. (Redrawn from Kidston and Scott.)

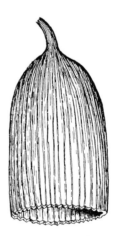

Fig. 28. *Whittleseya*, a campanulate polleniferous organ attributed to certain medullosan pteridosperms (*Alethopteris, Pachytesta*). Carboniferous. (Redrawn from Halle.)

Lyginopteris. The stem has a mesarch siphonostele with a very large pith and an abundant development of secondary wood. This is surrounded by a thick cortex which is differentiated into two zones made up of thin-walled and thick-walled cells. In *Lyginopteris* there are conspicuous leaf traces. The protoxylem has tracheids with spiral markings, and the metaxylem has the centrifugal tracheids scalariform and the centripetal with bordered pits. All of the tracheids of the secondary wood are pitted.

Medullosa. The stem is "polystelic," commonly with three steles, and with each stele surrounded by its own secondary xylem and phloem. In the secondary wood the pits seem to be restricted to the radial walls.

We note, then, that the primary wood is "cryptogamic" but that secondary wood, comparable to that found in gymnosperms, is present and is developed from a cambium. It was this fact that first led to the diagnosis of the group of pteridosperms. These petrified stem types, which are abundant in the Carboniferous and Permian, obviously show characters intermediate between those of ferns and those of cycads.

It is interesting now to place together the various detached parts of seed-ferns in order to visualize the general nature of each of these three main types of plants.

The lyginopterids (Fig. 26) are seed-ferns bearing *Sphenopteris* foliage, small seeds known as *Lagenostoma*, Fig. 29, and microsporangia known as *Crossotheca*. The small seeds are borne in cupules which fit as a husk around the lower portion of the seed. This cupule is usually divided into segments or lobes, with a superficial resemblance to the husk of a hazel nut. The seed is ovoid in shape, has a well-developed micropyle, and is covered by three integuments. The form-genus *Physostoma* (Fig. 1C) belongs also among the lyginopterids.

The medullosan seed-ferns (Fig. 26) usually bore *Neuropteris* or *Alethopteris* foliage and large seeds known as *Pachytesta* [including "*Trigonocarpus*," Fig. 29, or "*Rhabdocarpus*" (= *Neuropterocarpus*)]. The microsporangia are of the *Dolerotheca* or *Whittleseya* type, that is, campanulate structures bearing tubular sporangia.

There are in addition to the medullosans and lyginopterids a considerable number of supposed seed-ferns known exclusively from impressions and compressions. Some of these are undoubtedly pteridosperms, but others are controversial.

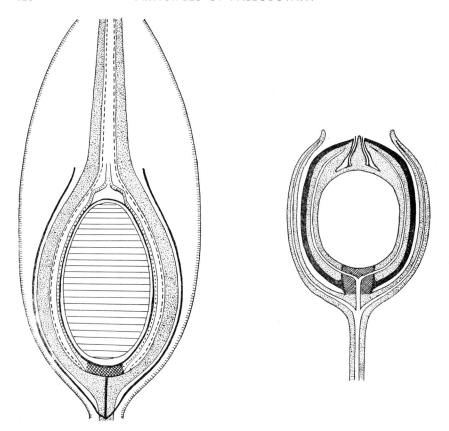

Fig. 29. Pteridosperm seed types. Left, *Pachytesta* (*Trigonocarpus*) *olivae-formis;* right, *Lagenostoma lomaxi*. *Pachytesta* is surrounded by a thick fleshy pericarp. *Lagenostoma* is enveloped in an open cupule. (Redrawn from Scott and Oliver.)

KNOWN SEED-BEARING FORMS

Many years ago White described seedlike bodies attached to sphenopteroid foliage which he named *Wardia fertilis*. Little more is known today concerning this form than at the time of its discovery. Subsequent discoveries, chiefly by Halle, have resulted in a growing list of seed-bearing genera, which collectively indicate great diversification of the pteridosperms, much greater than known petrified remains suggest.

Although the pteridosperms foreshadow the cycads and higher seed plants in a number of vegetative features, main interest centers in their remarkable fructifications. In the better-known forms which we have already considered, there are true seeds and pollen sacs borne in nonstrobilar arrangements. In *Lyginopteris* the seed is borne terminally upon short ramifications of a leaf. The microsporangia (pollen sacs) were usually produced upon pinnatifid branches.

When we consider the lesser-known forms, generalizations become difficult. The placement of seeds in these forms presents many problems.

Neuropteris heterophylla. The seed was placed terminally on the pinna, which for the remainder of its length possessed ordinary pinnules.

Neuropteris obliqua. The seeds are placed terminally on the pinna, which bears ordinary pinnules for its full length.

Neuropteris ovata. A number of seeds are borne singly but are arranged pinnately along the midrib; each seed replaces a pinnule.

Wardia fertilis. The small seeds are borne terminally on short pedicels, which correspond to reduced segments of the frond.

Pecopteris pluckeneti. In this form the seeds are attached to the margins of ordinary pinnules, at the ends of lateral veins; the fertile pinnules are slightly reduced.

Alethopteris norinii. The seed is attached to the rachis of an ultimate pinna bearing ordinary pinnules both above and below the seed.

Sphenopteris tenuis. A number of small seeds are borne upon the lower side of nonreduced pinnae.

Lescuropteris moorii. Numerous seeds are borne upon the upper surface of nonmodified pinnules.

Emplectopteris triangularis. This species, much like the former, has numerous seeds attached to the upper surface of pinnules, which show no signs of reduction.

In addition to these rather well-known forms, there are a number of more doubtful genera which exhibit seeds in attachment but for which there is insufficient data. The most difficult of these to interpret is *Pecopteris wongii.* The sterile form of this plant belongs to the group of *miltoni-abbreviata,* which has long been regarded as true ferns. Halle has found a single example which seems to show a seed in organic attachment. This seed is a smooth, ellipsoid structure which suggests the form-genus *Rhabdocarpus.* On the basis of this one specimen it is not possible to place great emphasis upon the supposed seed-fern nature of even a few species of *Pecopteris.*

In all these forms the seeds appear to have been borne singly. At least two forms, however, seem to have been polyspermic and thus produced structures analogous to a fruit. *Calathiospermum scoticum* is a cupulate-like structure presumed to contain six small seeds. A somewhat similar condition occurs in *Gnetopsis*, in which two to four seeds are produced within a cupulate investment. The cupule may prove to be of morphological significance in phylogeny, a suggestion which finds support among the Mesozoic pteridosperms.

MESOZOIC PTERIDOSPERMS

The Mesozoic pteridosperms were apparently much less important members of the flora than their Paleozoic progenitors. The known Mesozoic seed-ferns are referred to three families: CORYSTOSPERMACEAE, PELTASPERMACEAE, and CAYTONIACEAE, which are sometimes raised to ordinal taxonomic rank.

The PELTASPERMACEAE include several species referable to the genus *Lepidopteris*. *L. ottonis*, the best known, from the Rhaetic of Greenland, was shown by Harris to be a fernlike plant bearing microsporophylls and ovuliferous megasporophylls. The "microsporophyll" is a small branch system, each secondary branch forking several times, with the ultimate divisions bearing two short rows of pollen sacs (3 mm × 1 mm) producing oval pollen 30 microns in diameter. The ovate seeds (7 mm long, 4 mm diameter) are borne upon the lower surface of a branched peltate structure. The seeds have a curved beak, which formed the micropylar canal. *L. natalensis* from South Africa is closely related.

The CORYSTOSPERMACEAE recognized by Thomas in 1933 include several genera based upon megasporangiate structures and several upon microsporangial organs. The foliage is of the *Dicroidium* (*Thinnfeldia*) type. *Umkomasia* is a cupulate-branched inflorescence. The ovoid seeds (3-7 mm in length) have curved bifid micropyles. The cupules are usually stalked, and recurved mature seeds project beyond the cupules.

Pteruchus, the more common microsporangiate type, recalls *Crossotheca* in having clustered, pendulous sporangia borne upon the flattened tip of the fertile branches. The pollen grains are winged.

The CAYTONIALES have been variously interpreted since their discovery by Thomas. There are several genera, of which two, *Caytonia* and *Caytonanthus*, are well-known. Although first found in the Jurassic in England (1925), they have since been shown to have wide geographic distribution.

The fertile shoots were pinnatifid branches bearing carpel-like cases in which seeds were enclosed. The berry-like fruits attained a diameter of 5 mm. The structure is more or less homologous to an angiosperm carpel, thereby stimulating considerable debate as to the relation of *Caytonia* to the angiosperms. The microsporophylls, *Caytonanthus arberi*, is pinnately branched, the ultimate divisions bear synangia, each of which is comprised of four pollen sacs. The pollen is winged as in *Pteruchus*.

The small orthotropous seeds vary from 10 to 20 or more per fruit. The prominent micropylar beak found in the PELTASPERMA-CEAE and CORYSTOSPERMACEAE is absent in the CAYTONIACEAE.

The detached palmately compound leaves have been known for a century under the name of *Sagenopteris phillipsi*.

The enclosed seeds in a carpellary organ and the quadrilocular polleniferous synangium have suggested a relationship with the dicotyledons. Although the possibility that the angiosperms were ultimately derived from the pteridosperms cannot be disregarded, it would appear that the attainment of seed development within the megasporophyll, i.e., a fruitlike structure, in the CAYTONIACEAE is an independent evolution.

Among higher plants we find many features which suggest a pteridosperm ancestry for the gymnosperm and angiosperm groups.

Bibliography

ANDREWS, H. N. 1940. On the stelar anatomy of the pteridosperms, with particular reference to the secondary wood, *Ann. Mo. Bot. Gard.* 27: 51-118.

———. 1945. Some pteridosperm stems from Iowa, *Ann. Mo. Bot. Gard.* 32: 323-360.

HALLE, T. G. 1929. Some seed-bearing pteridosperms from the Permian of China, *Kungl. Svensk Vetensk. Handl.* 6, No. 8.

———. 1933. The structure of certain fossil spore-bearing organs believed to belong to pteridosperms, *Kungl. Svensk Vetensk. Handl.* 12, No. 6.

———. 1937. The position and arrangement of the spore-producing members of the Paleozoic pteridosperms, *C. R. 2e Congr. Avanc. Études Strat. Carb.*, Heerlen, 1935, 1: 227-235.

HARRIS, T. M. 1941. *Caytonanthus*, the microsporophyll of *Caytonia*, *Ann. Bot.* n.s. 5: 47-58.

HOSKINS, J. H., and A. T. CROSS. 1946. Studies in the Trigonocarpales, *Amer. Midl. Nat.* 36: 207-250, 331-361.

LONG, A. G. 1944. The prothallus of *Lagenostoma*. *Ann. Bot.* n.s. 8: 105-117.

OGURA, Y. 1948. A new example of seed-bearing pteridosperms from Manchuria, *Proc. Jap. Acad. Sci.* 24, No. 4: 1-4.

OLIVER, F., and D. H. SCOTT. 1904. On the structure of the Paleozoic seed *Lagenostoma Lomaxi*, *Roy. Soc. London Phil. Trans.* B 197: 193-247.

SCHOPF, J. M. 1948. Pteridosperm male fructifications. American species of *Dolerotheca*, with notes regarding certain allied forms, *Jour. Paleont.* 22: 681-724.

THOMAS, H. H. 1933. On some pteridospermous plants from the Mesozoic rocks of South Africa, *Roy. Soc. Lond. Phil. Trans.* B 222: 193-265.

11

CARBONIFEROUS FLORAS

The upper Devonian was a period of rapid plant evolution, marked by the advent of many new types of plants. The transition from the Devonian to the Carboniferous was gradual, although in some regions there is marked floral contrast. The luxuriance of Carboniferous vegetation is well-known, but it is usually overlooked that the so-called "Carboniferous flora" described in textbooks is only the middle Carboniferous swamp flora which grew along the margins of the great marine embayments.

In America the Carboniferous is usually divided into two periods, the Mississippian (lower Carboniferous) and the Pennsylvanian (upper Carboniferous). However, in western Europe these Carboniferous divisions are not accepted, although the floral differences are the same.

The earliest Mississippian was a time of considerable sea expansion in many different parts of the world. The most abundant vegetation—now represented by thick beds of coal—grew along these shallow seas. Such conditions occurred along the Appalachian trough, northern Alaska, the eastern Arctic, Scotland, western Europe, and in southern Siberia. It is presumed that the most rapid evolution of new plant types took place under these conditions.

The late Devonian was, on the contrary, a time when the seas were restricted or contracted, and when mountains and synclines were formed. The results of these orogenic movements were changes in the climatic and environmental conditions. The biological manifestations were in part the extinction of older types and the modification of existing types. The Mississippian floras are elaborations of these modified types, and the Carboniferous, which is longer in duration than the whole of the Cenozoic, is marked by a definite floral sequence.

There is a gradual shift in the dominance of various plant groups. Late Devonian floras generally contain numerous arborescent

Fig. 30. An Upper Devonian flora, characterized by arborescent lycopsids and fernlike plants. Notable forms are indicated by (1) Cyclostigma, (2) arborescent lycopods, (3) Sphenopteridium, (4) Archaeopteris, and (5) Pseudobornia. (By permission from Vegetationsbilder der Vorzeit, by K. Mägdefrau. Copyright, 1948, by Gustav Fischer Verlag, Jena.)

Fig. 31. (See next page for caption.)

lycopsids, various ferns, and precursors of other advanced groups (Fig. 30). In the lower Carboniferous the coenopterid ferns and the lepidodendrids are the chief members of the vegetation (Fig. 31). The coenopterids become less important with the increasing abundance of so-called marattiaceous ferns, and the lepidodendrids decline gradually until their virtual absence in Permian times—except in moist ecological associations. During mid-Carboniferous times the CORDAITALES began to diversify and become conspicuous, and the pteridosperms have gained ascendancy.

The great floral associations of the Carboniferous—*Lepidodendron, Cordaites, Glossopteris*, to name only a few—are not evident from a study of petrified remains. The magnificence of these forest types can be appreciated only by a study of great numbers of impression fossils.

The coal-ball floras give us intimate knowledge of the internal structure of many genera and occasionally some clue as to the community of types. Coal-balls have been found in England, Belgium, Holland, Germany, Russia (Donetz Basin), China, and the United States. The abundance of coal-balls in Iowa, Illinois, Kansas, and Indiana has stimulated an energetic school of American paleobotanists.

About 600 species of structurally preserved plants have been described from Carboniferous rocks. This number is small in comparison with the nearly 10,000 nominal species based upon impressions, casts, etc. The fundamental difficulty in studying fossil plants is the inability, often impossibility, of correlating external form with internal structure.

LOWER CARBONIFEROUS FLORAS

The lower Carboniferous floras are composed largely of lycopsids of the *Cyclostigma, Lepidodendropsis*, and *Lepidodendron* of the *corrugatum* types. The fernlike impressions belong to the form-

---

Fig. 31. A Carboniferous landscape, combining younger and older types. The genera portrayed include: (Ad) *Adiantites*, (As) *Asterocalamites*, (C) *Cardiopteris*, (Cal) *Calamites*, (Cd) *Cordaites*, (Et) *Etapteris*, (Lg) *Lyginopteris*, (Ln) *Lepidodendron*, (N) *Neuropteris*, (Ps) *Psygmophyllum*, (Ps) *Psaronius*, (Pt) *Pitys*, (R) *Rachopteris*, (S) *Stauropteris*, (Sa) *Stigmaria*, (Sg) *Sigillaria*, (Sp) *Sphenophyllum* (U) *Ulodendron*, (W) *Walchia*. (Drawn by Edward Vulliamy. By permission from *Plant Life Through the Ages*, by A. C. Seward. Copyright, 1931, by Cambridge University Press, London.)

Fig. 32. (See next page for caption.)

genera *Triphyllopteris* and the *Aneimites* types. These are soon accompanied by *Cardiopteris, Rhacopteris, Rhodea,* and an increasing number of sphenopterids. In America this association is known as the Pocono or the Price flora. It is very widely distributed over western Europe, Siberia, and the Balkans. The same flora (with some apparent endemics) occurs in Australia, South Africa, Brazil, and Argentina. This flora in continental Europe is known as the Culm flora and in the British Isles as the Calciferous flora. It is to be observed that the remarkable southern hemisphere extension of this association suggests a widespread moderate and uniform climate.

UPPER CARBONIFEROUS FLORAS

The Pennsylvanian or upper Carboniferous is better known paleobotanically than the Mississippian. The European subdivisions are in ascending order: Namurian, Westphalian, and Stephanian. The Westphalian or "Middle Coal Measures" are usually further subdivided into "A," "B," "C," and "D." The American equivalents of these divisions are as follows: Pottsville (Namurian to Westphalian B), Allegheny (Westphalian C), Conemaugh (Westphalian D and lower Stephanian), and the Monongahela and Washington (remainder of the Stephanian).

Following the recession of the sea at the close of the Mississippian, there were formed new land surfaces and complicated synclines, which in turn were followed by subsidence of the land. The many marine limestones which occur in the coal-bearing series of Europe and America attest to the instability of the land.

The Westphalian is the period of the well-known fernlike coal-plants: *Sphenopteris, Neuropteris, Alethopteris, Mariopteris,*

Fig. 32. An upper Carboniferous landscape. Probably the most satisfying and celebrated reconstruction of the Pennsylvanian flora. The large erect trunks on the left show the distinction between *Lepidodendron* (with spirally disposed leaf scars) and *Sigillaria* (with vertical ribs). Prostrate trunks of *Lepidodendron* appear in the foreground. The small erect plant with whorled leaves in the foreground is *Sphenophyllum*. To the right is the arborescent sphenopsid *Calamites,* with articulated trunk and whorled leaves. The large fernlike plant on the left is the pteridosperm *Neuropteris*. Seeds are shown as if borne terminally upon the tips of pinnae. Actual attachment in this species (*N. decipiens*) is not known. The great trunks in the left background and center are *Cordaites*. (By permission from the Chicago Museum of Natural History, copyright holder.)

Fig. 33. (See next page for caption.)

Lonchopteris, and many others. It witnessed too the maximum development of *Lepidodendron, Calamites,* and *Sphenophyllum* (see Figs. 32 and 33). It was the age of the coal-balls. The flora is phenomenally similar wherever it occurs. The flora of the Heraclea basin in Asia Minor shows the same succession as the Pottsville of the Appalachian province. A fairly large number of local genera occur in Europe and America, although this number is apparently diminishing as little-known regions are being explored. *Lonchopteris,* hitherto believed to be restricted to the Westphalian of western Europe, has been found in Nova Scotia; and the sphenopsid *Cingularia,* with a similar European range, has been found in West Virginia and Illinois.

Toward the close of the Westphalian a gradual uplift known as the Hercynian revolution caused the expulsion of the sea from continental western Europe. The Stephanian is usually dated by this orogenic movement, although the more precise correlations are based on the occurrences of fossil plants. In North America, particularly in the Appalachian province, there is a marked change in sedimentation in the Conemaugh, with the final marine incursion in mid-Conemaugh times. This change is usually regarded as an early evidence of the Appalachian revolution, which, although it reached its maximum intensity in the succeeding Permian, has been provisionally correlated or dated with the Hercynian.

The Stephanian is marked by the great development of the ferns and pteridosperms: *Pecopteris, Callipteridium,* and *Odontopteris.* Toward its close there appear *Taeniopteris, Lescuropteris, Gigantopteris,* and the earliest true conifers, *Walchia.* The curious NOEGGERATHIALES become abundant (*Tingia* and *Plagiozamites*). At the same time there is a rapid extinction of the older forms such as *Lepidodendron, Sigillaria, Calamites, Alethopteris,* and the large-pinnuled neuropterids. In eastern America the floral changes are

Fig. 33. Late Carboniferous landscape. An artist's conception of the so-called "Coal Flora." Notice the swamp environment, the implication of lush growth, and the accumulation of debris on the forest floor. In the center foreground are fallen trunks of *Sigillaria* and a standing hollow trunk. The *Stigmaria* base with ribbon-like rootlets is shown on a *Lepidodendron.* *Caulopteris* tree-ferns appear at the left. A group of *Calamites* of several species are shown at the right center. *Cordaites,* with strap-shaped leaves, is shown at the far right. (By permission from *Prehistoric Animals,* by J. Augusta and Z. Burian, no date. Spring Books, London.)

much more gradual than in Europe, and the lines of demarcation are correspondingly indistinct.

The Stephanian floras are much less uniform in content and more restricted in distribution than those of either the Westphalian or Mississippian. Nevertheless the cosmopolitan aspect of the Stephanian flora is remarkable. Zalessky described eight plants from coal mines near Mukden in Manchukuo, and, of these, seven are found in western Europe and six are found in the Appalachian province. Again in Tete, in southern Africa, there occurs a small flora of eleven species, all of which are found also in western Europe, and nine of which occur also in Pennsylvania. The Stephanian floras of Sumatra, China, Japan, and southwestern United States are remarkably similar, and this similarity continues into the Permian.

PERMIAN FLORAS

The Permian period is characterized by the rapid extinction of older types and the abundance of *Callipteris, Gigantopteris, Taeniopteris,* and conifers such as *Walchia, Voltzia, Dicranophyllum,* and early ginkgoalean forms such as *Baiera* and *Saportea.* The Permian has usually been considered to have been marked by great aridity, chiefly because of the deposition of red sediments, salt, and gypsum.

CLIMATE OF THE CARBONIFEROUS

The early historical geologists construed the lushness of Carboniferous vegetation, the abundance of coal, and the cosmopolitan distribution of the flora, as evidences of almost world-wide tropical conditions. More recently, however, the same facts have been interpreted as indicators of a mild, relatively humid, and above all, equable climate. It was probably moderate in temperature, not tropical, possibly not even subtropical in most regions. There are numerous criteria in support of this view:

1. Great size and rank foliar development—may indicate vigorous nutrition, with possibly increased atmospheric carbon dioxide.
2. Succulent nature of many genera, as evidenced by the large quantity of cortical tissues in the stems; these usually indicate rapid growth in moist situations.
3. Spongy leaves and large intercellular spaces.

4. Aerial roots, which are very conspicuous among certain Carbon-iferous plants, are characteristic of swamp environments.
5. The absence of marked growth rings in secondary wood, indicating absence of marked seasonal changes.
6. Abundant coal indicates that the temperature was not so warm that decomposition was more rapid than "normal."
7. The placement of stomata along sunken grooves, as in the needle-like leaves of *Lepidodendron*, is open to dual interpretation. At any rate it is a condition which occurs among xerophytic plants.

Collectively these features indicate a warm temperate humid climate during Carboniferous times.

THE GONDWANA FLORAS

The general Carboniferous floral sequence which has been described is essentially a Northern Hemisphere flora with long projections or extensions into the Southern Hemisphere. There was, in a large part of the Southern Hemisphere, a fairly distinct flora known as the *Glossopteris* or "Gondwana" flora (Fig. 34). The geologist Suess postulated a great "Gondwanaland," of which Aus-tralia, part of Africa, South America, and Antarctica are remnants. The dominant vegetational types were *Glossopteris*, *Gangamopteris*, *Noeggerathiopsis*, *Neuropteridium*, *Phyllotheca*, and *Schizoneura*. The flora, marked at once by *Glossopteris*, occurs in South Africa, Tasmania, Australia, Argentina, Brazil, New Zealand, and in various parts of Antarctica, as well as in scattered more northerly localities, as in India.

There is a complete floral succession from upper Devonian to Triassic. The most significant aspect of the Gondwana flora is the effect of glaciation, because the quantities of glacial sediments recognized indicate a glaciation of far greater intensity than that of the Pleistocene. The chief effects have been observed in the southern half of the Eastern Hemisphere. There were several inter-vals between colder periods, and these intervals are represented by well-developed floras. There are waves of migration from the north as the climate became moderated. Thus in the earlier inter-vals lepidodendrids and ferns reached South America, Africa, and Australia, while in the later intervals *Walchia*, *Callipteris*, and even later (Triassic) genera appeared. It is noteworthy that the silicified woods found in the strata which are more or less intimately asso-ciated with the boulder beds show conspicuous growth rings.

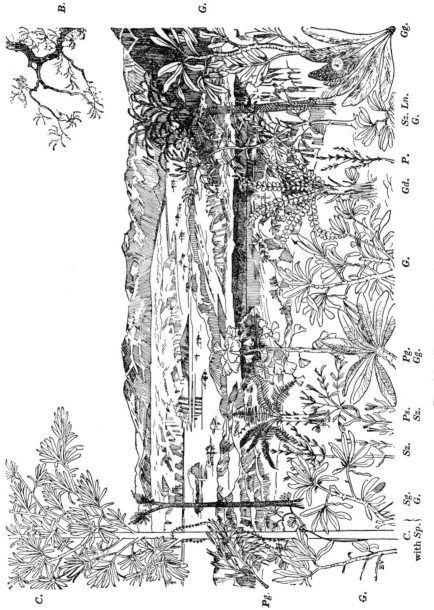

Fig. 34. (See next page for caption.)

Thus far, we have been concerned chiefly with the floral sequence and the chronology of the Carboniferous: the phytogeographic problems are of equal significance.

FLORAL PROVINCES IN THE LATE PALEOZOIC

More than a century ago it was recognized that the floras found in association with coal in America and in western Europe were remarkably similar. Lesquereux, for instance, believed that more than 80 per cent of the species in the American "coal flora" (i.e., Westphalian) were identical with well-known European forms. We know that this estimate is excessive because many of the species he believed to be identical have now been more critically identified and shown to be distinct. At the same time, this does not diminish the fundamental observation which he made—that the two floras were essentially similar. Such long-distance correlation is known as interregional correlation, and such studies have been carried on throughout the Northern Hemisphere. Paleobotanists consequently are now able to recognize several distinct geographical provinces in the Carboniferous.

It is generally agreed that toward the end of the Paleozoic era there existed four more or less well-defined botanical provinces. In the Southern Hemisphere there was the Gondwana continent with its very characteristic *Glossopteris* flora. This flora extended into India, which lies north of the Equator. The Gondwana flora was separated by a great mediterranean sea (called the "Tethys") from the other provinces which had more or less distinct floras of their own. These were, first, the Arctocarboniferous province, covering the area now known as western Europe and eastern North America; second, the province of the *Gigantopteris* flora, developed in parts of western North America and in China, but extending south into Sumatra; third, the Angara province, extending from the Ural Moun-

---

Fig. 34. The *Glossopteris* or Gondwana flora. This flora, essentially a Southern Hemisphere development, extended from lowest Carboniferous to early Triassic times. The plant content varied and the landscape shown here is Permocarboniferous. (B) *Buriadia*, (C) *Cordaites* (*Noeggerathiopsis*), (G) *Glossopteris*, (Gd) *Gondwanidium*, (Gg) *Gangamopteris*, (Ln) *Lepidodendron*, (P) *Phyllotheca*, (Pg) *Psygmophyllum*, (Ps) *Psaronius*, (Sg) *Sigillaria*, (Sp) *Sphenophyllum*, (Sz) *Schizoneura*. (Drawn by Edward Vulliamy. By permission from *Plant Life Through the Ages*, by A. C. Seward. Copyright, 1931, by Cambridge University Press, London.)

tains to the Pacific Coast, and southward into India as far as the
Tarbagatai Range, within a few degrees of Kashmir. The floras of
these three northern provinces have more in common with each
other than with the Gondwana flora. These divisions are somewhat
arbitrary because there are no sharp distinctions between the different provinces. Walton, for instance, has described a flora from
Southern Rhodesia in which there is a mixture of Arctocarboniferous
and *Glossopteris* types.

It is now necessary to consider the problem of the validity of
drawing distinctions between these several phytogeographic provinces. Schuchert, in a discussion of "Permian floral provinces and
their inter-relations," accepted only two floral provinces, the Arctocarboniferous and the Antarctocarboniferous (*Glossopteris* province). White was of the opinion that *Gigantopteris* was a genus of
lower Permian pteridosperms chiefly distributed on both shores of
the Pacific Ocean. Since the Asiatic flora contained non-American
(Eurasian) elements, and the Texas-Kansas region contained Appalachian elements, the distribution of *Gigantopteris* is primarily
explained by simple proximity, isthmian links, and barriers.
Schuchert accepted this opinion. Schuchert was also unwilling to
admit the Angara flora of central Russia as a distinct floral province because it is marked by numerous, typical undoubted Arctocarboniferous plants. However, these names remain in common use
as great conveniences.

The striking phenomenon of general Paleozoic distribution over
the Northern Hemisphere is by no means unique in the paleontologic
record. Knowlton has indicated the same relationship of Mesozoic
floras, Chaney for Cenozoic floras around the north Pacific basin,
and on a more limited scale, Fernald for the relict Recent floras. In
a somewhat different light, Berry has reviewed all of these floras in
relation to the past climate of the North Polar region. Still more
recently, there has appeared a paper by Kryshtofovich on a final
Tertiary link between Asia and Europe.

The importance of "cosmopolitan" distributions is chiefly their
bearing upon the broader problems of migration. The concept of
Wegener that the continents have tended to drift apart from a single
original land mass, "Pangea," has long been used as the basis for
explaining the general distribution of Paleozoic plants. Since
localized floral provinces first make their appearance during the late

Carboniferous, it was at this time that the continents were supposed to have split apart. A fundamental weakness in this reasoning is the belief that at no time subsequent to the Permian did a cosmopolitan flora develop. Such great floras are characteristic of each major geologic period.

There is a second aspect of the distribution of a given flora. Thus far we have considered its areal or horizontal extent, that is, its geographical spread. The geological record shows also the vertical spread, or in other words, the distribution in time. A flora or a given species develops in one place, known as its center of origin, and gradually spreads further and further away. This process of extension is simple migration, but migration takes place in time. A plant with a "successful" means of seed or spore dissemination may migrate hundreds of miles within a few years. On the other hand, even if no severe barriers stand in the way, the process may involve centuries. Attention is called to critical discussions of this problem by Jongmans (1952).

This aspect of change is well-known in the existing flora and has been termed "succession." Succession in its broader meaning signifies the order of events in the change of a flora. Paleobotanists have used the term to indicate the series of successive floras that have populated a particular area in more or less uninterrupted sequence.

The development of a cosmopolitan flora or the development of normal succession is usually interpreted as a result of equable climate with few climatic or physiographic barriers. It is difficult to refute this hypothesis because not only may it be true, but also the evidence against it is entirely negative.

A thesis underlying this problem is that plants are reliable indicators of climate. A hundred years ago, the Perry expedition into the Arctic brought back a small collection of fossil leaves from Greenland. Although we now know that the leaves were poplar, birch, and alder—at present genera with a circumpolar distribution in boreal regions, the conclusion was drawn from these specimens that the former climate of the Arctic was warm temperate. Paleobotanists made the geological climates warmer and warmer, until Heer was convinced that he found tropical palms in Greenland, Iceland, and Spitsbergen.

If the plants had been properly identified, and actually were what they had been named, then the inference as to climate might have been sound. Yet are we justified in saying that the inference would have been sound? Just because certain plants live today in tropical regions does not mean their ancestral species were also tropical. Nevertheless, this assumption is an underlying principle in the interpretation of geological climates.

The lushness of the Carboniferous vegetation was formerly believed to indicate that the Carboniferous was a period of torrid climate—at least in a large part of the Northern Hemisphere. It was suggested that the position of the equatorial zone has shifted to permit such rank growth at high latitudes. Drifting continents were also cited as substantiation.

To repeat, there is no evidence that the "coal flora" was tropical or even subtropical. One should not confuse mere size for lushness. Existing lycopods and equisetaleans are diminutive descendants of arborescent Carboniferous ancestors. More cannot be said than that.

The stomata of the leaves of most Carboniferous plants are normal in nature. Those of *Sigillaria* are frequently regarded to be of a xerophytic type. Functional xerophytism may be related to the occurrence of humic acids in a bog environment and may bear no connection to either temperature or climate.

Rocks with a red color are frequently described as indicating dry or arid climates, yet Barrell many years ago demonstrated that the great series of red sediments in the Upper Devonian and Mississippian were typical delta deposits which owed their red color to subaerial oxidation of iron. On the other hand, coarse red sediments with associated salt and gypsum deposits represent truly arid conditions of sedimentation. The Permian series of the American Southwest is an excellent example.

However the controversy over the value of these paleobotanical criteria may swing, it is probably true that a careful review of the paleontologic evidence will give a fair indication of past climate. Thick coriaceous leaves with sunken or modified stomata suggest xerophytism; floating or partially submerged aquatic plants readily reveal their nature; and a large flora with associated insects generally indicates favorable ecological conditions.

We shall have occasion to return again to these interesting fields of paleogeography and paleoclimatology. For the present we consider them as applications of the study of fossil plants to Paleozoic geography.

Bibliography

The literature concerning Carboniferous floras is voluminous. The following titles are for the most part well-illustrated and convey an excellent idea of the plant fragments which are commonly encountered. The references include titles pertaining to the various floristic regions.

ARNOLD, C. A. 1949. Fossil flora of the Michigan coal basin, *Contrib. Mus. Pal. Univ. Mich.* 7.

BELL, W. A. 1938. Fossil flora of Sidney coalfield, Nova Scotia. *Canada Bur. Mines Geol. Surv. Mem.* 215.

———. 1943. Carboniferous rocks and fossil floras of northern Nova Scotia. *Canada Bur. Mines Geol. Surv. Mem.* 238.

BERTRAND, P. 1930-1935. Flore fossile der bassin Houiller de la Sarre et de la Lorraine. *Études des Gîtes Minéraux de la France.* These elaborate and detailed monographs have been continued by P. Corsin, J. Danzé, and P. Danzé-Corsin.

CORSIN, P. 1932. Guide paleontologique dans le terrain Houiller du nord de la France. *Trav. et Mem. de'Univ. de Lille* 5.

DARRAH, W. C. 1937. Sur la présence d'équivalents des terrains stéphaniens dans l'Amérique du Nord, *Ann. Soc. Géol. du Nord* 61: 187-197.

———. 1937. American Carboniferous floras, *C. R. 2e Congr. Avanc. Études Strat. Carb.* 1: 109-129.

GOTHAN, W. 1913. Die Oberschlesische Steinkohlenflora, *Jahrb. preuss. geol. Landesanst.* 75.

HALLE, T. G. 1927. Paleozoic plants from central Shansi. *Paleont. Sinica* 2.

JONGMANS, W. J. 1939. Beiträge zur Kenntniss der Karbonflora in den östlichen Teilen des Anatolischen Kohlenbeckens, *Metaea* 2.

———. 1939. Die Kohlenbecken des Karbons und Perms in U.S.S.R. und Ostasiens, *Jvsl. Geol. Bur. Heerlen* 1934-1937.

———. 1940. Die Kohlenfelder von Gross Britannean (Jvsl. Geol. Bur. Heerlen 1938-1939).

JONGMANS, W. J., and W. GOTHAN. 1935. Die Paläobotanische Ergebnisse der Djambi Expedition (Batavia).

JONGMANS, W. J., W. GOTHAN, and W. C. DARRAH. 1937. Beiträge zur Kenntniss der Flora der Pocono-Schichten aus Pennsylvanien und Virginia, *C. R. 2e Congr. Avanc. Études Strat. Carb.* 1: 423-444.

KIDSTON, R. 1923-1925. Fossil plants of the Carboniferous rocks of Great Britain, *Mem. Geol. Surv. Gr. Brit.* 2.

LUTZ, J. 1933. Zur Kulmflora von Geigen bei Hof, *Palaeontographica* 78: 114–157.

POTONIÉ, H. 1896. Die floristische Gliederung des deutschen Carbon und Perm, *Jahrb. preuss. geol. Landesanst.* 9.

SAHNI, B. 1935. Permo-Carboniferous life provinces with special reference to India, *Current Science* 4: 385–390.

STOCKMANS, F. 1933. Les Neuropteridées des bassins Houillers de Belges. *Mém. Mus. Roy. d'Hist. Nat. de Belg.* 57.

TEIXEIRA, C. 1944. O antracolitico continental Português (Porto).

WHITE, D. 1899. Fossil flora of the lower coal measures of Missouri. *U.S. Geol. Surv. Mon.* 37.

———. 1900. Fossil flora of the Pottsville. *U.S. Geol. Surv. 20th Ann. Rept.*, Part 2.

———. 1929. Flora of the Hermit shale, Grand Canyon, Arizona. *Carn. Inst. Wash. Publ.* 405.

WHITE, I. C., and D. WHITE. 1908. Report on the fossil flora of the coal measures of Brazil. Imprensa Nacional, Rio de Janeiro.

ZALESSKY, M. D. 1918. Flore paléozoique de la serie d'Angara. *Mém. du Com. Géol. St. Petersb.* 174.

Zeiller, R. 1890. Bassin Houiller et Permien d'Autun et d'Épinac, flore fossile, *Études des Gîtes Minéraux de la France.*

——. 1906. Bassin Houiller et Permien de Blanzy et du Creusot, flore fossile, *Études des Gîtes Minéraux de la France.*

Special attention is directed to the published proceedings (Comptes Rendus) of the periodic International Congresses on Carboniferous Stratigraphy and Paleontology held at Heerlen, Netherlands, in 1927, 1935, 1951, and 1955.

12

THE PALEOBOTANY OF COALS

The several plant groups which we have thus far studied represent the dominant inhabitants of the Paleozoic swamps which produced coal. It is remarkable that our knowledge of these ancient plants is so complete; in a few cases we know more of the life history of Paleozoic plants than we do of a great number of plants living today. The original inspiration for much of this knowledge was research associated with the commercial exploitation of coal. It is probably true that the scope and technique of paleobotany have largely been determined by specialists in the Paleozoic floras who were forced to develop new methods to interpret unfamiliar plant groups.

The most useful applied branch of paleobotany is correlation, particularly as applied to the search for coals and petroleums. In the study of stratigraphy the plant content of a given rock may not only determine its age and its mode of deposition, but also the climate and physiographic environment under which the plants lived. These procedures have developed by a series of empirical studies on many coal basins and the methods have proved applicable to rocks of various types and of various geological ages. First there are the facts and theories concerning the origin of coal itself.

THE NATURE OF COAL

Coal is a carbonaceous sediment formed by the accumulation of plant debris and containing a variable amount of mineral in the form of ash. Most of this mineral represents mud and silt which is always present in accumulations of miscellaneous organic materials. One of the common or conventional assumptions concerning the origin of coal is that a coal bed begins its development as an accumulation of peat. This is extremely naïve because peat-forming materials, as we know them today, have left little or no fossil record. The plants of the Carboniferous which chiefly contributed in the accumulation of coal were arborescent—often attaining a height of 30 meters. The common peatmoss has a plant body scarcely reaching a height of 8 or 10 cm. The obvious result of this observation is the unwarranted assumption that by a study of existing peats one can reconstruct the history of coal formation in Paleozoic times.

A variation of this assumption considers the environment in which a peat forms the fundamental characteristic involved in the accumulation of plant debris. Since the days of Lyell, all geologists believe that past geologic changes can be measured in terms of the common changes that go on about us. It is true that the rates of change have been speeded up or slowed down, but the manner in which a change works has remained much the same. Thus the conditions of peat accumulation rather than the plant constituents are fundamental.

Geologists distinguish three types of peat formation. The first of these is the familiar *in situ* peat bog formed by the accumulation of successive generations of peat moss in a small depression with poor drainage. This type of peat formation may form at all latitudes and frequently at high altitudes but is most frequently found in cool temperate climates. The second type is the less common grass or sedge peat which most commonly occurs along a marine shore. Perhaps the best-known example is the common salt-marsh peat. Like the former, it accumulates in an area of frequent flooding and poor drainage. The third type is the carbonaceous accumulation formed by the deposition of transported materials into lagoons, bayous, and deltas. The most celebrated example of this class is the Dismal Swamp of Virginia. There are several variations of each of these types.

In a transported peat there results a crude sorting of materials so that the deposit may be made up largely of wood. In contrast, all kinds of materials in confusion—leaves and seeds and flowers mixed with wood and twigs—occur in an *in situ* swamp where the senile and dead plants have fallen where they grew.

Disregarding the initial stage in accumulation and considering a carbonaceous sediment in process of carbonization, the first major stage in coalification is lignite. A lignite is an organic sediment which has undergone a series of physical and chemical changes. Lignite, or brown coal as it is commonly called, contains up to 35 per cent of carbon, a considerable quantity of volatile materials, and a relatively large amount of water. "Lignite" and "brown coal" are poorly defined terms with no common agreement on meanings. Subsequent changes which result in bituminous and anthracite coal are further reductions in the amount of volatile ingredients and water with a resulting concentration of carbon. Much work remains toward an understanding of the form or forms in which this carbon occurs. Generally speaking, a good bituminous coal contains 55 to 70 per cent of carbon, while many anthracites have a carbon content in excess of 95 per cent. Schopf has attempted to define "coal" in keeping with present knowledge.

Jeffrey drew a distinction between lignite and brown coal. The former term is reserved for carbonaceous sediments made up almost exclusively of fossil wood. The latter is applied to an amorphous mass of miscellaneous plant debris which is usually finely divided. A lignite thus is typically a transported sediment, while a brown coal may represent an *in situ* accumulation.

Coal may be studied paleobotanically from four points of view: The one which least concerns us here is the standpoint of chemical composition. However, significant paleobotanical data have been derived from investigations of the resins, porphyrins, and other constituents of coals. The second method of approach is the thin section. Small pieces of coal may be ground until they become translucent (about 5 to 8 microns thick) and then studied with a microscope. It is also possible to prepare surface peels or transfers with a nitrocellulose solution from polished surfaces which have been etched with suitable acid. The third method is from the standpoint of photography. There are several procedures in use, but, in simple terms, a highly polished surface may be photographed with considerable magnification by the aid of reflected light. The fourth method is by complete maceration. In this case small samples of coals are completely macerated in acids, and subsequently alkalized. All of these methods, with the exception of the chemical one, study coal on the basis of its recognizable plant ingredients. Paleozoic coals contain chiefly wood, leaves, cuticles, and spores. These materials are present in varying quantities; sometimes one is entirely absent, at other times only one type of material may be present. An example of this type may be found in the cannel coal which is composed almost entirely of spores.

It is evident that a Paleozoic coal made up almost entirely of wood may be interpreted as a bituminized or carbonized lignite, and carrying the analogy one step further, a product resulting from a definitive environment. On the contrary, the familiar bituminous coal which contains many kinds of materials probably represents an *in situ* accumulation.

To be sure, one cannot study the origin of coal from small preparations and disregard the coal bed as a unit. It is known that certain coals, such as the Pittsburgh coal, extend over many thousands of square miles, with an average thickness of 5 or 6 feet throughout their range. Such an extensive accumulation can scarcely be transported. In many coal seams, and the Pittsburgh as well, there are upright trunks of such plants as *Lepidodendron* and *Sigillaria*, and these trunks penetrate through the coal seam to the rock above. The root systems of these trees frequently extend into the underclay and represent the plants as they lived in the original soil substratum. Such evidence has been cited since the days of Hutton as incontestable proof for the *in situ* accumulation of most coals.

COAL CONSTITUENTS

The terminology of coal constituents is not yet standardized, as virtually each country has developed its own system of nomenclature. The European system (with variants in England, Germany, France, and Holland) is based upon the work of Stopes, with subsequent refinements by Jongmans, Roos, Potonié, and Duparc. Stopes developed her descriptive system from the prior work of David White, which is still used in the United States. The White nomenclature, with some modification, has been adopted by the U. S. Geological Survey, the U. S. Bureau of Mines, and cooperating state geological surveys. Even in the United States, however, there is no general agreement, largely because of the infinite variety of coals, virtually no two being identical in structure or content. See Table 7.

TABLE 7

Comparison of Terms Applied to Coal Constituents

Petrographic Terms (Stopes)	U.S. Geological Survey (D. White)	Macroscopic Appearance
Vitrain	Anthraxylon	Brilliant black bands
Fusain	Fusain	Mineral charcoal, very friable
Clarain	Attritus	Laminated bright coal
Durain	Attritus	Dull (splint) coal, lamination poor or absent

The four petrographic terms are applicable to banded Carboniferous coals, whereas the White system, because it attempts to
indicate genetic relations, is more or less applicable to coals of all
geological ages. These terms will be considered in some detail
to indicate their paleobotanical significance.

1. Vitrain, which occurs as definite narrow bands, is brilliantly glossy,
   vitreous in its texture, and does not exhibit very fine banding. A
   band of vitrain may split up readily into small cubes or to fragments with conchoidal fracture.
2. Clarain, which occurs as bands of very variable thickness, has a
   pronounced gloss or shine; the surface is seen to be banded or
   striated. It has a definite and smooth surface when broken at
   right angles to the bedding plane.
3. Durain, which is hard, with a close, firm texture, appears rather
   granular even to the naked eye. A broken face is never truly
   smooth, but it always has a typical fibrous structure.

Stopes also examined coal microscopically, applying the method
of thin sections, and correlated the microscopic and macroscopic
features of the four constituents.

1. Vitrain is translucent, structureless, and uniform; in these characters it differs from all other parts of coal.
2. Clarain is essentially clean and also gives a translucent section,
   in which can be distinguished a great variety of recognizable
   exines, resin bodies, and other structures, most of them translucent; among this variety of material, stem tissues, leaf tissues,
   and other parts of the plant may be preserved or even fill the whole
   area of the sections.
3. Durain is essentially composed of fine opaque granules in which
   are embedded translucent micro- and megaspore exines in variable
   quantities.
4. Fusain is black, opaque, and shows cellular structure. The cells
   are generally empty.

We can distinguish microscopically the following constituents in
nearly all coals:

1. Structureless solidified gel
2. A substance which has a resemblance to this gel, but which exhibits
   cell structure more or less clearly
3. Exines of micro- and megaspores
4. Cuticles

5. Resinous bodies
6. Minute plant debris
7. Fusain

This classification, however, has some practical difficulties because it is impossible to describe the structure of a coal seam in these terms. For this reason Jongmans and Koopmans proposed to preserve the term *durain* for the microconglomerate, which practically cannot be described in detail. They proposed the following modified system of nomenclature:

1. **Vitrain:** entirely structureless coal substance, which soaks the other components of coal and serves as binding material.
2. **Durain:** microconglomerate of various minute plant fragments, soaked and held together by vitrain.
3. **Telain:** greater fragments of plant tissues, which are completely soaked with vitrain, i.e., the cell walls as well as the cell cavities.
4. **Fusain:** fragments of plant tissues which are not soaked with vitrain and show the character of charcoal.

Besides these principal constituents, there are various transitions between telain and fusain, which often may be observed in a polished surface preparation. Telain and fusain are derived from the same plant material, but they differ in the manner in which it was preserved.

A study of the maceration residue may give a clue to the constitution of a coal. For instance, if after maceration a number of bituminous bodies, consisting principally of spores, exines, and cuticles are left, we may conclude that the coal under examination consists mainly of durain. If, on the other hand, there are few spores, but resinous bodies and other indefinable bituminous bodies occur, we may conclude that the coal consists mainly of vitrain. In the same way, the amount of fusain contained in the coal may be estimated from the maceration results. In the past few years the investigation of macerols has opened a promising approach to the chemistry and petrography of coals.

Roos has observed that bituminous substances, which still occur in coals of low rank in the form of morphological remains, undergo a gradual change during coalification. The differences between the bituminous bodies and the other constituents of the coal, except fusain observed in thin sections or polished nonetched surfaces, decrease and even disappear as coalification proceeds, while they are less clearly perceptible on studying etched polished surfaces. The maceration of coals of higher rank results in a residue of indefinite finely divided bituminous bodies—the decomposition products of spores and cuticles. In this respect the microspores appear to be the most resistant.

One of the most promising developments from the microscopic study of coal has been correlation by means of spores and pollen grains. This specialism, now commonly called "palynology" (in its inclusive sense the study of pollen), has acquired an elaborate methodology and terminology.

In various kinds of coals, particularly cannels, we find a large number of spores which are usually well-preserved. The spore coat is generally cutinized and is thus highly resistant to desiccation. It is consequently possible to remove these spores from the mineral and other plant ingredients and to isolate the specimens for precise study.

In the majority of cases, the paleobotanist must content himself with fragmentary remains of fossil plants. It is not always possible to determine the name of the parent plant when dealing with a detached fragment. As a result, the coal technologist has used a series of arbitrary terms to indicate the superficial shape and form of the spores preserved in coal. The two major divisions of this artificial classification are based upon the spherical or ellipsoidal shape of the grain. These are further subdivided into smooth, rugose, winged, or other similar categories. The reader is referred to the Bibliography for representative monographic studies.

Turner has demonstrated that well-preserved wood and spores still remain even in anthracite coal, despite the alteration that has taken place in its chemical composition. Turner's preparations were made by flame-etching the polished surface of a coal specimen. By this method the carbon of the original cell walls was burned to mineral ash while the remaining materials in the specimen retained their amorphous black form. Similar work has been done with a nitrocellulose technique by which peels were made showing clearly the brown color of the original cells. Such work as this demonstrates rather clearly how necessary it is to approach the study of coal materials with suitable botanical methods.

It is almost universally believed that anthracite coal is a modified coal. All of the evidence available at the present time substantiates this opinion. It is interesting to note, however, that the coal has not undergone serious modification either in volume or in composition. Many anthracite coals show the bright bands so characteristic of bituminous coals and, just as commonly, certain anthracites exhibit the physical properties of cannels.

ALGAL COALS

The typical accumulations of coals with which the geologist is familiar are chiefly Paleozoic and predominately Carboniferous. There are many carbonaceous sediments composed to a large extent of plant materials which are found in Devonian and even in earlier times. Perhaps the most curious of these occurrences is the celebrated kerosene shale of Ostergotland in Sweden. This sediment is of Upper Cambrian age and has been shown to contain small spores which bear the triradiate scar typical of tracheophytes. Other kerosene shales are known from Esthonia, but these are of Ordovician age. The kerosene shales and the boghead coals are frequently regarded to be of algal origin.

The classic example of such a coal is the boghead of Autun in France. The organism supposed to contribute largely to the formation of this material is *Pila bibractensis,* which was described by Renault and C. E. Bertrand. There has been a great deal of controversy regarding the true nature of these supposed algal structures. It is usually argued that algae are poorly suited for preservation and that they decompose very rapidly. Those who are unwilling to accept *Pila* as algal consider it to be the flattened spore exine of a vascular plant. Jeffrey, in particular, belonged to this school. In defense of this position, it must be admitted that the bodies attributed to *Pila* retain a yellow resinous color which, so far as it is known, is characteristic of cutinized spores. Those who consider *Pila* to be algal point out that the various structures seem to be borne in colonies, which recall in many respects various members of the blue-green algae. White and Paul Bertrand held to this opinion. There is still a third opinion regarding *Pila* and related structures. This opinion, though it is probably indefensible, would have us believe that the small resinous structures are mineral sphaerulites. A second form, called *Reinschia,* is frequently cited in the literature and belongs to the same category as *Pila.*

The view that the colonial one-celled algae of the *Pila* and *Reinschia* type are spore exines, as held by Jeffrey, or that in general they, together with the generally recognized spore exines, like *Sporangites* in Tasmanites, are mere agglomerations of bitumen, as has recently been proposed by Potonié, has been more or less disproved, Thiessen having demonstrated the probable algal nature of *Pila* and *Reinschia* in connection with his studies of recent Coorongite. Both the algal nature of the genera last named and the spore exine structure of Tasmanites and other exines common in cannels and in oil shales have been proved by Stadnichenko through the comparison of the structural details revealed by the spore exines when heated in a microfurnace. The prevalence of true algal coals is now well established (Kosanke).

In most bituminous shales, including those with small quantities of organic matter, the organic debris visible in microscopical sections is relatively meager, consisting mainly of scattered remains of only the most resistant plant tissues. The black shales of the Devonian of western New York, Ohio, Illinois, and Kentucky consist mostly of thinly laminated, argillaceous silts or muds, in which resinoid or waxy spore exines and spores, mostly of large size and various types, are sparsely scattered, with some cuticular material in small bits.

An oil shale is a sapropelic shale—rich in organic matter—that yields petroleum by low temperature distillation. With considerable amounts of inorganic matter are spore and pollen exines and other resistant plant matter and occasionally resistant parts of animals. The debris is dominantly of aquatic origin and contains the products of animal and plant biochemical decomposition and preserved waxy or fatty plant tissues. The rich deposits of oil shale may be black, like the kerosene shale of New South Wales; blackish or brownish black with brilliant luster; brown, like the Tertiary oil shale of Brazil; buff or reddish, like the Platteville oil shale; or dark red, like some of the Esthonian deposits. Oil shales may be canneloid, with apparent massiveness and conchoidal fracture, banded or variously streaked, or earthy. Most of them weather in laminae, some of which may be flexible and paper-thin. Nearly all are tough and more or less elastic.

"Tcheremkhite" is an algal sapropel found in the vicinity of Tcheremkhova, Russia, which consists of yellowish or brownish-red humic mass, in which are found abundant small, reddish-brown pellets of various form, with occasional clear, yellow, cellular structures that closely resemble the Scotch boghead alga, *Pila*. The deposit is interpreted by Zalessky as a fluvial lagoon sapropel in which are buried pellets of peaty matter washed out from other deposits and redeposited.

Kuckersite is the Esthonian boghead which, where purest, consists almost exclusively of a colonial unicellular alga very closely resembling the living genus *Gloeocapsa*.

THE COALIFICATION PROCESS

From this array of facts and theories we can gather evidence concerning the process by which vegetable debris is converted into coal.

Nearly fifty years ago, White urged the importance of recognizing that the transformation of fresh plant matter into coal is chiefly accomplished through two consecutive and fundamentally different processes: (1) the biochemical; and (2) the dynamochemical process. More recently Schopf has presented an analysis of the aspects of the coalification processes, emphasizing the structures which contribute to the end products found in coals.

During the first of these processes, i.e., the accumulating of vegetable debris under the varying conditions of peat formation, the debris becomes more or less disintegrated or decomposed. The organic compounds of the original material are more or less broken and changed by those conditions. This process was termed "biochemical," because the more important transformations take place under the influence of, or in connection with, the vital activities of microorganisms, chief of which are the bacteria. The process ends with the cessation of anaerobic bacterial action as the result of exhaustion of the necessary supply of oxygen or the development of toxins. Studies of coal as well as of accumulating peat show that the biochemical process may be cut short, with only partial decomposition of the vegetable matter, as in the xyloid lignites of North Dakota and in woody or fibrous peat; or it may go further, as in some of the densely laminated coals, and even nearly to the obliteration of practically all the plant structures in some of the so-called "amorphous" coals and peats. The conditions involved vary with the rate of growth of the peat, degree of concentration of toxic substances, porosity of cover, temperature, water composition, and circulation, etc. There is reason to believe that anaerobic action continued at considerable depths in the bog and perhaps even for a time after the peat deposit has been buried by other sediments.

White called attention to the main point: that the important residual product of the biochemical process is a peat or an accumulation of equivalent rank.

On termination of the biochemical action we have only an unconsolidated, nondehydrated peat including methane and other decomposition products that have not yet escaped. If the process has gone on to an advanced stage, the resulting material is a black or more "mature" peat in which most of the plant matter has decayed; if it is less advanced, it may contain wood or other matter largely undecomposed. If the vegetable debris falls into more nearly "aseptic" water, the decay is relatively little and the peat is lighter brown and fibrous or xyloid.

The second or dynamochemical process is responsible for the chemical and physical alterations of the coal-forming matter. Its first physical expression is seen in the densification of the peat under the burden of overlying strata, by the expulsion of a part of the water, and in consolidation of the residual substances. Under its early action the mass is compacted, so that gases are further expelled, and the liquid putrefaction products that form the cementing pastes or binders of the coal are partly hardened, and the coal mass, reduced in volume, assumes its more typical geologic relation as a stratified sediment. It has been estimated that the reduction of an average peat, containing about 90 per cent of water in the middle depths of a bog or swamp, to a low-grade lignite containing 40 per cent of water represents a loss by weight of three-fourths of the original peat mass. The further transformation of this mass through the intermediate ranks to an anthracite is attended by a reduction of the water content to less than 3 per cent. Note how this theory is compatible with the observations on the constituents in thin sections on coal.

Simultaneously with the expulsion of water begins the escape of gases, mainly methane, from the peat. Some carbon dioxide and hydrogen sulfide also are liberated. As the process is carried further, additional changes in the chemical constitution of the coal take place, some of the residual products of the biochemical process are further reduced, and plant elements not previously affected are decomposed or altered, with consequent losses of the organic matter, mainly in the form of gases and water.

Aside from the more or less distinctly physical changes in the coal, resulting from the operation of the dynamochemical process, the most readily recognizable chemical changes are seen in its progressive loss of volatile matter. The volatile matter in ordinary peat dried at 100° C is about 70 per cent (ash, moisture, and sulfur free), and that of typical lignite is about 55 per cent on the same basis. The gradual elimination of this volatile matter under ordinary geologic conditions—that is, progressive "devolatilization" of the lignite or coal—is due to the geodynamic process. The ultimate stage of the process results in the approximately complete expulsion of the oxygen, nitrogen, and hydrogen. Stages at which the loss of the volatile matter is successively less are illustrated by anthracite, semianthracite, semibituminous, bituminous coal, etc. The reduction of the volatile "combustible" matter of the fuel is not accomplished without loss of a considerable part of the two chief heat-producing elements, hydrogen and carbon; but under normal geological conditions the changes are probably accomplished with relatively high conservation of carbon, whereas the loss of oxygen, which formed over 40 per cent of the original plant material, is proportionately much greater than that of the other combustible elements.

In summary we note the following: First, the accumulation and formation of coal is brought about largely by the action of biological processes; second, the plants preserved in or associated with coal are one of the chief sources of paleobotanical information; and third, through a study of the plant content of a given coal, much concerning its origin and properties can be determined.

Bibliography

BARGHOORN, E. S. 1949. Degradation of plant remains in organic sediments, *Bot. Mus. Leafl. Harvard Univ.* 14: 1-20.

BERTRAND, P. 1930. Les charbons d'algues. H. Vaillant-Carmanne, Liége.

CADY, G. H. 1942. Modern concepts of the physical constitution of coal, *Jour. Geol.* 50: 337-356.

CROSS, A. T. 1947. Spore floras of the Pennsylvanian of West Virginia and Kentucky, *Jour. Geol.* 55: 285-308.

DARRAH, W. C. 1941. Observations on the vegetable constituents of coals, *Econ. Geol.* 36: 589-611.

GHOSH, A. K., and J. SEN. 1948. A study of the microfossils and the correlation of some productive coal seams of the Raniganj coalfield, Bengal, India, *Trans. Min. Geol. Met. Inst. India* 43: 67-95.

JEFFREY, E. C. 1924. The origin and organization of coal, *Mem. Amer. Acad. Arts Sci.* 15: 1-52.

JONGMANS, W. J., and R. KOOPMANS. 1933. Kohlenpetrographische Nomenklatur, *Jvsl. Geol. Bur. Heerlen,* pp. 49-64.

JURASKY, K. A. 1928. Paläobotanische Braunkohlenstudien, I-III, *Senckenbergiana* 10.

KNOX, E. M. 1949. Microspores and their significance in biological problems, *Trans. Proc. Bot. Soc. Edinb.* 35: 109-119.

KOSANKE, R. M. 1950. Pennsylvanian spores of Illinois and their use in correlation. *Ill. St. Geol. Surv. Bull.* 74.

PARKS, B. C., and H. J. O'DONNELL. 1948. Determination of petrographic components of coal by examination of thin sections. *Amer. Inst. Min. Met. Tech. Publ.* 2492.

———. 1956. Petrography of American Coals. *U.S. Bur. Mines Bull.* 550.

RAISTRICK, A., and C. MARSHALL. 1939. *The Nature and Origin of Coal and Coal Seams.* English Universities Press, London.

ROOS, G. 1937. Comparative researches on the variations of the constituents of coal, *C. R. 2e Congr. Avanc. Études Strat. Carb.* 2: 1057-1161.

SCHOPF, J. M. 1947. Botanical aspects of coal petrography. Coal from the Coos Bay Field in southwestern Oregon, *Amer. Jour. Bot.* 34: 335-345.

———. 1948. Variable coalification: the processes involved in coal formation, *Econ. Geol.* 43: 207-225.

———. 1956. A definition of coal, *Econ. Geol.* 51: 521-527.

SPACKMAN, W. 1958. The maceral concept and the study of modern environments as a means of understanding the nature of coal, *Trans. N.Y. Acad. Sci.,* ser. II, 20: 411-423.

STOPES, M. C. 1935. On the petrology of the banded bituminous coals, *Fuels in Sci. and Pract.* 14: 4-13.

VANKREVELEN, D. W., and J. SCHUYER. 1957. *Coal Science.* Elsevier Publishing Co., Amsterdam.

WHITE, D., R. THIESSEN, and C. A. DAVIS. 1913. The origin of coal. *U.S. Bur. Mines Bull.* 38.

13

CORDAITALES AND GINKGOALES

Jeffrey has applied the name "ARCHIGYMNOSPERMAE" to those gymnosperms which retain motile sperms to accomplish fertilization and have pycnoxylic wood. The sporophyte of the pteridosperms, bennettitaleans, and cycadeans are quite fernlike, but the two groups we now consider never possess a fernlike habit. In the manner of fertilization and the minute anatomy of the wood, however, they are archigymnospermous.

In point of time, the CORDAITALES, and doubtfully the GINKGOALES, began their development during the Devonian. Thus they antedate both the BENNETTITALES and CYCADALES. This fact forces upon us a caution concerning the antiquity of the diversification of the main lines of seed-producing plants.

THE CORDAITALES

The CORDAITALES attained their maximum development during the Paleozoic, persisted into the early Mesozoic, and are now entirely extinct. The GINKGOALES reached their culmination during the late Mesozoic and diminished, until now a single species exists—and that probably owes its present existence to cultivation.

Cordaites was a forest tree with a tall main axis and spirally disposed, spreading branches. The unisexual strobili were borne in loose aggregations on an axis forming thereby a compound inflorescence. The seeds were platyspermic. The leaves were simple, usually spatulate, with a collateral and mesarch structure. The stamens and ovules were borne with accompanying sterile bracts, which until recently have been poorly understood. *Cordaites*, Fig. 35, presents a superficial resemblance to the conifer *Agathis*.

The stem has a large pith with discoid structure that is broken up by transverse diaphragms with space between them. Casts of these pith cavities ("*Artisia*") are familiar fossils. A number of genera

154

based upon the minute anatomy of stem types have been distinguished.

The CORDAITALES are usually subdivided into three families:
POROXYLACEAE, PITYACEAE, and CORDAITACEAE. It is possible that
the PITYACEAE should be segregated as an independent order.

The POROXYLACEAE contains only one genus with three or four
species confined to the Permo-Carboniferous of central France.
Poroxylon, Fig. 35, is usually regarded as a primitive cordaitalean
because of its affinities with the pteridosperm *Lyginopteris.* In
Poroxylon there is a cylindrical stele with a relatively large pith.
Around the solid pith is a row of strands of exarch centripetal xylem.
There is evidence that some species possessed mesarch strands.
These strands recall the xylem of the collateral leaf-traces of *Lyginopteris,* but in *Poroxylon* there are no well-defined centrifugal elements. The secondary xylem is similar to that of *Lyginopteris,*
although there is less parenchyma. The cortex is parenchymatous
and contains numerous secretory sacs. No endodermis has been
observed. The leaf-traces are double and extend through several
internodes before the centripetal tracheids are exhausted. Each
leaf-trace has an arc of secondary centrifugal xylem around the
bundle as it courses through the secondary wood. The leaves were
broad and linear. The fructification is unknown.

The PITYACEAE are probably a comprehensive group which includes only relatively related forms. Some of the genera referred
here are of great antiquity. *Callixylon,* which in late years has engaged the interests of several American paleobotanists, is a characteristic Devonian tree. Arnold has given us the clearest account of
the genus.

The two most pronounced features of the anatomy of *Callixylon*
are the mesarch primary wood bundles at the margin of the pith in
contact with secondary wood and the arrangement of pits on the
radial walls of the tracheids. In *Callixylon* the inner portion of the
xylem cylinder is divided into wedge-shaped masses, which gives to
the stem a superficial resemblance to that of *Calamites.* There is a
large pith of thin-walled parenchyma. The medullary rays are
usually narrow and uniseriate, 3 to 15 cells deep. The tracheids of
the wood converge toward the center where there is a primary xylem
strand. In most species there are several rows of contiguous and
alternate bordered pits on the radial walls of the tracheids. Similar
abundant but scattered pits occur on the tangential walls.

Fig. 35. Paleozoic Gymnosperms. A composite reconstruction comparing typical forms. These genera do not occur contemporaneously. Left, *Poroxylon* (Carboniferous) with large linear leaves, a cordaite. Left center, *Cordaites*, a tall arborescent form (late Devonian to Permian, Triassic?). Right center, *Walchia*, a voltzialean conifer, shown as a low tree with needle-like leaves and araucarian habit (Carboniferous and Permian). Far right, *Baiera*, with incised palmate leaves, a ginkgophyte (Permian to Jurassic). (By permission from the Brooklyn Botanic Garden.)

The largest specimen known had a stem about 5 cm in diameter. In *Callixylon zalesskyi* Arnold the occurrence of leaf-traces indicates a spiral disposal of the leaves. Apparently the leaves were larger than those found in existing conifers but smaller than those of the typical CORDAITALES.

Callixylon is closely related to *Pitys* (Fig. 31) which Witham described in 1833. Again in *Pitys* the secondary xylem of the wood possesses the so-called araucarian type of pitting. There is a large pith and numerous small primary xylem strands with mesarch structure. The leaf-traces are single. The most completely known species is *Pitys withami*, which was first described by Lindley and Hutton in 1826. The first specimen was an incomplete trunk 12 meters long, but a few years later Witham described a still larger specimen 15 meters long and 3.6 meters in diameter. Nothing is known of the foliage, inflorescence, or fruit. Gordon has described another species, *P. dayi*, which bore short, fleshy leaves unlike those of *Cordaites*.

The genus *Mesoxylon* is the most abundant member of the COR-DAITACEAE, and probably includes the majority of familiar cordaitean species of the middle and upper Carboniferous. The genus was defined by Scott and Maslen for stems of cordaitaleans in which centripetal xylem is present in the stele where it takes part in the formation of the leaf-trace. Scott interpreted *Mesoxylon* as intermediate between the typical *Cordaites* and *Poroxylon*. A double leaf-trace is present in all known species. Axillary buds are known in *Mesoxylon sutcliffii*. The stem is densely clothed with leaf bases into each of which pass eight bundles from the divided leaf-trace. The medullary rays are uniseriate, rarely biseriate. There is usually the distinct zone of periderm, the presence of xylem parenchyma, and the discoid pith. The axillary buds mentioned above are believed to represent the female inflorescence. The best known species are *M. sutcliffii* and *M. thompsonii*. The latter abounds in Iowa coal-balls (Traverse 1950).

We observe, then, that although the CORDAITALES in their stem anatomy show some resemblance to the pteridosperms, and have the typical archigymnospermous large pith, the wood structure resembles that of the conifers.

Cordaites has an endarch siphonostele, with spirally marked tracheids bordering on the pith. The protoxylem cells are small and are followed by cells of greater diameter with spiral markings;

these are followed by scalariform tracheids, and finally the pitted tracheids of the secondary wood. *Mesoxylon, Pitys,* and *Callixylon* have various amounts of centripetal xylem. In *Poroxylon,* all of the metaxylem is centripetal.

The multiseriate pitting, resembling that of the genus *Araucaria,* is characteristic for all of the CORDAITALES. The pits are bordered, in one, two, three, or five rows, but are usually so crowded that they appear to have hexagonal outline. The pits are more or less restricted to the radial walls, but some tracheids have been observed to have pits on the tangential walls. The medullary rays are narrow, but in the PITYACEAE they may reach a width of several cells.

The leaves are in striking contrast with those of the pteridosperms, BENNETTITALES and CYCADALES. They are much smaller, even the largest seldom exceeding a meter in length, while the smaller are needle-like. They are coriaceous, with the margins entire, and the venation beyond the base is parallel (Fig. 36).

The name *Cordaites* was originally applied to leaves, and the form-genus, in its broader sense, is subdivided on the basis of leaf characters. *Cordaites,* section *Eu-Cordaites* of Grand'Eury, includes those in which the leaves are broad, with rounded apex and with strong veins alternating with weaker ones. The *Poa-Cordaites* had long, linear, grasslike leaves. The *Dory-Cordaites* contain those with broad lanceolate leaves with acute apex and rather fine equal veins.

The internal structure of the leaf suggests that the CORDAITALES were chiefly xerophytic. The epidermal cells are rather thick-walled, and the hypodermal cells on both sides of the leaf have thick walls. Needle-like and cladified leaves have been observed in association with *Pitys.* This is significant because these types of leaves became dominant in the CONIFERALES.

Little concerning the roots of CORDAITALES has been published. The form *Amyelon* unquestionably belongs with *Mesoxylon,* perhaps to other stem-genera as well. Specimens of *Amyelon* are extremely abundant in Iowa coal-balls.

The fructifications have sometimes been described as catkins. The fertile branch is really a compound inflorescence, the individual flowers being strobili. The ovulate and staminate strobili were borne on separate branches. The male and female strobili are similar, there being a thick axis bearing spirally disposed bracts. The pollen sacs are borne erectly upon slender sporophylls. The oval pollen are winged. The best known staminate strobili are *Cordaianthus penjoni* (originally described by Renault and subsequently reinvestigated by C. E. Bertrand and Florin) and *Cordaianthus shuleri* (Fig. 1D).

Many pollen grains show a multicellular body within the intine, but the central portion of the gametophyte was hollow, presumably producing free nuclei.

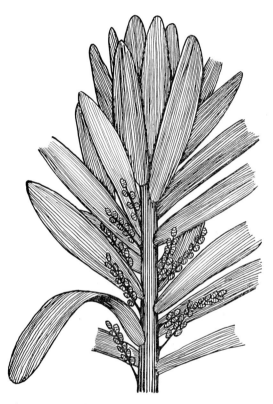

Fig. 36. *Cordaites.* Grand'Eury's classic reconstruction of a branch bearing spatulate leaves and compound inflorescences. (Redrawn from Grand'Eury.)

The construction of the ovulate strobili was similar to that of the staminate. Bracts were disposed spirally upon the axis; and the ovules, like the pollen sacs, were produced terminally upon sporophylls. The fundamentally simple organization of the fructification has been appreciated only recently through the meticulous research of Florin, who has reinvestigated all known classic European material.

The extremes of construction, with intermediate forms, have been found. In *Cordaianthus pseudofluitans*, the older and more primitive type, the orthotropous but pendant ovules are produced on long repeatedly dichotomized megasporophylls. In *C. zeilleri*, the ovules are erectly borne upon reduced unbranched megasporophylls. In *C. shuleri* the ovules are borne upon rather long unbranched megasporophylls, two, three, or four per strobilus. *C. shuleri* is related to the well-known compression forms described as *C. pitcairnei* (Fig. 37). The persistence of dichotomy in the fructification is significant, while the tendency toward reduction foreshadows the direction of modification in the conifer and ginkgophyte lines.

Fig. 37. *Cordaianthus pitcairnei.* A compound inflorescence consisting of an axis bearing numerous strobili with spirally disposed bracts. This specimen shows several mature seeds of the *Cordaicarpus* type. Carboniferous. (Redrawn from Berry.)

The ovules of *Cordaianthus* were bilaterally symmetrical and usually developed into a winged platyspermic seed. About a dozen form-genera, sorely in need of critical study, have been described, and of these *Cardiocarpus* (structurally preserved) and *Cordaicarpus* (compression) may be cited as typical. The ovule had a thick integument of two layers, an outer fleshy and an inner stony layer (Fig. 38). Although well-preserved pollen grains have been found in the pollen chamber, no pollen tubes have been observed.

The CORDAITALES show a combination of anatomical characters which indicate affinities with the pteridosperms and the conifers.

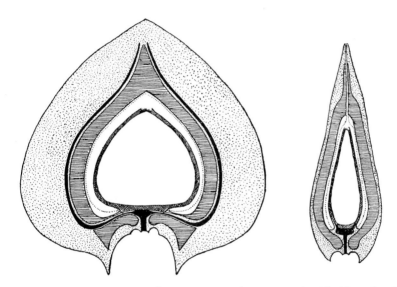

Fig. 38. *Mitrospermum,* a platyspermic cordaitean seed probably referable to *Mesoxylon.* Shown in frontal and lateral sections. (Redrawn from Arber.)

GINKGOALES

Although many Mesozoic and Cenozoic forms are attributed to the GINKGOALES, *Ginkgo biloba* is the sole living representative of the order. The tree has the general habit of a conifer, with a central shaft and wide-spreading branches. It may attain a height of more than 25 meters and a diameter exceeding 1.5 meters. The deciduous leaves are very characteristic in form and venation. The petiole is long and slender, the lobed blade is broadly wedge-shaped, and the venation is conspicuously dichotomous.

The branches are dimorphic; one kind being long shoots that elongate rapidly and bear scattered leaves, the other being the numerous short shoots that elongate very slowly and bear only a few leaves in a cluster. The short shoot elongates slightly each year.

The transverse section of the stem of *Ginkgo* shows a comparatively narrow zone of cortex, a thick and compact cylinder of secondary wood developed by a persistent cambium, and a small pith. In the short shoots, however, the pith is large and the zone of wood comparatively narrow. The primary xylem is endarch, and there is no distinct mesarch structure except in the bundles of the cotyledons. There is a double leaf-trace, as in most of the primitive gymnosperms, each of the strands forking at the base of the blade, and the resulting four strands breaking up into the characteristic dichotomous system of veins.

There is great variation in the size and in the lobing of the leaves of *Ginkgo*. The blades are often deeply cut and with more than two lobes, and the same tree may show every gradation between deeply lobed leaves and those with nearly entire margins. In the genus *Ginkgo*, the lobed condition is always found in the leaves of seedlings and usually on the long shoots. The leaves on the short shoots are generally entire.

In anatomical structure the leaves of *Ginkgo* resemble in general those of the CYCADALES. There is a moderately thick cuticle; the stomata are mostly restricted to the abaxial surface, the guard cells being somewhat below the level of the epidermis; and there is a distinct palisade tissue in the larger leaves, but not in the leaves of the dwarf branches.

The strobili of *Ginkgo* are monosporangiate, and the plants are dioecious, as in the CYCADALES.

The staminate strobili consist of numerous microsporophylls rising in loose catkin-like clusters from the axils of the scale leaves developed at the summit of the dwarf shoot.

The stamens suggest the *Crossotheca* type among pteridosperms. Incidentally *Antholithus Zeilleri*, which was once regarded as the staminate strobilus of *Baiera*, a ginkgophyte, belongs to the pteridosperm *Lepidopteris*.

The ovulate strobili of *Ginkgo* are very much reduced and are borne in groups at the summit of the short shoot. The individual strobilus consists of a long stalk arising from the axil of a bract and bearing at its apex usually two ovules, one of which aborts, although both ovules frequently develop. Occasionally more than two ovules, indeed as many as twenty, may appear as a complex, and this has been interpreted as evidence that the strobilus of *Ginkgo* has been derived from one bearing several or many ovules. This interpretation has found support in *Trichopitys*.

Around the base of the ovule of *Ginkgo* there is a more or less conspicuous "collar." This collar has been likened to the cupule of pteridosperms.

The evidence suggests that this fructification is a strobilus bearing two (or more) megasporophylls which are usually reduced to the so-called "collars," but which sometimes take on their original leaflike form. These abnormal ovuliferous leaves are supposedly suggestive of the ovuliferous leaves of the pteridosperms.

During the Mesozoic the GINKGOALES were represented by a series of isolated leaves, some of which are similar to *Ginkgo* in form and in structure. Ginkgo-like male and female reproductive organs are associated with a few species of leaves, but very little is known about them. The form-genera based upon leaf characters may be indicated as follows:

Leaf more or less deeply indented .... *Ginkgo* (*Ginkgoites*)
Leaf divided into several segments .... *Baiera*
Leaf divided into filiform segments .... *Czekanowskia*

Although this arbitrary classification is simple, it is very inaccurate because the extent to which the leaf is divided varies and the genera overlap. The affinity with *Ginkgo*, however, has been confirmed by cuticular studies. Extreme forms of *G. biloba* with the lamina dissected into narrow segments as in *Baiera*, are common.

Baiera spectabilis Nathorst is one of the best-known species of *Baiera* (Figs. 35 and 49); it has large leaves which are always wedge-shaped, though the extent to which they are divided is very variable. Among the other well-known Rhaetic species are *B. paucipartita* Nathorst, with small leaves on short shoots and *B. taeniata* Schenk, with much-divided leaves. *Baiera* occurs in all the larger Triassic and Jurassic floras, particularly fine species being known from Australia and South Africa.

In *Czekanowskia*, as in certain species of *Baiera*, the leaves are borne in groups of about ten on scaly short shoots. The outline of the leaf is wedge-shaped, but the segments are filiform and possess only a single vein. The cuticle is similar to that of *Ginkgo* and *Baiera,* except that the epidermal cells are narrower. *Czekanowskia* is common in the northern Rhaetic and Jurassic. It has been found in the supposed Permian of Angara Land.

While *Czekanowskia* has been accepted as ginkgophyte, recent discoveries by Harris (1951) suggest that it may belong to a new order perhaps related to the GINKGOALES in the same sense that the taxads are related to the true conifers. The fructification of *Czekanowskia* turns out to be a *Leptostrobus,* with two-valved capsules, each valve containing two rows of small seeds. Such an ovulate construction would automatically exclude *Czekanowskia* from the GINKGOALES.

Phoenicopsis, a genus with ribbon-shaped leaves, is present in early Jurassic floras. A narrow leaf form, *P. tenuis,* occurs in the Rhaetic of Greenland and has a typical ginkgoalean cuticle.

DOUBTFUL PALEOZOIC GINKGOPHYTES

Thus far the supposed Paleozoic representatives of the ginkgophytes have been disregarded, largely because the evidence is controversial and opinion divided.

The earliest undisputed ginkgophyte, and a remarkably significant form it is, is *Trichopitys heteromorpha,* described in 1875 by Saporta. This Permian form, found at Lodeve, France, was originally interpreted as a ginkgoalean. Although Zeiller concurred, most botanists disregarded the form. Florin (1949) has reinvestigated the material and confirmed and elaborated the description. The branches bear long narrow dichotomously divided leaves, in the axils of some of which occur short shoots with numerous ovules. The ovule-bearing complex is very like that found teratologically in *Ginkgo.*

Numerous other species have been attributed to *Trichopitys,* but none of them apparently has valid claim. Still other leaf forms with variously dichotomized laminae have been referred to the ginkgophytes. Among Devonian floras there are many "*Psygmophyllum,*" "*Platyphyllum,*" and "*Ginkgophyllum.*" There is no substantial evidence for their reference to this group. It is even questionable as to whether they are seed plants. Høeg (1941) has reviewed the evidence critically.

Among Carboniferous forms which may possibly belong to the ginkgophytes are *Psygmophyllum, Dicranophyllum,* and *Baiera,* but for all of them proof is lacking.

Neither the CORDAITALES nor GINKGOALES gave rise to higher plant groups, but they attest to the rapidly diversifying pattern of tracheophytes in the late Paleozoic. Their common origin, and perhaps that of the conifers, may some day be traced to the Devonian.

Bibliography

ANDREWS, H. N., and C. J. FELIX. 1952. The gametophyte of *Cardiocarpus spinatus* Graham, *Ann. Mo. Bot. Gard.* 39: 127-135.

ARNOLD, C. A. 1930. The genus *Callixylon* from the upper Devonian of central and western New York, *Pap. Mich. Acad. Arts, Sci. Lett.* 11: 1-50.

DARRAH, W. C. 1940. The fossil flora of Iowa coal-balls, III. *Cordaianthus. Bot. Mus. Leafl. Harv. Univ.* 8.

———. 1951. A new cordaitean seed, *Paleobot. Notices* 3: 1-24.

FLORIN, F. 1936. Die fossilen Ginkgophyten von Franz-Josef Land, *Palaeontographica* B 81, 82.

———. 1936. On the structure of the pollen grains in the CORDAITALES, *Svensk Bot. Tidskr.* 30: 624-651.

———. 1938-1945. Die Koniferen des Oberkarbons und des unteren Perms, I-VIII, *Palaeontographica* B 85.

———. 1949. The morphology of *Trichopitys heteromorpha* Saporta, *Acta Hort. Berg.* 15, Part 5.

———. 1950. On female reproductive organs in the Cordaitineae, *Acta Hort. Berg.* 15, Part 6.

———. 1951. Evolution in the cordaites and conifers, *Acta Hort. Berg.* 15, Part 11.

HARRIS, T. M. 1935. The fossil flora of Scoresby Sound, East Greenland. *Meddel. om Grønland* 112.

———. 1951. The fructification of *Czekanowskia* and its allies, *Roy Soc. Lond. Phil. Trans.* B 235: 483-508.

KIDSTON, R., and W. H. LANG. 1923. On *Palaeopitys Milleri* M'Nab, *Trans. Roy. Soc. Edinb.* 53: 409-416.

SEWARD, A. C., and J. GOWAN. 1900. The Maidenhair Tree (*Ginkgo Biloba*), *Ann. Bot.* 14: 109-154.

TRAVERSE, A. 1950. The primary vascular body of *Mesoxylon Thompsonii*, a new American cordaitalean, *Amer. Jour. Bot.* 37: 318-325.

14

BENNETTITALES AND CYCADALES

During the Carboniferous, the pteridosperms reached their maximum development and began to decline. Two great evolutionary lines began to differentiate from this complex: one called the BEN-NETTITALES and the other the CYCADALES. The BENNETTITALES rapidly reached their culmination in the Jurassic and became extinct in the Upper Cretaceous, while the CYCADALES still exist in various tropical and subtropical regions.

THE BENNETTITALES

The BENNETTITALES are gymnosperms, commonly—but not always —with the internodes of the shortened stem suppressed, usually with a crown of large compound leaves, with axillary unisexual or bisexual cones, and with the pollen sacs and ovules borne terminally.

The CYCADALES are gymnosperms with the stems and leaves as in the BENNETTITALES, but the pollen sacs and ovules are foliar and aggregated into terminal cones. The cycads are dioecious. The embryo in both orders is dicotyledonous.

The BENNETTITALES were much more abundant during the Mesozoic than were the CYCADALES. It is pertinent to note that the cycads have never been conspicuous or dominant if reliance can be placed upon the evidence at hand.

Because the BENNETTITALES possess a bisexual fructification which has been compared to a perfect flower, attempts have been made to derive the flowering plants from a bennettitalean ancestor. Well-preserved specimens of bennettitaleans have been found in the Triassic, Jurassic, and Cretaceous in England, Scotland, Belgium, Poland, Russia, Italy, the United States, and India.

Buckland in 1827 described the genus *Cycadeoidea* (Fig. 47) from the Isle of Portland. Ward (1885-1905) investigated bennettitaleans from various Jurassic and Cretaceous localities in the

United States. He was followed by Wieland of Yale University, who has been the outstanding specialist of the BENNETTITALES. In two great works, *American Fossil Cycads* and the *La Flora Liassica de la Mixteca Alta*, and a host of shorter contributions, Wieland has been largely responsible for the present status of our knowledge concerning the fossil cycads.

Many other students of fossil plants have been engaged in research on members of the BENNETTITALES, chiefly Carruthers (1867-1893), Saporta (1875-1891), Nathorst (1875-1913), Lignier (1892-1913), and Solms-Laubach (1885-1895), and among present paleobotanists, Thomas, Harris, and Florin. Recent discoveries among other primitive gymnosperm groups have so revised our interpretation of the morphology of the fertile organs that thorough re-examination of the cycadeoids is needed. It is now clear, though Wieland so argued for many years, that it is to the *Williamsonia* group we must look for a key to the cycadophyte phylogeny.

The four best known bennettitalean genera may be characterized by the following key. A number of other forms, presenting somewhat different features, have been recognized.

1. Stem covered by an armor of the leaf bases, and mostly unbranched.
    2. Flowers sunken between the leaf base and generally perfect . . . . *Cycadeoidea.*
    2. Flowers mostly long-stemmed and not sunken between leaf bases. Mostly with unisexual flowers . . . . *Williamsonia.*
1. Stem smooth, bifurcately branched; flowers perfect.
    3. Leaves bunched in the forks of the branches; stamens united below into a tube . . . . *Wielandiella.*
    3. Leaves spirally arranged; stamens free . . . . *Williamsoniella.*

Cycadeoidea. Mostly Cretaceous.
Williamsonia. Triassic to Cretaceous.
Wielandiella. Triassic and Jurassic.
Williamsoniella. Triassic and Jurassic.

Cycadeoidea (*Bennettites*) possessed short, stout, rounded, or barrel-shaped trunks at the top of which emerged a crown of fronds. Some stems are almost globular. In all examples known to us, there is a dense armor of spirally disposed leaf bases, interrupted by the axillary rosette-like fructifications. This fructification is strobiloid but has been usually discussed as a flower. Ramenta are always present.

Wieland fully described *Cycadeoidea dacotensis* MacBride, which is known from a number of exceptionally well-preserved specimens with flowers. The flower is constructed around a central ovuliferous receptacle, which is pyriform. This receptacle is surrounded by a whorl of incurved, pinnatifid microsporophylls which bear multi-locular pollen sacs (Fig. 39). Outside of this fertile whorl is a whorl

Fig. 39. *Cycadeoidea dacotensis.* Schematic reconstruction of a flower. The pinnatifid sporophyll on the left side is in the bud condition; that on the right, extended as when mature. (Redrawn from Wieland.)

of sterile hairy bracts. There are 10 to 20 compound "stamens," each producing nearly a hundred pollen sacs. The receptacle is covered with ovules and interseminal scales.

Wieland also described two "ripe fruits": *Cycadeoidea dartoni* and *Cycadeoidea wielandi*. The ripened seeds are borne terminally upon elongate, slender pedicels; they are erect, and the micropyle is directed outward. Many slender interseminal scales fill the fruit, and the tips of these scales extend beyond the seeds and expand to form an almost continuous envelope enclosing the seeds (Fig. 40).

The cycadeoids have large flowers while in contrast the Williamsonians have small flowers, many no larger than those found in the RANUNCULACEAE. Some authors have separated these forms in an order, the "MICROFLORAE."

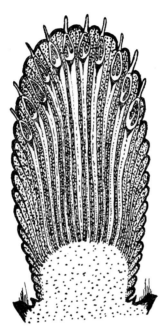

Fig. 40. *Cycadeoidea*. The ovulate strobilus with bracts and foliage leaves removed. Sporophylls bearing single, terminal, orthotropous ovules are intermixed with similar sterile appendages. (Redrawn from Wieland.)

Williamsonia Carruthers (Fig. 47) is known from more than a score of species. The most completely investigated is *Williamsonia gigas* (Fig. 41), which is believed to have been bisporangiate, although the megasporophylls are the essential and conspicuous organs. The ovulate strobilus consists of a central pyriform receptacle surrounded by caducous megasporophylls, and interseminal scales surrounded by bracts. Near the apex there were persistent interseminal scales which extended to form a funnel-like appendage

Fig. 41. *Williamsonia gigas,* showing columnar stem, frondose leaves, and globular fruits. This reconstruction, drawn by Williamson in 1868, is considered to be essentially correct. (Redrawn from Williamson.)

at the top. *Williamsonia spectabilis* and *Williamsonia whitbyensis* are fine examples of the microsporangiate organs. The "flower" consists of a corolla-like or funnel-shaped tube divided for more than half its length into some 9 to 20 linear segments or microsporophylls. These segments bear two rows of multilocular synangia which are filled with narrow ellipsoid pollen 58 to 65 microns in length. In some flowers the microsporophylls are pinnatifid (Fig. 42).

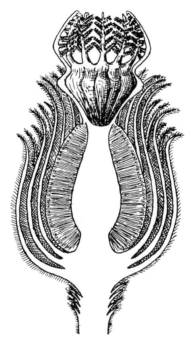

Fig. 42. A *Williamsonia* flower. The microsporangiate disc at the summit is usually found detached. Some paleobotanists question whether this form is truly bisporangiate. (Redrawn from Hirmer.)

Williamsoniella Thomas is best known from the type species, *W. coronata*, which is of Jurassic age (Fig. 43). The strobilus consists of a central axis bearing both megasporophylls and microsporophylls. The peduncle is covered with interseminal scales and ovules. There is a whorl of 12 to 16 fleshy microsporophylls around the basal interseminal scales. Each sporophyll bears on the upper surface two rows of pollen sacs. Thomas suggested the foliage is that known as *Taeniopteris vittata*. Subsequently Zimmermann figured a specimen with leaves in organic connection and corroborated this opinion. Fig. 43 is redrawn from Zimmermann's reconstruction.

Wielandiella (Fig. 47) Nathorst is a curious genus which stands apart from all other BENNETTITALES. Its bisporangiate flowers agree in general morphology with those of *Cycadeoidea*, but the repeatedly forked, smooth, slender stem is unusual among living and most fossil cycads. The foliage is known as *Anomozamites*. The strobilus consists of a small pyriform axis surrounded by a ring or collar marked by parallel striations which are caused by the short, reduced sporo-

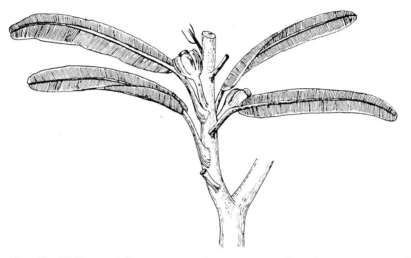

Fig. 43. *Williamsoniella coronata*. Reconstruction, based upon an actual specimen, of a branch bearing *Taeniopteris* leaves and two flowers. (Redrawn from Zimmermann.)

phylls. The sporophylls bear oval pollen which vary in size but have an average length of 40 microns. Nathorst believed that the axis of this strobilus type was surrounded by a whorl of megasporophylls which have been lost. *Wielandiella* is important because there is at least a superficial resemblance between its "flower" and the flower of some of the magnolians.

The vascular system of the bennettitaleans is an endarch siphonostele, the highest type found in gymnosperms and characteristic of many angiosperms. In transverse section the stem shows the large pith, scanty wood, and thick cortex. The scanty zone of wood, as in most of the living cycads, shows no growth rings.

Cycadeoidea jenneyana is exceptional in having a rather broad zone of wood and showing distinct growth rings.

The leaf-trace bundles pass directly through the cortex into the leaves, consequently there is no girdling, such as occurs in living cycads.

The tracheids are normally scalariform, but those of the proto-xylem, next to the pith, are spiral. Lignier has observed bordered pits on the radial walls of tracheids of *Cyadeoidea micromela,* and there are bordered pits in *Cycadeoidea dartoni.*

The leaves of the BENNETTITALES and the CYCADALES are very similar. In both, the usual form is the pinnate leaf, which is inter-preted as a filicinean characteristic. In various forms, e.g., *Wil-liamsoniella coronata,* the leaves are simple and entire. This is another argument favoring the separation of the "microflorae" from other bennettitaleans.

The leaves of *Cycadeoidea ingens* reach a length of 3 meters. They are thick, and their internal structure shows that they were leathery and more or less xerophytic. On the upper side there are some thick-walled hypodermal cells and a well-marked palisade layer. There is a single row of mesarch bundles, with a strong bundle sheath connected with the upper part of the leaf by sclerenchyma cells. Below the bundles is a wavy line of thick-walled cells beneath which is a thick layer, extending to the lower epidermis of thick-walled cells. The principal leaf form-genera attributed to the BENNETTITALES are *Pterophyllum, Ptilophyllum, Zamites, Anomozamites, Otozamites, Dictyozamites,* and *Taeniop-teris* (in part).

The most striking feature of the BENNETTITALES is the strobilus. They are all axillary, and in some cases there is evidence that a strobilus was borne in the axil of every leaf. At the bases of foliage leaves and entirely covering the scale leaves is a dense ramentum of scales several cells wide and thick. This is a typical fern char-acteristic and not present in the CYCADALES, in which the ramentum consists of elongate unicellular hairs.

The strobili of the BENNETTITALES are typically bisporangiate, with leaflike microsporophylls arranged around the central recepta-cle consisting of innumerable small megasporophylls, each bearing a single terminal ovule. The megasporophylls are slender peduncles without vestiges of lateral pinnae.

Wieland has considered the cycadeoids to be monocarpic. It has been noted that in some of the specimens there are strobili only in the upper portion and that these strobili are of approximately the same age. In some there are no vegetative leaves at the tip and no indication that there would be any. Wieland concluded that many of the BENNETTITALES flowered once and died. Such behavior is well-known in angiosperms. None of the living cycads is mono-carpic.

The microsporophylls are similar to the vegetative leaves but are reduced in size. The pinnules bear synangia on both sides, and this had led Wieland to regard the pinnule as bipinnate. In the synangia sporophylls are twice pinnate.

The microsporangia are multilocular and thus have been termed synangia and pollen sacs. Chamberlain objected to "synangia," since the term implies a fusion of separate sporangia to form a single large synangium. The structure is similar to that found in the marat-tiaceous ferns. There is an outer layer of thick-walled cells, followed by thin-walled cells and then a tapetum.

The solitary megasporangium is borne terminally on a slender stalk, which has been interpreted as the rachis of the sporophyll. In the CYCADALES, all the ovules are lateral, while in the BENNETTITALES, all are terminal. Chamberlain suggested that the ancestral stock bore ovules both laterally and at the apex, the lateral ovules, in the BENNETTITALES, became sterile and disappeared; while in the CYCADALES the top of the sporophyll became sterile and the lateral ones remained. The megaspore-producing members of the cyca-dophytes are so varied that this simple hypothesis cannot apply to the phylum in toto.

The ovules are small, many of them not more than 5 mm in length; a few of them exceed 1 cm. The best illustrations available are drawn from later stages in *Cycadeoidea dartoni* and *Cycadeoidea moreri*. The outer layer is thick, the middle layer is stony, and the thinner inner layer appears to be membranaceous. The hypocotyl of the dicotyledonous embryo is more extensive than in the living cycads, and the suspensor apparently was small.

There are several small natural groups which are closely related to the BENNETTITALES and CYCADALES. However, our knowledge of them is still meager and we are obliged to consider their systematic positions as being uncertain.

The first of these are the NILSSONIALES, an order which extends from the mid-Triassic to the upper Cretaceous and is widely distributed in Europe, Greenland, Alaska, and Japan. The leaves have a more or less pinnate arrangement. They have a very thin epidermis, dorsal stomata, and apparently were not xerophytic. The seeds occur in the midst of bunched leaves. In general features, these small seeds recall the sporocarps of the fern *Marsilia*—with which they were once confused.

In considering the relationships of the NILSSONIALES, it is necessary to diagnose the genus *Beania* which Carruthers instituted for a branched fertile shoot from the rich Jurassic flora of Gristhorpe in Yorkshire. The sessile seeds are borne in adaxial pairs on loosely disposed sporophylls, much as in the CYCADALES. The sterile form of *Beania,* that is, the plant to which it belonged, is not adequately known, but the constant association with *Nilssonia* leaves and peculiar compressed microsporangiate cones suggests that it belongs to the NILSSONIALES.

THE CYCADALES

We have already observed that the true cycads have not left a rich record, nor are they particularly abundant in the existing flora.

Beania and the Rhaetic *Bjuvia* (*Paleocycas*) simplex approach in their sporangiate structures the true cycads, but it is not possible to assign them to any group of existing cycads. Nevertheless there are complicating factors which suggest close bennettitalean affinities, particularly the *Nilssonia* foliage of the former and *Taeniopteris* of the latter.

The present distribution of cycads is indicative of antiquity and gradual extinction. There is a single family (CYCADACEAE), which is composed of 9 genera, and 95 species. No genus is common to both the eastern and western hemispheres. *Dioon, Ceratozamia, Microcycas*, and *Zamia* are confined to the western hemisphere. All but a few of the 35 species of *Zamia* are restricted to the northern hemisphere, although several extend along the Andes southward into Chile. *Cycas, Encephalartos, Stangeria, Macrozamia*, and *Bowenia* are confined to the eastern hemisphere, and all but *Cycas* are limited to the southern hemisphere. Certain species of *Cycas* range from Japan, southward into Australia.

Kräusel critically reviewed the Cenozoic occurrences of the CYCADACEAE and a resume demonstrates how the problem now stands, as shown in Table 8.

TABLE 8

Cenozoic Cycads and Their Distribution

Name	Locality	Age	Status
Anomozamites muelleri Ettingshausen	Australia	Tertiary	Doubtful
Bucklandia niersteinensis Kräusel	Germany	Miocene	*Encephalartos?*
Ceratozamites vicetinus Meschenelli	Italy	Oligocene	Doubtful
Cycadites escheri Heer	Switzerland	Miocene	Doubtful
Cycas fujiana Yokoyama	Japan	Low Tertiary	*Cycas*
Encephalartos gorceixianus Saporta	Greece	Oligocene	*Encephalartos*
Zamia mississippiensis Berry	U. S.	Eocene	*Zamia*
Zamia praecedens (Ettingshausen) Krasser	Brazil	Tertiary	Doubtful
Zamia wilcoxensis Berry	U. S.	Eocene	*Zamia*
Zamia tertiaria Engelhart	Chile	Oligocene	*Zamia*
Zamiostrobus saportanus Schimper	France	Miocene	Doubtful
Zamites epibius Saporta	France	Oligocene	*Zamia?*
Zamites palaeocenicus Saporta & Marion	Belgium	Eocene	Doubtful
Zamites tertiarius Heer	Switzerland	Miocene	Doubtful

Thus we see the same progressive extermination as evidenced earlier by the lycopsids and sphenopsids.

In all probability, the cycads had evolved to their present degree and spread to their present ranges long before the beginning of the Cenozoic.

RELATIONSHIPS AMONG THE CYCADOPHYTES

All of the evidence available points to the derivation of the BEN-NETTITALES and CYCADALES from the pteridosperms, and it is usually assumed that the two orders have evolved from a common ancestor. The barrel-shaped trunk in both groups suggests such an origin. The strobilus, on the contrary, is very different in the two lines. In the BENNETTITALES the strobili are axillary and in the CYCADALES they are terminal. Lateral leaflets of the megasporophyll are absent in the BENNETTITALES, but they are present in the CYCADALES. Chamberlain theorized that these leaflets have been lost, assuming, of course, that the ancestral stock possessed lateral leaflets on the megasporophyll. The divergence probably commenced during the Carboniferous or Permian.

More and more paleobotanists have come to regard the william-sonian alliance (MICROFLORAE) as the most significant group of the cycadophytes. There are many enigmatic forms, known from frag-mentary remains, which promise unexpected discoveries in the future.

The PTERIDOSPERMAE, BENNETTITALES, and CYCADALES form a nat-ural group of plants phylogenetically related by the common reten-tion of such cryptogamic features as pinnatifid sporophylls, large pith, and fernlike foliage. Circinnate vernation is present in the three groups.

Numerous attempts have been made to link the bennettitaleans with the origin of angiosperms. We shall return to this problem later.

Bibliography

FLORIN, R. 1933. Die Spaltöffnungsapparate der *Williamsonia-, Williamsoniella-,* und *Wielandiella*-Bluten, *Ark. f. Bot.* 25: 1-20.

———. 1933. Studien über die CYCADALES des Mesozoikums, *Kungl. Svensk Vetensk. Handl.* 3, Part 12.

HARRIS, T. M. 1932. Fossil flora of Scoresby Sound, East Greenland. *Meddel. om Grønland,* Vol. 85.

———. 1941. Cones of extinct CYCADALES from the Jurassic rocks of Yorkshire, *Roy. Soc. Lond. Phil. Trans.* B 231: 75-98.

———. 1942. *Wonnacottia,* a new bennettitalean microsporophyll, *Ann. Bot.* n.s. 6: 578-592.

KRÄUSEL, R. 1928. Paläobotanische Notizen, IX. Die Tertiäre Verbreitung der Cy-cadeen, *Senckenbergiana* 10: 103-111.

SAHNI, B. 1932. A petrified *Williamsonia* from the Rajmahal Hills, India, *Pal. Indica* 20, Part 3.

THOMAS, H. H. 1915. On *Williamsoniella,* a new type of bennettitalean flower, *Roy. Soc. Lond. Phil. Trans.* B 207: 113-148.

WIELAND, G. R. 1906-1916. American fossil cycads. *Carn. Inst. Wash. Publ.* 34.

———. 1920. Distribution and relationships of the cycadeoids, *Amer. Jour. Bot.* 7: 125-145.

———. 1934. Fossil cycads, with special reference to *Raumeria Reichenbachiana* Goeppert of the Zwinger of Dresden, *Palaeontographica* B 79: 85-130.

15

THE CONIFERALES

The second major division of the gymnosperms is the CONIFERO-PHYTA, which, according to Jeffrey, should be classed with the GNETALES in the metagymnosperms, because fertilization is accomplished by means of a pollen tube instead of by motile sperm.

The conifers have left an extensive paleontological record as far back as the upper Carboniferous, but only during the past two decades have botanists recognized the importance of the most ancient members.

The living conifers comprise a very heterogeneous group of plants. There are 40 recognized genera including 380 species, and thus represent almost 80 per cent of the existing gymnosperms. They are very widely distributed over the world, and many of the species are important members of great forest communities. The classification of the living conifers is by no means satisfactory. Pilger (*Natürliche Pflanzenfamilien Bd.* 13, 1926) recognizes seven families: TAXACEAE, PODOCARPACEAE, ARAUCARIACEAE, CEPHALOTAXACEAE, PINACEAE, TAXODIACEAE, and CUPRESSACEAE. Five of these families are known as far back in geological time as the Jurassic: TAXACEAE, ARAUCARIACEAE, PINACEAE, TAXODIACEAE, and CUPRESSACEAE. The PODOCARPACEAE are probably as old as the Jurassic, being represented by the extinct genus *Stachyotaxus*. Undoubted PODOCARPACEAE and probably CEPHALOTAXACEAE occur in the Cretaceous. It is evident that the diversification of the conifers took place in early Mesozoic times.

The conifers show the futility of attempting to establish phylogenetical relationships of existing families without regard for extinct representatives. There has long been a controversy over the relative antiquity and primitive nature of the "araucarineans" and "abietineans." It is now recognized that neither phyletic line is ancestral to the other, and that both are developments from older coniferous plants.

As long ago as 1920 Sahni suggested that the TAXACEAE should be segregated from the true conifers. More recently Zimmermann proposed a grouping of the seven coniferous families into two orders, the Taxales (Taxaceae and Podocarpaceae) and the Coniferales (with the remaining five families). To these two orders he adds a third, the extinct Voltziales.

THE VOLTZIALES

The earliest true conifers are found in the late Carboniferous and Permian.

The form-genus *Walchia*, including compressions of araucarian-like foliage, was created by Sternberg in 1826. For more than a cen-

Fig. 44. *Lebachia piniformis.* Reconstruction of the stem apex showing arau-carian-like branching. Lower Permian. (By permission from Die Coniferen des Oberkarbons und unteren Perms, *Palaeontographia,* 85B. Copyright, 1944, by E. Schweizerbach Verlag, Stuttgart.)

tury it served as a catch-all for Paleozoic conifers. About 1930 Florin commenced elaborate investigations of the cordaites and conifers and soon demonstrated that the group was of extraordinary interest. Owing to the fact that most of the remains consisted of vegetative shoots, he studied first the cuticular structure.

Florin distinguished three genera: *Lebachia* (Fig. 44), in which the stomata occur irregularly in four bands; *Ernestiodendron,* in which the stomata are in single rows; and *Lecrosia*, in which the branching is irregular rather than pinnatifid as in other walchians.

Subsequent investigations showed the spore-producing members to be strikingly like those of the CORDAITALES. In *Lebachia* the cones are borne singly at the tips of ultimate branches, Fig. 45. The

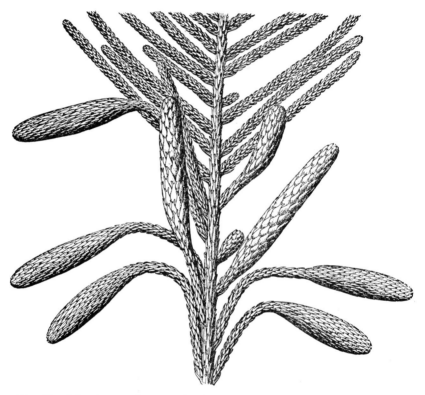

Fig. 45. *Lebachia piniformis.* The basal portion of a fertile lateral shoot system, with upright female cones and pendant male cones, placed singly and terminally on branchlets. (By permission from Die Coniferen des Oberkarbons und unteren Perms, *Palaeontographia*, 85B. Copyright, 1944, by E. Schweizerbach Verlag, Stuttgart.)

axillary short (dwarf) shoot is a radial shoot with bracts, each with a fertile scale bearing an erect ovule. In *Lecrosia* the ovuliferous scale bears two ovules, and in *Ernestiodendron* there are three or more. In all these genera the ovules are terminal, developing as platyspermic seeds. The staminate strobili produced pollen similar to that of *Cordaites*.

Later members of the Voltziales show modifications of this simple organization. In *Pseudovoltzia* the ovuliferous scale is five-lobed but bears only two or three inverted ovules. In *Ulmannia* the number of ovules is reduced to one.

In all of the Voltziales the bract and ovuliferous scales are not fused and the number of ovules on each scale varies from one to three. So far as is known, the platyspermic seeds are always provided with narrow wings and the pollen grains have air bladders. The wood is of the "araucarian" type, having alternate polygonal pits on the tracheids.

FOSSIL CONIFEROUS WOODS

Perhaps the most abundant and spectacular coniferous fossils are petrified woods. The Petrified Forest (Triassic) of Arizona, a famous tourist attraction, consists of scattered trunks of *Araucarioxylon arizonicum* (Fig. 47). The scientific study of fossil conifer wood dates from Goeppert's *De Coniferarum structura anatomica* which was published in 1841 and which was followed by his more comprehensive *Monographie des Coniferes fossiles*, 1850. The form-genera, now in wide use, were proposed by Kraus (see Schimper, 1872, *Traité des Paléontologie végétale*, vol. 2, pp. 363-385). The "genera" he recognized are: *Cupressoxylon, Cedroxylon, Pityoxylon, Araucarioxylon,* and *Taxoxylon.* Each name suggests that the fossil wood shows structure comparable to that found in a family or genus of living conifers. The work of Jeffrey and his students from 1905 to 1925 on Cretaceous coniferous lignites showed that this terminology was very misleading and that coniferous wood is extremely variable.

Bailey, in an attempt to interpret this seemingly endless and overlapping variation, called attention to the range of variability within a single living species (*Sequoia sempervirens*) and concluded that although it is possible to distinguish the wood of *Sequoia* from that of the Taxaceae, Araucariaceae, and the Pinoideae, it is difficult to distinguish it in all cases from that of the Podocarpaceae, Cupressaceae, and other genera belonging to the Taxodiaceae.

Bailey raised the question whether the supposed transitional Mesozoic genera fall within the range of structural variability of living coniferous genera. Although most paleobotanists agree that such genera as *Protopiceoxylon, Protocedroxylon, Planoxylon,* and *Araucariopitys* are generalized or transitional forms, differences of opinion have arisen concerning their classification and phylogenetic significance. One group of investigators considers them to be fore-runners of the PINACEAE which exhibit evidences of an araucarian or cordaitean ancestry, whereas another group asserts that they are primitive araucarian conifers which retained vestiges of a pinaceous ancestry.

Nearly a score of form-genera of Mesozoic conifers have been instituted for woods of supposedly intermediate or transitional struc-ture. This assemblage of hypothetical genera forms the bulk of evidence concerning the relative antiquity of the araucarians and abietineans. The controversy no longer arouses interest because, as we have seen, fully half of the time of coniferous evolution antedates the occurrence of undoubted members of either line.

Nevertheless, to appraise the paleobotanical literature, we cannot ignore the argument for regarding these Mesozoic conifers as gen-eralized or transitional forms. This opinion assumes that the occur-rence of so-called araucarian tracheary pitting in combination with structures that are not essentially araucarian is of phylogenetic sig-nificance because similar combinations of structural characters do not occur in living representatives of the CONIFERAE. Bailey argued that both of these premises are unreliable.

According to Bailey, there are three groups of genera in the PINACEAE whose wood may be distinguished with a considerable degree of certainty:

1. *Pinus*
2. *Picea, Pseudotsuga,* and *Larix*
3. *Keteleeria, Cedrus, Pseudolarix, Abies,* and *Tsuga*
    a. *Pinoxylon.* (*Pityoxylon,* in part.) For woods which fall within the range of structural variability of the genus *Pinus.*
    b. *Piceoxylon.* (*Pityoxylon,* in part.) For woods which fall within the range of structural variability of *Picea, Larix,* and *Pseudotsuga.*
    c. *Cedroxylon.* For woods which fall within the range of structural variability of *Keteleeria, Pseudolarix, Cedrus, Tsuga,* and *Abies.* (Here should be included *Planoxylon, Pinoxylon, Protopiceoxy-lon, Thylloxylon, Protocedroxylon* or *Metacedroxylon, Araucari-opitys,* and *Metacupressinoxylon.*)

The evidence from comparative anatomy of coniferous woods substantiates the conclusion based upon the study of so-called impressions: that the existing coniferous families have had their origins in middle Mesozoic times.

EARLY MESOZOIC CONIFERS

Before considering the geological history of the existing coniferous families, brief mention should be made of four early Mesozoic genera which show affinities with the VOLTZIALES but are clearly more complex.

Stachyotaxus (Fig. 49) is the best known Rhaetic conifer. Its foliage resembles that of *Sequoia sempervirens,* and though the male cones are not remarkable, the female cones are unique. Each cone scale consists of a bract bearing two one-seeded cupules. The seed has a free nucellus and the micropyle often contains pollen grains. *Stachyotaxus* is sometimes referred to the PODOCARPACEAE.

Palyssia, which has narrow, spirally arranged leaves and lax female cones with narrow cone scales, is another peculiar Rhaetic conifer. Each cone scale bears two rows of cupulate seeds, about twelve in all. Although the cone scale of *Palyssia* has been compared with that of *Cunninghamia,* it is not certain to what family this genus is related.

Cheirolepis has small, spirally arranged leaves and oval cones composed of five-lobed cone scales, each bearing two seeds. This genus, and perhaps also *Leptostrobus* and *Swedenborgia,* all of which possess strongly lobed cone scales, are probably related to the Triassic *Voltzia.* The cone scales consist of a bract scale and a very deeply lobed ovuliferous scale, which appears to be composed of an axis and several separate leaves.

Schizolepis is a small cone with bifid or trifid cone scales. Gothan and Seward tentatively considered it to be an early Abietinean, but it is more probably a member of the VOLTZIALES. Shoots bearing linear leaves are sometimes associated with *Schizolepis* and are presumed to be the vegetative form of this plant.

TRIASSIC ARAUCARIANS

Wieland (1929) proposed a new genus *Proaraucaria* for the Patagonian Triassic petrified cone known previously as *Araucarites mirabilis* Spegazzini (= *A. windhauseni* Gothan). The name suggests the "primitive" nature of the cone scale, which has a deep sulcus between the bract and scale. Darrow has also studied well-preserved specimens of the cones of this species and observed that the cone scales have broad wings and prominent ligules, and in addition have broad leaves and embryos with two cotyledons. Thus in this form there are combined the chief characteristics of the *Eutacta* and *Colymbea* sections of the genus *Araucaria*. The embryos of *Proaraucaria mirabilis* are similar to those found in the *Colymbea* section of the genus.

Wieland (1935) also described, from the Triassic of Patagonia, *Pararaucaria patagonica*, which he regarded as combining certain abietinean features with the obvious araucarinean characteristics. The single seed is enclosed in the fused cone scale, but the cone axis has a woody cylinder with a large pith or medulla. *Pararaucaria*, like *Proaraucaria*, is an undoubted member of the ARAUCARIACEAE.

Although araucarians can thus be traced back into the Triassic, abietineans, in the restricted pinean sense, go back only to the Jurassic. Jeffrey instituted the curious genus *Prepinus* for short shoots bearing numerous spirally disposed leaves. There is an indeterminate number (20 or more) of long needles borne in each bundle. There are several species from the middle Cretaceous of Gay Head, Massachusetts, and Staten Island, New York, and England. It is an interesting type approaching the genus *Pinus*.

CENOZOIC RADIATION OF CONIFERS

The Cenozoic history of the conifers is the manifestation of a twofold process: the early Cenozoic is marked by a gradual geographic radiation of genera and species, and the late Cenozoic is marked by gradual restriction, isolation, and extinction. During the Eocene to Miocene there gradually developed a tendency toward cosmopolitanism, but the development of mountains and arid regions over large areas in North America, South America, Africa, and Asia and the subsequent Pliocene cooling and the Pleistocene glaciations reversed the process.

All of the existing families of the conifers were represented throughout the Cenozoic. The ARAUCARIACEAE were gradually restricted to the southern hemisphere, although *Araucaria* is present in the Eocene of Europe and *Dammara* in the Eocene of Eurasia. Among the TAXACEAE there are several widely distributed members —*Taxus* and *Torreya* being nearly general over the northern hemisphere. The Podocarpaceae and Cephalotaxaceae are represented by leaves and fruit which occur in Eurasia and North America. Other genera, such as *Pinus, Glyptostrobus, Taxodium,* and *Arthrotaxus,* and, to a lesser extent *Cryptomeria,* are generally distributed over the north temperate zone. *Sequoia* by Miocene times is truly cosmopolitan. *Taxodium* and *Glyptostrobus* did not extend into the southern hemisphere.

However, even other genera (*Callitris, Widdringtonia,* etc.) possessed great geographic ranges in the Cenozoic, but these genera were more restricted than in the Mesozoic. Apparently they were excluded from North America soon after the Mesozoic but they retained a hold in Eurasia.

Considerable popular interest has attended the chain of events which followed the discovery by Miki that certain supposed species of *Sequoia* and *Taxodium* from the Cenozoic of Japan belonged to a distinct genus, which he called *Metasequoia* (Fig. 46). The long-recognized confusion of compressions of *Sequoia* and *Taxodium* in the Cretaceous and Tertiary floras of western North America was thereby unexpectedly clarified (Chaney). Meanwhile, surviving trees of *Metasequoia* were found in central China and thus detailed taxonomic, cytologic, and anatomical comparisons of all three taxodiaceous genera were possible. Here is an instance where a genus was correctly recognized in the fossil state before it was found living. It is an excellent example of the validity of the methodology of paleobotany despite the fragmentary material available for study.

The gradual segregation and isolation of the moribund conifers is evidenced by the large number of monotypic and localized ("endemic") genera in the extant flora.

Genera known from only one species:

Metasequoia	China
Cryptomeria	China and Japan
Thujopsis	Japan
Sciadopitys	Japan
Pseudolarix	China
Cunninghamia	China and Japan
Taiwania	Formosa
Microcachrys	Tasmania
Diselma	Tasmania
Acmopyle	New Caledonia
Polypodiopsis	New Caledonia
Callitropsis	New Caledonia
Saxegothaea	Chile
Pilgerodendron	Southern Chile ("*Cedrus uvifera*")

Fig. 46. *Metasequoia*. This is a unique and remarkable example of a genus recognized from fossil fragments before it was found living. Paleobotanists were puzzled for many years over the apparent confusion of mingling of fossil *Sequoia* and *Taxodium* and related forms. Miki correctly segregated late Cenozoic remains as a distinct genus, which he named *Metasequoia*. Subsequently, living specimens were found in China. The sketch shown here was drawn at the type locality, especially for the Chronica Botanica Company. (Courtesy of F. Verdoorn.)

Genera known from two species:

Cedrus (2 or 3)	Eurasia (Mediterranean and Himalayan region)
Keteleeria	China
Glyptostrobus	China
Pseudotsuga	North America
Sequoia (sometimes separated in two monotypic genera)	California
Taxodium	North America and Mexico
Actinostrobus	Australasia
Fitzroya	Southern Chile and Tasmania
Pherosphaera	Australia and Tasmania

Localized genera with more than two species:

Folienia	(3)	China
Torreya	(4)	United States and Japan
Arthrotaxus	(3)	Tasmania and Victoria
Cephalotaxus	(6)	Eastern Asia

The term "monotypy" takes on a peculiar significance to the paleobotanist and the phytogeographer. A monotypic genus is usually (always?) an old genus, and the endemic "home" is that remnant of its former range which has most resisted geological change. Extinction of the genus is inevitable. Relict endemism not only signifies a restricted range but an isolation phenomenon. Geological change is one of the chief factors involved in extinction— perhaps it is the prime factor. Those species which are able to migrate with the change, or change with it, survive; those unable to change ("adapt") perish. It is in this connection that the factor of racial old age or senescence is involved. Young, "virile," "plastic" species are better able to cope with the environment—i.e., with physiographic change—than old, "rigid" species which have lost, presumably, their plasticity. In this concept we are face to face with the problem of the inheritance of acquired characteristics, not necessarily in the classic sense of Lamarck but some modified interpretation.

The conifers, although still a conspicuous and important plant group, are decadent and moribund. This gradual process of extinction is to be observed in all gymnosperms—the pteridosperms were the first to disappear, the cordaitaleans almost simultaneously died out, and the bennettitaleans followed. The GINKGOALES are reduced to a single representative, the cycadeans to less than a hundred species, and the conifers to four hundred species. The gnetaleans, with scarcely seventy species, have left practically no fossil record.

There is a very doubtful report of *Ephedrites* in the Eocene of western Europe and a more doubtful fruit (Jurassic) attributed to *Welwitschia*.

PHYLOGENY OF THE CONIFERS

The phylogeny of the members within the CONIFERALES is probably better understood than ever before, although their ultimate derivation is still a matter of conjecture. The abietinean and araucarinean lines of development both had their origins in the VOLTZIALES by the segregation of characteristics established in the VOLTZIALES. The voltzian group is above all characterized by the production of terminal ovoid seeds (first erect, then inverted), provided with narrow wings, borne upon ovuliferous scales in varying numbers (1 to 3, or more), and by pollen with air bladders. The bract and scale are separate, that is, not fused. Many of these characters appear among the abietineans. In the vegetative features —which are just as important—the plants appear to be araucarinean. The general habit resembles *Araucaria excelsa*. The wood so far as known is of the "*Dadoxylon*" or "*Araucarioxylon*" type.

The taxads, including the TAXACEAE and PODOCARPACEAE series, had their origin in early Mesozoic times, probably from a voltzian stock. *Palyssia* and *Schizolepis,* and *Stachyotaxus* are pertinent to this problem. From all that is known of the conifers, it is generally believed that they are monophyletic, developing from the CORDAITALES during the Carboniferous.

The conifers illustrate two principles of paleontology: radiation, or evolutionary diversification with a resulting geographic spread, followed by gradual restriction and extinction, and phylogenesis, or gradual specialization and diversification from a common stock, with the segregation of certain characteristics in several developmental lines.

Bibliography

BAILEY, I. W. 1933. The cambium and its derivative tissues, VII. Problems in identifying the wood of Mesozoic conifers, Ann. Bot. 47: 145-157.

BAILEY, I. W., and A. F. FAULL. 1934. The cambium and its derivative tissues, IX. Structural variability in the redwood, Sequoia sempervirens, and its significance in the identification of fossil woods, Jour. Arn. Arbor. 15: 233-254.

CHANEY, R. W. 1950. A revision of fossil Sequoia and Taxodium in western North America based on the recent discovery of Metasequoia, Trans. Amer. Phil. Soc. 40, Part 3.

Darrow, B. S. 1936. A fossil araucarian embryo from the Cerro Cuadrado of Patagonia, *Bot. Gaz.* 98: 328-338.

Florin, R. 1939-1945. Die Koniferen des Oberkarbons und des unteren Perm, *Palaeontographica* B 85.

———. 1951. Evolution in the cordaites and conifers, *Acta Hort. Berg.* 15, Part 11.

Gothan, W. 1905. Zur Anatomie lebender und fossiler Gymnospermen-Hölzer, *Abh. Kon. Preuss. Geol. Landes.* 44.

Kon'no, E. 1944. Contribution to our knowledge of *Swedenborgia*, *Jap. Jour. Geol. and Geogr.* 19: 27-66.

Kräusel, R. 1919. Die fossilen Koniferenholzer, *Palaeontographica* B 62.

Mason, H. 1927. Fossil records of some western American conifers. *Carn. Inst. Wash. Publ.* 346.

Penny, J. S. 1947. Studies on the conifers of the Magothy flora, *Amer. Jour. Bot.* 34: 281-296.

Simpson, J. B. 1949. Fossil pollen of the *Metasequoia* type, *Nature* 163: 771-772.

Wieland, G. R. 1935. The Cerro Cuadrado petrified forest. *Carn. Inst. Wash. Publ.* 449.

16

MESOZOIC FLORAS

The Mesozoic Era has been popularly known as the age of reptiles (as named by Agassiz) and the age of gymnosperms (by Brongniart). These designations indicate the dominant groups of animals and plants which were living during this time.

TIME SUBDIVISIONS OF THE MESOZOIC

The Mesozoic is usually divided into three periods: Triassic, Jurassic, and Cretaceous. Together the Triassic and Jurassic comprise the early Mesozoic, while the Cretaceous is known as the late Mesozoic. The late Mesozoic is sometimes subdivided by American geologists into the Comanchian (lower) and the restricted Cretaceous (upper). This distinction is not accepted by European geologists, so that the Cretaceous is here used in its inclusive sense.

According to the time computations of earth history obtained by the radioactive method, the Paleozoic endured for 350 million years, the Mesozoic for 120 million, and the Cenozoic for 60 million. Thus the Mesozoic is only one-third as long as the Paleozoic, yet it is twice as long as the Cenozoic. The Triassic and Jurassic involve the first half of the Mesozoic, and the Cretaceous, which is as long as all of the Cenozoic, involves the later half. When the spectacular evolutionary trends are viewed against these relative time values, the successions of events do not appear sudden or unpredictable.

In several parts of the world the Permian passes so gradually into the Triassic that it is difficult to separate them. This is particularly true of the continental formations in Russia, India, and Brazil, but it also applies to the marine series in the Himalayas. However, in general there is a great unconformity between the Paleozoic and the Mesozoic. In many parts of the world, as in the Cordilleras of western America and the Atlantic border of eastern North America, there are extensive igneous rocks showing that in the Triassic there was widespread vulcanism. Great lava flows occurred in North America, South America, South Africa, and New Zealand.

At the close of the Mesozoic, the diastrophic movements resulted in a general elevation of all the continents, with consequent withdrawal of the epeiric seas. Presumably the land masses were higher above the sea than at present, though the distribution of land and sea was quite similar to that which exists at the present time.

The early Mesozoic was a time of great instability. Coal beds occurred in Virginia, Germany, Sweden, Antarctica, and many other localities. Both the Triassic and Jurassic series include widely distributed marine limestones and dolomites. The climate was, in general, rather mild. A luxuriant vegetation covered not only many parts of boreal Europe, America, Greenland, and Spitsbergen, but also New Zealand, Antarctica, and Grahamland. There is some evidence indicating fairly definite climatic zones.

Paradoxically however, there are tillites in the Triassic of central Africa (3°–5° S. Lat.) west of Lake Tanganyika. The tillite contains great boulders, many of which are striated. It is possible that these tillites were produced by more or less local montane glaciers. There is also evidence of glaciation in the Triassic of New Zealand.

During the lower Cretaceous there were in western North America three widespread marine transgressions, and the same region was again inundated in the upper Cretaceous by a great sea extending from the Gulf of Mexico to the Arctic Ocean. This sea was gradually restricted from the north (i.e., by the withdrawal of the Arctic sea) until, at the close of the Cretaceous, it was much more limited in extent—barely reaching the border between the United States and Canada in the Rocky Mountain region.

The Atlantic province was likewise covered by the sea from Massachusetts to South Carolina. The sediments deposited in this region include many fine lignites (studied by Jeffrey and his students) and impressions (studied by Hollick).

At the close of the Cretaceous there took place a great revolution, known as the Laramide. Mountain folding began in Alaska and progressed southward. The Sierra Nevadas and the Cordilleras had already been uplifted, but the great Rocky Mountains were formed by the Laramide orogeny. The Cordilleras were elevated further. Contemporaneously, the Andes were uplifted from Trinidad to Cape Horn. There were also intense diastrophic movements on the other continents.

A marine gulf over northern Europe greatly expanded during the upper Cretaceous and flooded surfaces which had been exposed land since the Paleozoic. The alpine orogeny caused the general retirement of this sea, lifted the land, and formed mountains from Spain to Hungary. Some lava flows occurred in the Pyrenees and Carpathians. Northern Africa, including most of the Sahara plateau, was widely inundated, as were both the eastern and western coasts. Asia was not greatly affected by the upper Cretaceous transgression, and most of the sedimentary rocks are of continental origin.

The greatest volcanic activity is to be observed in India where the basaltic plateau known as the "Deccan Traps" have a thickness of two thousand feet and cover an area of almost 250,000 square miles. These lava flows were subterranean and were subsequently exposed by erosion in Cenozoic times.

These diastrophic movements have had a profound effect upon the evolution of plant and animal life. Old land masses were inundated or eroded away. New deltas and plateaus were open to invasion by vigorous organisms.

As we have seen, the conspicuous plants of the early Mesozoic were conifers and bennettitaleans (Fig. 47). The ferns and ginkgoaleans were also abundant members of the floras, but the lycopsids and sphenopsids were of minor significance.

Perhaps the most remarkable feature of the early Mesozoic flora is its homogeneity, both in space and in time. The flora, which is markedly distinct from that of the late Paleozoic, does not vary greatly from the middle Triassic to almost the end of the lower Cretaceous. The specific content of the floral succession changes, of course, but the generic content is strikingly constant.

REPRESENTATIVE MESOZOIC FLORAS

There is no international standardization of the various subdivisions of the Triassic system. Except in North America, the terms in widest use are based upon deposits in western Europe. The lowest (earliest) division is the Keuper, the middle called the Bunter, and the upper, the Rhaetic. The Lunz flora from Austria and Germany is the best-known Keuper flora, Fig. 48. Many years ago a similar plant association was found in the Richmond basin of Virginia, but this flora is in need of critical revision. Some of its members, like *Macrotaeniopteris*, various ferns, and cycadophyte fructifications, are of considerable interest.

Fig. 47. Mesozoic gymnosperms. A selection of typical genera illustrating the major groups. Extreme left, *Araucarioxylon* (Triassic). *Araucarioxylon*, which is represented in the paleobotanical record by many pertified woods, is the chief species in the well-known Petrified Forest of Arizona. Left center, *Wielandiella* (Triassic) and *Williamsonia*, right center (Jurassic and Cretaceous) are cycadophytes. Note the strobiles in the axils of branches. On the extreme right are the shortened trunks of *Cycadeoidea* (Jurassic and Cretaceous) with expanded strobiles ("inflorescences") and frondose leaves arising from the summit of the trunk. (By permission from Brooklyn Botanic Garden.)

Fig. 48. (See next page for caption.)

The richest northern hemisphere Rhaetic flora has been found in the vicinity of Scoresby Sound in East Greenland. Similar but smaller floras occur in England and Sweden. Harris, employing modern techniques, has recognized nearly 60 plants, and these portray the characteristic vegetation of the time (Fig. 49).

Daugherty recognized 42 species from the Petrified Forest of Arizona, including silicified woods, microfossils, and impressions. The petrified wood occurs as great exposed logs of *Araucarioxylon arizonicum* and *Woodworthia arizonica*. They have been visited by thousands of tourists. In addition to these well-known conifers, there is the curious *Schilderia adamanica* of unknown affinity, possibly GNETALES. The prominent impression genera include *Todites, Cladophlebis, Neocalamites, Podozamites, Baiera, Ctenis, Macrotaeniopteris,* and *Otozamites.*

Halle has described a flora of 61 species from Hope Bay, Grahamland, lat. 53° 15′ S. Almost half of the total number of species are ferns, and the remainder consists chiefly of cycadophytes and conifers. Some of the species, like *Cladophlebis denticulata*, are truly cosmopolitan.

Other Triassic floras occur in Asia, the Gondwana province of the southern hemisphere, in Mexico, and southwestern United States. The Triassic plants of Massachusetts, Connecticut, New Jersey, and Pennsylvania, in eastern United States, are preserved in coarse sediments and thus are for the most part of limited interest.

The most widely used subdivisions of the Jurassic are likewise derived from European deposits. The Yorkshire Oolitic has long been the world standard for lower Jurassic. The divisions of the Jurassic are Liassic, Oolitic or Dogger, and Malm (which in turn is subdivided into Oxfordian, Kimmeridgian, and Portlandian).

Although many Jurassic floras have been described, few have been studied with modern methods (Fig. 50). A notable exception is Harris' investigation of the Yorkshire deltaic succession. In more than fifty "Notes," Harris has redescribed this remarkable flora.

Fig. 48. Triassic (Keuper) flora of Germany. (1) *Equisetites*, (2) *Neocalamites*, (3) *Danaeopsis*, (4) *Cheiropteris*, (5) *Sphenozamites*, (6) *Scythophylium*, (7) *Dioonitocarpidium*, (8) *Pterophyllum*, (9) *Voltzia*, (10) a reptile. The association contains sphenopsids, ferns, cycadophytes, and conifers. (By permission from *Vegetationsbilder der Vorzeit*, by K. Mägdefrau. Copyright, 1948, by Gustav Fischer Verlag, Jena.)

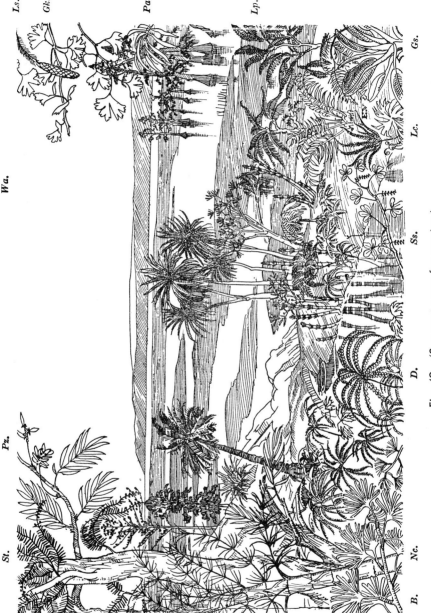

Fig. 49. (See next page for caption.)

Two other Jurassic floras deserve special mention, the Solen-hofen limestone of Bavaria and the silicified plants of the Rajmahal Hills of India. For more than a century the Solenhofen lithographic limestone has yielded fine specimens of insects, fish, reptiles, and birds, as well as algae, ferns, cycads, and conifers. Although the flora is of ecologic rather than phylogenetic interest, it is justly celebrated.

The Jurassic from the Rajmahal Hills is strikingly different. Here the deposits consist of fresh-water shales interbedded with exten-sive lava flows. This cycle of sedimentation affords many mag-nificent structurally preserved plants, some of singular beauty and interest. While the impression forms resemble, quite closely, con-temporary floras of other regions, the petrified plants caution us that there is much to learn about Mesozoic groups, indeed to expect the unexpected. Most of the Rajmahal plants are bennettitaleans, cycads, and conifers of conventional aspect, but among them are several types which cannot be classified with known groups. Two of these will be discussed briefly: *Homoxylon* and *Pentoxylon*.

Homoxylon rajmahalense is a peculiar cycadophyte with an angiosperm-like stem, with wood resembling that of such homoxylous angiosperms as *Drimys*, *Tetracentron*, and *Trochodendron*. Its botanical affinities, however, remain rather uncertain.

Far better known, yet more puzzling, is a group of gymnosperms named by Sahni (1948), the PENTOXYLEAE. The writer has deliberately refrained from introducing this remarkable group in earlier chapters.

The best known member, *Pentoxylon sahnii* Srivastava (1935) was provisionally described as a small tree or shrub of xerophytic habit, bearing deciduous *Taeniopteris* leaves and unisexual flowers on short shoots. These short shoots resemble a miniature cycad in

Fig. 49. The Rhaetic flora of Greenland. By all means the best known Rha-etic flora, this rich association contains all the principal lower Mesozoic plant groups. (B) *Baiera* and (Gk) *Ginkgoites* are ginkgophytes; (D) *Dictyophyllum*, and (Lc) *Laccopteris* are ferns; (Lp) *Lepidopteris* and (Gs) *Glossopteris* are pteri-dosperms, as is (Ss) *Sagenopteris* (Caytoniales); (Ls) *Lycostrobus*, a lycopsid; (Nc) *Neocalamites* is a sphenopsid; (Pa) *Pelourdea*, of unknown affinity, is be-lieved to be a cordaite; (Pz) *Podozamites* and (Wa) *Wielandiella* are bennetti-taleans; (St) *Stachyotaxus*, a conifer. (Drawn by Edward Vulliamy. By permis-sion from *Plant Life Through the Ages*, by A. C. Seward. Copyright, 1931, by Cambridge University Press, London.)

Fig. 50. (See next page for caption.)

having persistent leaf bases. The ovulate cones (*Carnoconites*) were fleshy, with numerous spirally disposed sessile ovules attached directly to the axis, with no megasporophyll or ovuliferous scale. Apparently there were no interseminal scales. The integument is thick, with a well-developed bicarinate stony layer and thin pericarp. The stems in cross-section show a ring of five (rarely six) bundles which lie close together, leaving little space for soft tissue. The secondary wood is compact with well-marked growth rings and uniseriate medullary rays. The radial walls of the tracheids show bordered pits of the cordaitean or araucarian type.

These plants cannot be referred to any known group of gymnosperms, though they show relationship with the bennettitaleans and conifers. Should future discoveries show the PENTOXYLEAE to be widespread and diversified, the whole question of cycadophyte evolution will have to be reconsidered.

So many baffling plant groups, of ordinal rank or higher, have been recognized in the Mesozoic that we must remain dissatisfied with present interpretations of the gymnosperms and angiosperms.

An extensive and well-described succession of Mesozoic floras occurs in the Japanese Islands extending from Rhaetic to lower Cretaceous in almost unbroken sequence. Yokoyama (1889, 1891, 1894) and Yabe *et al.* (1905) demonstrated the general features of this rich floral sequence and more recently Oishi (1940) published an excellent summary of knowledge of the Japanese Mesozoic which deserves wider recognition.

The oldest of three paleobotanical subdivisions is called the *Dictyophyllum* series. The prominent genera are: *Dictyophyllum, Clathropteris, Thaumatopteris, Hausmannia, Ptilozamites, Nilssonia,* and *Baiera*. Tropical and subtropical ferns of the MARATTIACEAE and DIPTERIDACEAE dominate the association. A total of 120 species has been described from central and southwestern Honsyu. This flora in Japan ranges from upper Triassic to mid-Jurassic.

Fig. 50. An upper Jurassic landscape. The tall *Williamsonia* on the left are somewhat better portrayed than in Fig. 47, but the strobili are not indicated. The short globular trunks of *Cycadeoidea* are shown near them. The smooth-stemmed *Williamsoniella* with entire leaves (*Taeniopteris*) and axillary strobili, appears on the right. The low equisetalean in the foreground is *Equisetites*. The animals represented are *Brontosaurus*, *Allosaurus*, and a *Compsognathus* dinosaur. (By permission from the American Museum of Natural History.)

Fig. 51. (See next page for caption.)

The next subdivision is called the *Onychiopsis* series and extends through the upper Jurassic and lower Cretaceous. The flora contains about 130 species, with *Onychiopsis, Cladophlebis, Coniopteris, Nilssonia,* and *Zamiophyllum* predominant. A small number of forms occur in both the *Dictyophyllum* and *Onychiopsis* series.

The third floral subdivision is characterized by the presence of angiosperms, including *Cretovarium, Nelumbium, Trochodendroides, Protophyllum, Nyssa,* and woods (*Juglandoxylon, Fagoxylon,* and *Dryoxylon*). The known species, which number 80, have been found in Honsyu, Hokkaido, and Tyosen.

The *Onychiopsis* series is notably similar to the Wealden of western Europe and the upper Newark and Potomac of eastern United States.

The lowest Cretaceous floras (i.e., Wealden) are very similar to those of Jurassic. The cycadophytes such as *Williamsonia* and *Cycadeoidea* were still abundant, the ginkgoaleans were common, and ferns belonging to the MATONIACEAE were widely distributed (Fig. 51). The CAYTONIALES (*Sagenopteris*) were still fairly conspicuous members of the floras.

MESOZOIC FERNS

All humid Mesozoic floras contain abundant ferns of rather modern aspect. Numerous existing families are represented by handsome forms.

The OSMUNDACEAE are represented by leaves and by petrified stems. These stems have been described by Kidston and Gwynne-Vaughan. The Mesozoic OSMUNDACEAE belong to two main types— one having expanded fertile pinnules, like *Todea* and *Cladophlebis,* and the other in which the fertile pinnules have no lamina, like *Osmunda.* The best-known genus of the *Todea* type is *Todites,* to which a series of very similar species has been assigned.—*T.* (*Acrostichides*) *rhombifolius* from the Keuper, *T. Goppertianus* and *T. Williamsoni* from the Rhaetic, the Lias, and the Oolite.

Fig. 51. The Wealden lower Cretaceous flora. Although showing some resemblance to the Rhaetic floras, the bennettitaleans show greater dominance and variety. (1) *Matonium,* a fern; (2) *Onychiopsis* (Polypodiaceae), a fern; (3) *Williamsonia,* (4) *Cycadeoidea,* and (5) *Nilssonia* are bennettitaleans; (6) *Ginkgoites;* (7) *Sphenolepidium,* a conifer; (8) *Iguanodon,* a reptile. (By permission from Vegetationsbilder der Vorzeit, by K. Mägdefrau. Copyright, 1948, Gustav Fischer Verlag, Jena.)

Schizaeaceae. There are two early Mesozoic genera with sporangia similar to those found in the SCHIZAEACEAE—*Klukia,* a fern with large, much divided fronds, and *Norimbergia,* a small fern with fronds scarcely 10 cm long. *Klukia* is fairly common in the Jurassic but has not been identified with certainty in the Rhaetic. *Norimbergia* is confined to the lower Jurassic of Germany. The family was possibly represented in the Carboniferous by *Senftenbergia,* but it is not certain whether this genus should be included, because the sporangia have a multiseriate annulus extending to the apex of the sporangium.

Gleicheniaceae. The GLEICHENIACEAE were at their maximum development in the upper Cretaceous, but at least one fertile species of *Gleichenites* is known from the middle Jurassic, and there are several probable Triassic species. In the details of the pinnae, the sori, and the sporangia, these older Mesozoic species are very like the living *Gleichenia.*

Matoniaceae. The chief fossil genus is *Laccopteris* (Fig. 36), which first occurs in the middle Triassic and is common throughout the Jurassic. Its leaf is like that of *Matonia pectinata,* and the sorus is like that of *Matonia,* but without an indusium. The sporangia have a conspicuous and complete annulus.

Dipteridaceae. The DIPTERIDACEAE were abundant. It is believed that most of the Mesozoic forms had creeping rhizomes and erect petioles bearing large palmate fronds. They are classified in two subfamilies: DIPTERIDEAE and CAMPTOPTERIDEAE, which are distinguished by the branching of the frond, straightforward dichotomy in the DIPTERIDEAE, and unequal dichotomy giving katadromic sympodia in the CAMPTOPTERIDEAE.

The best-known genera of the CAMPTOPTERIDEAE are *Clathropteris* and *Thaumatopteris.*

The DIPTERIDEAE are represented by *Hausmannia,* a group of small ferns resembling *Dipteris* in habit and in the form of the leaf.

APPEARANCE OF THE ANGIOSPERMS

The grand problem of the Mesozoic is, of course, the appearance of the angiosperms. A supposed palm leaf has been found in the Triassic of Arizona. In the Rhaetic of Greenland there is a leaf of an unknown plant named *Furcula granulifera* by Harris. Probably this is an angiosperm.

In the lower Cretaceous of western Greenland there occurs what is believed to be the earliest angiosperm flora, varied leaves associated with the ferns *Laccopteris, Cladophlebis,* and *Hausmannia* and *Ginkgoites.* The leaves have been referred to *Magnolia, Platanus, Liriodendron, Cinnamomum, Artocarpus,* and *Dalbergia.*

This meager flora has been found on Disko and Upernivik Islands, some 300 miles north of the Arctic Circle. Note that the families include MAGNOLIACEAE, LAURACEAE, PLATANACEAE, and MENISPERMACEAE. These well-characterized families give little clue to the probable origin of the flowering plants.

One of the most suggestive discoveries of recent years is that of Simpson (1937), who has found in macerations of Jurassic coal from Brora, Scotland, many pollens belonging to conifers and undoubted angiosperms. The pollens are attributable to the NYMPHAEACEAE and probably to the MAGNOLIACEAE. Similar pollens have been recognized in other Jurassic sediments. Since the cuticularized and cutinized pollens and spores are among the most resistant of plant structures, this source of information will become increasingly important in the search for the earliest angiosperms.

Probably the most that can be said for the newer evidence relating to the antiquity of the angiosperms is that the origin of the flowering plant is not so much "an abominable mystery" as an absorbing problem with many new clues at hand.

Bibliography

DARRAH, W. C. 1936. Antarctic fossil plants, *Science* 83: 390-391.
DAUGHERTY, L. H. 1941. The upper Triassic flora of Arizona. *Carn. Inst. Wash. Publ.* 526.
EDWARDS, W. N. 1934. Jurassic plants from New Zealand, *Ann. and Mag. Nat. Hist.* X, 13: 81-109.
HALLE, T. G. 1913. Mesozoic flora of Graham Land. *Wiss. Ergeb. Schwed. Süd-Polar Exped.* 1901-1903, 3.
HARRIS, T. M. 1926. The Rhaetic flora of East Greenland, *Meddel. om Grønland* 68.
———. 1931. Rhaetic floras, *Biol. Rev.* 6: 133-162.
———. 1931-1937. The fossil flora of Scoresby Sound, East Greenland, *Meddel. om Grønland* 85, 112.
———. 1942-1952. Notes on the Jurassic flora of Yorkshire, 1-57, *Ann. Mag. Nat. Hist.* 11, 12.
LUNDBLAD, A. B. 1950. Studies in the Rhaeto-Liassic floras of Sweden, *Kungl. Svensk. Vet. Handl.* IV, Parts 1, 8.
OISHI, S. 1940. The Mesozoic floras of Japan, *Jour. Fac. Sci. Hokkaido Imp. Univ.* 4: 5.
SAHNI, B. 1948. The PENTOXYLEAE. A new group of Jurassic gymnosperms from the Rajmahal Hills of India, *Bot. Gaz.* 110: 47-80.

Simpson, J. B. 1937. Fossil pollen in Scottish Jurassic coal, *Nature* 139: 673.

Sinnott, E. W. 1914. Some Jurassic Osmundaceae from New Zealand, *Ann. Bot.* 28: 471-479.

Sitholey, R. V. 1944. Jurassic plants from the Tabbowa series in Ceylon, *Spolia Zeylandica* 24: 1-17.

Walkom, A. B. 1921. Mesozoic floras of New South Wales. *Mem. Geol. Surv. N.S.W.* 12.

Ward, L. F. 1905. Status of the older Mesozoic floras of the United States. *U.S. Geol. Surv. Mon.* 12. Obsolete, but contains descriptions of eastern American floras in need of reinvestigation.

Wieland, G. R. 1914. La flora liassica de la Miexteca Alta. *Bot. Inst. Geol. Mex.* 31.

Zeiller, R. 1903. *Flore fossile des gîtes de charbon du Tonkin.* Imprimerie Nationale, Paris.

17

ORIGIN OF THE ANGIOSPERMS

Among plants of the early Mesozoic we have encountered several structures which among living plants are characteristic of the angiosperms.

These are of three types:

1. The bisexual "flower"
2. The "ovules" enclosed in an "ovary"
3. The expanded entire leaf (i.e., with a blade)

These structures evolved independently among various groups of gymnosperms.

We will now proceed to study the most perplexing problem in paleobotany—the origin of the angiosperms. It is fallacious to argue from the vantage point of any one theory. The evidence should be considered from three points of view: the earliest undoubted remains of angiosperms, the several main theories of angiosperm origin based on fossil remains, and finally the demands of the recent botanist in finding the early beginnings of the flowering plants.

To be sure, we are hampered in all of these speculations because of our narrowed point of view. The refuge of every doubter is in the incompleteness of the fossil record. Yet there can be little doubt that we have most, if not all, of the clues to angiosperm origin, but botanists have not been able to put them into a logical story.

Leaf compressions are the most abundant angiosperm remains, but fossil leaves do not always offer trustworthy evidence as to botanical relationship. A number of plant families have been recognized in the upper Cretaceous. The FAGACEAE, the MAGNOLIACEAE, and the SALICACEAE are known not only from leaves but also from seeds and fruits. The correctness of these identities cannot be denied. In other cases the evidence is by no means conclusive, so that many of the determinations published widely are open to question. The BETULACEAE in particular come under this category, as do the LAURACEAE and the PLATANACEAE.

205

There is a curious leaf type known as *Credneria* (Fig. 52) which roughly suggests a leaf of the plane family. No fruits or flowers belonging to this plant are known. However, there are certain features worthy of attention. In this, as in many other Cretaceous leaves, there are three or five prominent veins arranged palmately. In many forms these veins extend into three lobes. In a few forms, as in *Aspidophyllum* (Fig. 53), there is also a peculiar flange of tis-

Fig. 52. *Credneria.* An upper Cretaceous leaf form of unknown botanical affinity. (Drawn by G. W. Dillon.)

sue around the petiole. This leaf form, with many variations, occurs so generally (Fig. 54) that it probably has phylogenetic significance, particularly because the leaves exhibiting this form cannot be referred with certainty to any known families. It is commonly believed that such a leaf is primitive. The venation has a tantalizing resemblance to that of certain frondose pteridosperm leaves.

The MAGNOLIACEAE have interested botanists for many years because the family has been interpreted as the most primitive among living angiosperms. There are two magnoliaceous genera based upon leaf types which have abundant Cretaceous representatives, *Magnolia* and *Liriodendron*. Although a few fruits have been referred to the magnolia family, there is insufficient evidence to consider the MAGNOLIACEAE a preponderant Cretaceous group (Fig. 55).

Fig. 53. *Aspidophyllum.* A common leaf form in the Cretaceous Dakota sandstone. Note characteristic venation. Affinity unknown. (Drawn by G. W. Dillon.)

THE EARLIEST KNOWN ANGIOSPERMS

The earliest undoubted remains of angiosperms are palmlike leaves from the Triassic of southwestern Colorado described by Brown in 1956. From Jurassic coal of Brora, Scotland, Simpson recognized several types of pollen, including two referable to the NYMPHAEACEAE (cf. *Nelumbium* and *Castalia*). In addition, to these should be added the curious leaf named by Harris *Furcula granulifera* from the Upper Triassic of east Greenland. Were this form, however fragmentary, found in rocks of later geologic age, it

would be accepted as a dicotyledon without hesitation. The venation and stomatal structure are of forms known only among the
dicotyledons. With the supposed occurrence of Triassic palms, more
credence should be given to *Furcula*.

A few significant angiosperm remains occur in the lower Cretaceous. We find, aside from the various forms from western Greenland, a number of fossil woods which can be placed with some

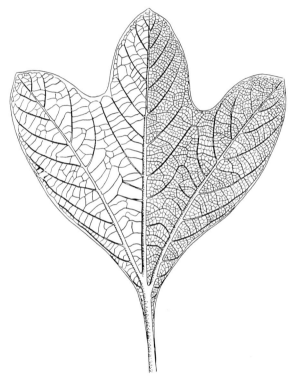

Fig. 54. *Araliopsis*. Although the name implies relationship with *Aralia*, the
systematic position of this Cretaceous leaf form is uncertain. (Drawn by G. W.
Dillon.)

confidence in modern plant families. In 1912 Stopes described a
series of six woods from England. In all of these, large vessels and
typical medullary rays are present. One of the genera, *Sabulia*,
is compared with the modern DIPTEROCARPACEAE. These records
are chiefly interesting because they show all of the characteristics
found in typical angiospermous woods. A few years earlier Lignier
described a wood belonging to the HAMAMELIDACEAE from the

Cretaceous of France. Similar structures have been found in the Cretaceous of Japan and have been described by Stopes and Fuji.

The earliest well-developed floras which are predominantly angiosperm occur on both sides of the Atlantic Ocean in beds sup-

Fig. 55. *Sterculia*. A common Cretaceous leaf form attributed to the Sterculiaceae. (Drawn by G. W. Dillon.)

posed to be contemporaneous. This has sometimes been assumed to indicate that the angiosperms evolved in Greenland and migrated southward into Europe and America where they became firmly established during late Mesozoic times; but there is no evidence to substantiate this. In Greenland during the upper Cretaceous there is a large flora of two hundred species which belong to types widely distributed over the northern hemisphere throughout the Cretaceous. Before entering into a discussion of this flora, it is well to bear in mind that large Cretaceous floras have been described from western North America. The Dakota flora, particularly well-developed in Kansas, has more than five hundred nominal species. Similar floras are known in Montana and Colorado. In South America (e.g., Argentina) similar floras are known to occur. Even on the Antarctic there are undoubted records of angiosperms. It has already been mentioned that fossil woods are found in Japan, and there are also extensive leaf floras. Cretaceous floras are known also from Australia and Africa.

The most striking monocotyledonous remains of which we have definitive knowledge in the Cretaceous are such fruits as a coconut from France and widely distributed specimens of *Sparganium*. There are a great number of leaves attributed to palms and *Smilax*. A most interesting occurrence is a fossil flower from the upper Cretaceous of Japan. This plant, named *Cretovarium japonicum*, is a member of the LILIACEAE. It has, in addition to well-preserved ovules in a tripartite ovary, the remains of a somewhat poorly preserved perianth. From these few examples it will be observed that a considerable number of families of the angiosperms were already present in the Cretaceous.

Thomas and many other paleobotanists have argued that in the light of these occurrences, it is necessary to search far into the geologic record to find the ancestors of the flowering plants.

SOME THEORIES OF ANGIOSPERM ORIGIN

The several theories concerning angiosperm origin based upon fossil materials trace the ultimate derivation of flowering plants from the pteridosperms. This derivation is implied rather than proved. The seed-ferns themselves are almost certainly not directly ancestral to the angiosperms, but they show certain evolutionary tendencies which arrest our attention:

1. The seed habit, achieved independently by several groups.
2. Both "megasporophylls" and "microsporophylls," using the terms in a broad sense, began a series of modifications including the cupulate seed and the united campanulate staminate disc.

If the pteridosperm stock became strobiloid and attained the cycadean level, three tendencies could be derived:

1. BENNETTITALES, with the strobili bisexual and the female sporophyll more reduced than the male.
2. MICROFLORAE, which are much like the former but with dichotomously branched smooth stems.
3. CYCADALES, with unisexual strobili and with the male and female sporophylls equally reduced.

Note that the CAYTONIALES, now regarded as Mesozoic pteridosperms, cannot be placed into this scheme, nor do the MICROFLORAE possess the barrel-shaped trunk so characteristic of the cycadophytes. None of these groups furnishes us with a perianth.

Wieland in 1906 suggested that the BENNETTITALES were the ancestors of the flowering plants. His theory immediately attracted many botanists, notably Arber and Parkin. The assumption which Wieland made was that the strobiloid flower found among many dicotyledons is primitive. There is by no means universal agreement that this is true.

In Wieland's argument the various structures considered to be restricted to the angiosperms have homologies among the fossil cycads. Thus there are stamens, carpels, receptacles, and dicotyledonous embryos among the members of the BENNETTITALES. These are structures involved in the evolution of a flower. There are two difficulties involved in such a comparison. In the first place, is it justifiable to compare the compound stamen of a fossil cycad with the simple stamen known in the MAGNOLIALES? In the second place, what is the morphogenic origin of the carpel?

Paleobotany offers little toward an answer to these baffling questions. The "new morphology" casts aside supposed homologies based upon leaf and stem conversions and does not accept the notion that the carpel is of foliar origin.

In *Caytonia*, a state of angiospermy is observable. The ovules are enclosed in an "ovary" which closes late in life. Possibly these peculiar structures are analogous, not homologous, with the angiosperm carpel. Yet it is significant that angiospermy appears among several Mesozoic pteridosperm and perhaps cycadophyte groups.

In angiosperm woods, vessels are characteristic, but they are present among the GNETALES; why not among fossil gymnosperms? Seeds with dicotyledonous embryos occur among the pteridosperms, cordaites, and various cycadophytes. Complete, that is, bisexual, flowers, occur in the MICROFLORAE and in other BENNETTITALES. Ovules enclosed in an ovary-like fruit occur in the CAYTONIALES. Pollen producing a pollen tube occurs in the CAYTONIALES. If all of these characteristics were united in one plant, we would have a Triassic or Jurassic angiosperm.

The general opinion among recent botanists holds that despite the fact that one part of the RANALES series is essentially woody and another part essentially herbaceous, the group is homogeneous. This ranalean complex is frequently considered by morphologists as a type from which all other angiosperms could be derived.

Stimulated by Wieland's interpretation of the BENNETTITALES, morphologists seized upon the magnolian flower, typified by *Liriodendron,* and proclamed they had found the avenue by which the angiosperm had arrived. As objections and difficulties accumulated, a gloomy pessimism shrouded the theory, leading to a general distrust of such evidence based upon comparative morphology. Recently, however, interest in the RANALES has been revived. There occurs among the woody ranaleans a combination of primitive characters which presents an entirely different picture as to the direction of angiosperm evolution. Bailey (1949) is the most outspoken proponent, but by no means does he stand alone.

Briefly the evidence is this. There exists today a hundred species of primitively vesselless dicotyledons. These are trees, belonging to a dozen genera in six or seven families, mostly in the RANALES (WINTERACEAE, TROCHODENDRACEAE, TETRACENTRACEAE). The gymnospermous affinities of the homoxylous structure of both the primary and secondary xylem has long been recognized. But there are other features which imply primitiveness. The only distally monocolpate form of pollen among the dicotyledons occurs in these families. Bailey and Swamy (1951) have shown also that among the vesselless ranaleans is to be found a comparably primitive carpel, conduplicate in form and ontogenesis. This conduplicate carpel (e.g., *Drimys* in the WINTERACEAE) is styleless, unsealed, has a diffused stigmatic surface, and has laminal rather than marginal placentation of the ovules. Various lines of specialization occur in the several families. There is a geographic factor which also suggests antiquity. Five of the nine genera occur in New Caledonia, and of these, three are endemic. The RANALES alone among angiosperms retain so many primitive characteristics.

There is little paleobotanical evidence to show the relative antiquity of the monocotyledons and dicotyledons. The evidence of comparative anatomy suggests that the monocots were derived from a ranalean ancestry. A few botanists regard the palms as being the most primitive monocot family. The palms are arborescent—an unusual condition among monocotyledons. Palms are relatively abundant from the Cretaceous to the Miocene, but one Triassic form has been recognized. The fossil evidence suggests that the dicotyledons are of earlier origin and diversification, but the evidence is chiefly inferential.

There are other theories of flowering plant origin based upon comparative studies of living plants. One of these derives the angiosperms from the curious GNETALES. Since there are no fossil records of members of the GNETALES, we are not justified in devoting much attention to this theory. This theory assumes that the amentiferous, wind-pollinated, unisexual, naked-flowered families of angiosperms are primitive. Wettstein has been the leading proponent of this hypothesis. There is no fossil evidence for either side, and it is believed by many that these plants have been reduced from a complete flowered stock.

We find throughout all of these disputed arguments two aspects of the major problem. The first is the purely speculative argument based on comparison of hypothetical ancestors with assumed primitive plants. We do not know definitely what is primitive or what is advanced, nor what is generalized nor what is modified by reduction. For instance, some angiosperms like the cactus have secondarily lost vessels. In the second place there occur among many living and extinct gymnosperms structures which are usually considered to be characteristic of the angiosperms. On the other hand, a number of angiosperms possess characters which appear to be persistent traits from a gymnosperm ancestry. Of this much we may be certain: the ancestry of the angiosperms will be demonstrated, but as yet we do not know that ancestry. All of the theories ultimately lead back to the seed-ferns in the broadest sense in which we observe first true seeds and true pollen. Probably both the typical gymnosperm and the typical angiosperm have evolved from this early group.

It is still generally believed that the ancient flowers of the fossil cycads most nearly represent the ancestral type of the angiosperms.

It is difficult to escape the conviction that the Mesozoic pteridosperms and cycadophytes shed some light on the early floral structure of the true flowering plants. Scott once said of the cycadeoids that they "for the first time brought the origin of the flowering plants within the range of scientific discussion." Considering the NILSSONIALES and MICROFLORAE as "fossil cycads," this view still holds.

The presence of a bell-shaped disc uniting the stamens has led to some speculation, particularly since it has also been found among other cycadeoids, as in the MICROFLORAE. Wieland suggested that this disc or "campanula" makes a "perfect corolla." The possibility has also been suggested that this structure may have been present also among some members of the primitive flowering stock and that it represents an early stage in the evolution of the corolla of many flowers of the tubular type. There is little evidence to support this hypothesis.

THE HERBACEOUS HABIT

Though there is still some dispute as to whether arborescent or herbaceous habit is primitive and ancestral, the overwhelming evidence supports the view that the woody habit is ancestral. Any theory of angiosperm origin which is based on a herbaceous ancestry is without paleobotanical evidence. The herbaceous habit was probably not acquired early. It appeared simultaneously in a number of diverse phylogenetic lines.

The most striking difference in general habit of growth among angiosperms is that between woody and herbaceous plants. The former series comprise trees and shrubs, and have persistent, woody, aerial stems which increase in size from year to year by the activity of the cambium, and which usually attain considerable height and thickness. Herbaceous plants, on the other hand, are usually short-lived and limited in growth, at least in their aerial portions, and possess stems which are usually smaller and of softer texture. The stelar construction is extremely complicated.

These two great groups are more or less equal in number of species, woody forms predominating in the tropics and herbs in more temperate regions. Nearly half the families of the angiosperms include both woody and herbaceous members, and even in a large percentage of the genera there are species from both groups. Sinnott and Bailey have said: "It is quite evident, therefore, that whichever of these two classes is the more recent, it must have arisen quite independently many different times, and from numerous ancient stocks. The whole question as to the origin of these plant types, their relative antiquity, and the way in which they have been developed and become dispersed is consequently of great botanical interest."

It is still widely accepted that the most ancient angiosperms were herbaceous, and that the woody and arborescent members of the phylum have been derived from them by an increase in the extent of the cambium and in the amount of its activity.

The alternative hypothesis is that woody plants are the more ancient and that herbaceous forms have been derived from them by reduction. This concept has been generally held by paleobotanists for a great many years. Hallier in 1905, in discussing the origin of the angiosperms, states that from their arborescent habit (etc.) the MAGNOLIALES are, "without doubt," the oldest living angiosperm families, and down from them, through the BERBERIDACEAE, RANUNCULACEAE, and NYMPHAEACEAE, through to the MONOCOTYLE-DONS, there has been a line of reduction from the ancient arborescent forms to lianas, shrubs, herbs, and waterplants.

Paleobotanical evidence certainly indicates that the arborescent angiosperms are more ancient than the herbaceous ones, for the overwhelming majority of fossil angiosperms are related to forms which today are always trees and shrubs. The objection frequently raised to this conclusion is that the absence of herbaceous leaf impressions is not due to the absence of herbs, but rather to the fact that leaves of such plants are generally more delicate and less apt to be preserved. This is a gross exaggeration of fact. Every large angiosperm flora includes preserved flowers, aquatic plants, and fruits. Absence of herbaceous forms is due to their actual absence.

Herbs are not lacking as fossils. In the middle Cretaceous of the Potomac occur specimens variously assigned to *Plantago*, XYRIDACEAE, and CYPERACEAE. In the Florissant (Miocene) there occurs a leaf referred to *Carduus*. From the Miocene onward, especially from Spitsbergen and Switzerland investigated by Heer, herbaceous forms appear to be increasingly abundant. In the Tertiary flora of Switzerland, Heer supposed that 24 per cent of the angiosperms were herbaceous. The number of herbs is much greater in the more recent than in the older formations.

Since very few herbs are found from the Cretaceous and comparatively more from the Tertiary, it appears in general that woody plants are more ancient than herbs.

Sinnott and Bailey made an interesting case as to the relative antiquity of herbs and woody plants from a study of the present distribution over the earth of the members of these two groups. One of the most conspicuous facts brought out by their study of distribution is the great contrast between temperate and tropical regions in the proportion of herbaceous flora.

Of course, in all these regions the monocotyledons, which comprise 25 to 30 per cent of the angiospermous vegetation, are with comparatively few exceptions, herbaceous. The accompanying table shows that in the north temperate zone herbs are the dominant dicotyledons, but that in the tropics the situation is reversed and woody plants are the prevailing type of vegetation. A comparison of the percentage of herbs in various families in their temperate and tropical ranges indicates the phenomenon, as shown in Table 9.

TABLE 9

Relative Proportions of Herbaceous Species
(Data from Sinnott and Bailey)

Family	North Temperate Zone (%)	Brazil (%)	India (%)	Tropical Africa (%)
AMARANTHACEAE	100	79	44	84
LEGUMINOSAE	90	22	38	41
EUPHORBIACEAE	95	14	10	29
VIOLACEAE	100	6	52	18
LYTHRACEAE	100	30	42	76
CONVOLVULACEAE	100	42	52	65
VERBENACEAE	100	20	4	7
RUBIACEAE	100	20	39	19
COMPOSITAE	100	39	91	80

An overwhelming majority of arborescent dicotyledons is confined to the tropics, where they constitute from 25 per cent to 40 per cent of the species instead of from 1 to 5 per cent, as in temperate regions. Dorf (1938) used the criteria proposed by Sinnott and Bailey in his investigation of the Cretaceous Medicine Bow flora and found strikingly similar results.

If woody plants were originally the dominant type of dicotyledonous vegetation throughout the world, the question arises as to where herbaceous forms were first developed and what were the causes for their origin. The present distribution of herbs throughout the various regions of the world provides scant evidence for a solution. Since herbaceous plants attain predominance today in the great land mass of the north temperate zone, the more profound change in the growth habit of its vegetation must have occurred in this region.

During Cretaceous and Cenozoic times many genera and families of trees flourished in the north temperate zone which are either absent or rare in this area at present, but of which many still occur in warmer regions. The presence of *Ficus, Eucalyptus, Diospyros, Cinnamomum, Aralia,* and various proteaceous genera as fossils in northern Europe and America may be cited as examples.

Herbs have a short life-cycle, and are therefore able to survive unfavorable seasons, such as periods of cold, underground or in the form of seeds. Their great development in temperate regions has probably been the result of progressive refrigeration of the climate during the course of the later Cenozoic and Pleistocene.

The advent of colder conditions resulted in the extermination of a large part of the vegetation of the north temperate zone, but this extermination was proportionately much greater among woody plants than among herbs. The present flora of Europe contains a decidedly smaller element of woody plants than does that of corresponding temperate North America because of the inability of the plants in the former region to migrate southward on the encroachment of glaciation.

None of these hypotheses can be proved at this time. We will, however, reconsider them after further consideration of the angiosperm fossil record.

Bibliography

ARBER, E. A. N., and J. PARKIN. 1907. The origin of angiosperms, *Jour. Linn. Soc. Lond.* 38: 29-80.

BAILEY, I. W. 1949. Origin of the angiosperms. Need of broadened outlook, *Jour. Arnold Arbor.* 30: 64-70.

BAILEY, I. W., and B. G. L. SWAMY. 1951. The conduplicate carpel of dicotyledons and its initial trends of specialization, *Am. Jour. Bot.* 38: 373-379.

EDWARDS, W. N. 1935. The systematic value of cuticular characters in recent and fossil angiosperms, *Biol. Rev.* 10: 442-459.

EMBERGER, L. 1950. La valeur morphologique et l'origine de la fleur, *Ann. Biol.* 26: 279-296.

ERDTMAN, G. 1948. Did dicotyledonous plants exist in early Jurassic times? *Geol. Foren. i Stockholm Forh.* 70: 265-271.

JUST, T. 1948. Gymnosperms and the origin of angiosperms, *Bot. Gaz.* 110: 91-103.

Sahni, B. 1932. *Homoxylon rajmahalense* gen. et sp. nov. A fossil angiospermous wood, devoid of vessels, from the Rajmahal Hills, Behar, *Mem. Geol. Surv. India* n.s. 20.
Sinnott, E. W., and I. W. Bailey. 1914. Investigations on the phylogeny of the angiosperms, 4. The origin and dispersal of herbaceous angiosperms, *Ann. Bot.* 23: 547-600.
Stopes, M. C. 1912. Petrifactions of the earliest European angiosperms, *Phil. Trans. Roy. Soc. Lond.* B 203: 75-100.
Stopes, M. C., and K. Fujii. 1910. Studies on the structure and affinities of Cretaceous plants, *Roy. Soc. Lond. Phil. Trans.* B 201: 1-90.
Takhtajian, A. L. 1958. *Origins of Angiospermous Plants.* (Transl. O. H. Gankin.) American Institute of Biological Science, Washington. Follows the magnolian-homoxylous-*Degeneria* theory, but without citation of non-Russian works.
Thomas, H. H. 1925. The Caytoniales, a new group of angiospermous plants from the Jurassic rocks of Yorkshire, *Roy. Soc. Lond. Phil. Trans.* B 213: 229-363.
Thompson, W. P., and I. W. Bailey. 1916. Are *Tetracentron, Trochodendron,* and *Drimys* specialized or primitive types? *Mem. N.Y. Bot. Gard.* 6: 27-32.

For those who wish to know more about the geological history of families and genera of angiosperms, the following summaries will be helpful:

Berry, E. W. 1923. *Tree Ancestors.* The Williams & Wilkins Co., Baltimore.
Darrah, W. C. 1939. *Textbook of Paleobotany,* Chap. 16. D. Appleton-Century Co., New York.
Gunderson, A. 1950. *Families of Dicotyledons.* A Chronica Botanica Publication. The Ronald Press Co., New York.

No critical or complete survey of the fossil angiosperms has been attempted in this century.

18

UPPER CRETACEOUS FLORAS

The upper Cretaceous floras are of peculiar importance in the study of fossil plants. Although angiosperms appear in the late Jurassic, and may perhaps occur earlier, it is not until mid-Cretaceous times that they become numerous. Suddenly—and suddenly is the proper word—a rapid diversification and radiation of the flowering plants occurred.

Seward called the upper Cretaceous "the dawn of a new era" and Lesquereux many years ago observed that "the flora of the globe has become modified as by a new creation" (Figs. 56 and 57).

There has been no adequate explanation for this apparently sudden modernization of the earth's flora. The angiosperms appear in familiar form, not in small variety but in great numbers of existing families and genera. It is this perplexing paradox which has obscured the origin of the angiosperms. Monocotyledons and dicotyledons occur simultaneously, LILIACEAE and PALMAE; MAGNOLIACEAE and ASCLEPIADACEAE.

The taxonomy of fossil angiosperms is in a deplorable condition, although modern investigations have eliminated many of the more obvious erroneous determinations of the early monographers. The identification of leaf impressions is in many instances accurate and trustworthy; oftentimes it is hazardous. As noted in the previous chapter, there are many Cretaceous leaf forms (e.g., *Credneria*, *Protophyllum*) which cannot be referred to existing genera or even families. In some floras they are the most abundant fossils. Recognizing these limitations, we will consider several representative floras.

THE SUCCESSION OF CRETACEOUS FLORAS

An approximate sequence of upper Cretaceous floras is indicated by Table 10.

The "Denver" and "Laramie" floras, as described in older mono-

Fig. 56. The upper Cretaceous (Cenomanian) flora of Bohemia. Left foreground, *Credneria*; center, various palms ("*Sabalites*"); far right, *Araliopsis*. The reconstruction, published in 1879, is probably as correct as present knowledge warrants. (From Saporta, *Le Monde des Plantes avant l'Apparition de l'Homme.*)

Fig. 57. The upper Cretaceous (Senonian) flora. Semi-schematic portrayal of typical angiosperms and conifers: (1) a mono-cot; (2) Magnolia; (3) Credneria; (4) Salix; (5) Quercus; (6) Geinitzia; (7) Sequoia; (8) Gleichenia, a fern. (By permission from Vegetationsbilder der Vorzeit, by K. Mägdefrau. Copyright, 1948, Gustav Fischer Verlag, Jena.)

graphs, overlap upper Cretaceous and basal Eocene (Paleocene). The Medicine Bow, for instance, is correlated with "Lower Laramie."

It has already been noted that the continents were submerged over extensive areas in the Mesozoic and vast regions were again elevated during the Laramide revolution, at which time the seas were pushed back to approximately their present position. The Atlantic Coastal Plain preserves an extensive sequence of Cretaceous and Eocene floras (see Dorf, 1952) while in western United States there are many continental deposits, less easily correlated perhaps, but showing the sequence of floras in remarkable detail.

TABLE 10

The Sequence of Upper Cretaceous Floras

	Western United States	Eastern United States	Europe
Upper Cretaceous	(Denver) (Laramie)	–	Danian
	Lance	Ripley	–
	Medicine Bow	Ripley	Senonian
	Fox Hills	Magothy	Turonian
	Mesa Verde	Tuscaloosa	–
	Dakota	Raritan	Cenomanian
Mid-Cretaceous	–	Potomac (upper)	Albion (Gault) Aptian

THE ATLANTIC COASTAL PLAIN PROVINCE

In Maryland and Virginia, the lower Cretaceous series of clays, sands, and sandstones have been called the Potomac Formations. There are three distinct divisions, the oldest of which is known as the Patuxent. The Patuxent flora is comprised of approximately a hundred species, of which forty are conifers. The aspect is very similar to that of a late Jurassic flora. It has been mentioned earlier that plants of the lowest Cretaceous are types which persisted from Jurassic times.

This persistence of older types into the lower Cretaceous has been observed in England, Belgium, Germany, France, Portugal, and North America. In America, this phenomenon is particularly well illustrated by the Patuxent flora.

Along the Atlantic Coastal Plain the Patuxent is succeeded by the Raritan, a rich flora which contains 70 per cent angiosperms and a small remnant of the persistent Jurassic types.

The Raritan flora, which is slightly older than the Dakota, occurs from Martha's Vineyard (Massachusetts) to the Potomac River. There are approximately 300 species, of which 220 are angiosperms. The conifers are represented by about fifty species while the ferns and cycads total some twenty species. *Liriodendron, Liriodendropsis, Aralia, Araliopsis, Diospyros, Sassafras, Magnolia,* and *Eucalyptus* are abundant.

The Magothy flora, numbering more than three hundred species, succeeded the Raritan in the Atlantic Coastal Plain. *Liriodendron, Magnolia, Aralia,* and *Ficus* are again abundant. *Quercus* is represented by six species. The monocotyledons, although rare and poorly preserved, include grasses, sedges, *Typha,* and palms. Conifers held about the same proportion as in the Raritan.

Plant-bearing beds of approximately the same age are found along the Atlantic Coastal Plain from North Carolina to Texas.

Attention has already been called to the supposition that these floras have originated in the north and spread southward in successive waves of migration. Slight evidence is to be found in the large upper Cretaceous floras of Greenland. These floras, known respectively as the Atane (older) and Patoot (younger) floras, combined included about three hundred species. Many of these species occur as far south as Texas, there being, for example, forty-seven in the Raritan, thirty-seven in the Magothy, and thirty-six in the Dakota flora, with smaller numbers in the several Coastal Plain florules. It is possible that critical study would reduce this number somewhat.

ARCTIC CRETACEOUS FLORAS

The Greenland floras show much the same mixture of conifers and hardwoods as already mentioned, i.e., *Sequoia, Juniperus, Taxodium, Pinus,* and *Ginkgo,* with *Acer, Cornus, Juglans, Diospyros, Ficus, Liriodendron, Laurus, Cinnamomum, Eucalyptus,* and *Platanus.* Ferns, some of them evidently tree-ferns, were more abundant and varied in the Greenland floras than in the eastern United States.

Perhaps the most interesting member of the Greenland flora is breadfruit (*Artocarpus*), which is represented by both leaves and fruits. As the breadfruit is found living at the present day within 20 degrees of the equator, its presence so far north in Greenland in upper Cretaceous time suggests a similar climate, provided, of course, its ecological requirements then were similar to those demanded at present.

Strictly Arctic upper Cretaceous floras are limited to Alaska and Greenland, but others of similar age and content are found in northern Europe and eastern Asia. The most extensive is that from the two horizons in West Greenland known, as stated above, as the Atane and Patoot. These have in large part been described by Heer and there is an obvious overspeciation. The upper Cretaceous flora from the Atane beds has nearly 200 nominal species, including 30 ferns, 12 cycads, 9 ginkgoes, 25 conifers, 4 monocotyledons, and 100 dicotyledons.

The Patoot flora includes 20 ferns, 20 conifers, 2 monocotyledons, and 80 dicotyledons, and thus shows a similar composition.

Early Cenozoic plants from the Arctic have been encountered at very many localities, usually associated with coal. Incidentally, Berry noted that this coal, plants with their roots in place as in the case of *Equisetum* (in Spitsbergen), the association with fresh water mollusks (Greenland), aquatic beetles (in Spitsbergen and Iceland), and also the presence of fresh water diatoms in the matrix and the mixture of branches and delicate foliage, proves that these Arctic floras and the associated coals cannot represent drift material from lower latitudes as has sometimes been suggested. That the climate was more temperate than at present is supported by collateral evidence.

During the upper Cretaceous there took place a great extension of subtropical floras into the temperate zone. This northward movement reached its maximum in upper Eocene (Jackson) to middle Oligocene (Vicksburg) time. Plants or coal of lower Tertiary age are found at numerous widely distributed localities. These completely encircle the pole and reach to within 8.5° of it, as in Grinnell Land.

Recently there have appeared several critical papers (Seward, Seward and Conway) on the Cretaceous floras of western Greenland. In these works attempts have been made to evaluate the many species previously identified and described on meager data. "*Populus*" *arctica* and "*Populus*" *richardsonii* have turned out to belong to *Trochodendroides*. Other plants, which had been referred to *Dalbergia, Crataegus, Juglans, Rhamnus,* etc., are at best doubtful.

THE TUSCALOOSA FLORA (Atlantic Coastal Plain)

We return to the Atlantic Coastal Plain to consider one of the most remarkable transition floras thus far recognized. The Tuscaloosa flora was described in 1919 by Berry, who recognized 151 species. There were in addition a number of unidentifiable seeds in the collections, a suggestion of the occurrence of forms which when studied may shed new light upon the problems of angiosperm history. The Tuscaloosa flora represents 87 genera in 48 families and 31 orders, approximately half of which are not represented in existing floras. This is somewhat misleading, however, because many of these are form-genera, like *Laurophyllum, Capparites,* and *Leguminosites,* which may indicate close relationship to living forms. All the species are of course extinct, none of them surviving in the abundant lower Eocene floras of the Mississippi embayment. The striking difference, in addition to the great modernization of the Eocene angiosperms, is the disappearance of the Mesozoic gymnospermous types like *Androvettia, Abietites, Brachyphyllum, Protophyllocladus, Widdringtonites, Podozamites, Protodammara,* and *Geinitzia.*

The CONIFERALES of the Tuscaloosa flora include such modern types as *Pinus, Dammara,* and *Sequoia,* and the extinct phylloclad type *Androvettia,* as well as *Protophyllocladus, Brachyphyllum, Protodammara,* and *Geinitzia.*

As in all known upper Cretaceous floras, the angiosperms constitute the major part of the Tuscaloosa. It may be noted that the monocotyledons are represented by a single fragmentary grasslike form referred to the form-genus *Cyperacites.* Berry suggested that "this scarcity of monocotyledons is largely due to the fact that the lack of differentiation of their foliage into lamina and petiole precludes the regular shedding of their leaves which therefore hang on and are flayed by the wind until they become almost unrecognizable."

The order RANALES, which in the Tuscaloosa includes fifteen species, has one supposed member of the RANUNCULACEAE referred to the genus *Dewalquea.* This genus, which is quite abundant, is a curious type which appeared with apparent suddenness in the Atane beds of Greenland, and in "contemporaneous" deposits in the Raritan formation of New Jersey, the Tuscaloosa formation of Alabama, and the Cenomanian of Bohemia. It persisted into the

Paleocene (i.e., basal Eocene) of western Europe, especially the
Gelinden of Belgium. The Ranales include nine species of Magnoliaceae, probably overspeciated (i.e., leaves referred to *Magnolia*), and five species of Menispermaceae.

THE ROCKY MOUNTAIN PROVINCE

Brief consideration of three floras from central United States will
suggest the homogeneity of the upper Cretaceous floras. Although
the species differ among different floras, the similar association is
striking.

The Dakota flora, occurring in Kansas, Nebraska, and neighboring
states, contains more than 550 nominal species, undoubtedly a greatly
exaggerated number. At any rate, the chief features are evident.
The composition is almost entirely angiosperm, there being barely
30 forms referable to the ferns, cycads, and conifers combined, and
these being relatively rare. To what extent ecological factors are
responsible for this distribution has not been ascertained.
Liriodendron, Sassafras, Aralia, Diospyros, and *Magnolia* are each
represented by many species. In addition to these genera supposedly identical with existing groups, there are many other of
uncertain systematic position, the most conspicuous of them being
Aspidophyllum, Protophyllum, and *Credneria.* This remarkable association, despite disappointing preservation, deserves critical revision and thorough field investigation.

The Medicine Bow flora from southern Wyoming and northwestern Colorado contains several score of recognizable species distributed as follows: dicotyledons, 45; monocotyledons, 8; ferns, 3;
and conifers, 2. The conspicuous genera are *Sabalites, Ficus,
Trochodendroides, Magnolia, Juglans, Credneria, Cinnamomum,
Laurus, Viburnum, Zizyphus, Rhamnus,* and *Sequoia.* It may be
inferred from this association that it flourished in a warm temperate
or subtropical climate.

The Lance flora, of 70 species, includes 55 dicotyledons, 6
monocotyledons, 2 conifers, 4 ferns, and a ginkgo (the widespread
Ginkgo adiantoides). The more abundant genera are *Sabalites,
Laurophyllum, Platanophyllum* ("*Sassafras*"), *Dryophyllum, Dombeyopsis, Fraxinus, Viburnum, Ficus, Vitis, Grewiopsis,* and *Sequoia.*
The assignment of a supposed *Sassafras* (*S. montana*) to *Platanophyllum* casts some suspicion upon other early species frequently referred
to the genus solely upon polymorphic leaves.

Rich Cretaceous floras have also been found in Canada. These are similar to those of the Rocky Mountain province.

OTHER REPRESENTATIVE FLORAS

In South America, in the province of Santa Cruz, Argentina, there occurs a rich upper Cretaceous flora in need of careful revision and other floras from Patagonia largely undescribed.

Ettingshausen (*Beiträge zur Kenntnis der Kreideflora Australiens,* 1895) published a flora of 64 species that may be of Eocene rather than Cretaceous age. The chief families are PROTEACEAE, FAGACEAE, MYRTACEAE, LEGUMINOSAE, and LAURACEAE. On the whole the flora is poorly described. Ettingshausen also studied supposedly Cretaceous plants from New Zealand. A number of these forms have been studied individually by modern methods, but no reinterpretation of the flora is as yet justified.

Other Cretaceous floras are known from Japan, Siberia, Egypt, Cameroons, Nigeria, Sweden, Germany, France, England, Portugal, Italy, Austria, Czechoslovakia, Hungary, and the Balkans. Many individual species from these localities have been studied with modern methods, but no extensive revisions are available.

There are two important aspects of the evolutionary development of the angiosperms during the upper Cretaceous. The first of these is the apparent rapidity with which the diversification of the families of flowering plants took form. The meager beginnings of this process of diversification which are evident in the middle Cretaceous give no hint of the explosive radiation which followed. The real modernization of the angiosperms occurred in the Cenozoic, but the lines of descent were well established by the close of the Cretaceous.

The other aspect is the phenomenal geographic spread of the angiosperms over the world in the Cretaceous. This process has been termed the "upper Cretaceous radiation." It was the last "cosmopolitan" flora in the true sense of the word. The rapid radiation of the diversifying flowering plants certainly is indicative of an equable climate.

Bibliography

There are hundreds of monographs on Cretaceous floras. They are based almost exclusively upon leaf impressions and, in older works, superficial resemblances served as evidence of relationship. Most of the references given here represent critical studies which attempt interpretation of floras as well as description.

BELL, W. A. 1949. Uppermost Cretaceous and Paleocene floras of western Alberta. *Canada Dept. Mines and Resources Geol. Surv. Bull.* 13.

BERRY, E. W. 1916. The upper Cretaceous floras of the world. *Md. Geol. Surv. Rept. Upper Cret.* 1916: 183-313.

———. 1919. Upper Cretaceous floras of the eastern Gulf region in Tennessee, Mississippi, Alabama and Georgia. *U.S. Geol. Surv. Prof. Pap.* 112.

———. 1935. A preliminary contribution to the floras of the Whitemud and Ravenscrag formations. *Canada Dept. Mines Geol. Surv. Mem.* 12.

DORF, E. 1938-1942. Upper Cretaceous floras of the Rocky Mountain region. *Carn. Inst. Wash. Publ.* 508. An excellent example of present methods of interpretation.

———. 1952. Critical analysis of Cretaceous stratigraphy and paleontology of Atlantic Coastal Plain, *Bull. Amer. Assoc. Pet. Geol.* 36: 2161-2184.

FRIČ, A., and A. BAYER. 1901. Studien im Gebiete der bömischen Kreideformation. *Arch. naturwiss. Landes. Böhmen* 2.

KNOWLTON, F. H. 1922. The Laramie flora of the Denver Basin. *U.S. Geol. Surv. Prof. Pap.* 130.

LESQUEREUX, L. 1891. The flora of the Dakota Group. *U.S. Geol. Surv. Mont.* 17. Posthumous. Badly obsolete, but a classic. Included here because many Dakota specimens are preserved in museums.

SEWARD, A. C. 1925. Notes sur la flora Cretacique du Groenland, *Livre Jubil. Soc. géol. Belg.*, Liége.

———. 1926. The Cretaceous plant-bearing rocks of western Greenland, *Roy. Soc. Lond. Phil. Trans.* B 215: 57-175.

SEWARD, A. C., and V. CONWAY. 1935. Additional plants from western Greenland, *Kungl. Svensk Vetensk. Handl.* 15, Part 3.

———. 1935. Fossil plants from Kingigtok and Kagdlunguak, West Greenland, *Meddel. om Grønland* 93, Part 5.

STOPES, M. C. 1913-1915. *The Cretaceous Flora.* 2 vols. Brit. Mus. Nat. Hist. Cat., London. Primarily a useful checklist.

VELENOVSKY, J., and L. VINIKLAR. 1920-1926. *Flora Cretacea Bohemiae.* 2 vols. Roz. Stat. Geol. Ust. Gesk. Rep., Prague.

19

CENOZOIC FLORAS

In considering the upper Cretaceous floras we have seen how the angiosperms achieved dominance over other plant groups and in what manner they resemble their living descendants. Just as there was a persistence of Jurassic genera into the lower Cretaceous, there was a persistence of upper Cretaceous forms into the Eocene. Although this is more striking among the gymnosperms, it is also true among the angiosperms.

It is quite possible to overemphasize the similarity of certain Cretaceous genera with existing groups and confuse similarity for identity. Hence *Araliopsis*, while resembling *Aralia*, is not identical with it. In recent years paleobotanists have been much more cautious in defining generic affinities for leaf impressions and increasing numbers of form-genera have been substituted for established generic names, e.g., *Ficophyllum, Celastrophyllum, Platanophyllum,* and *Saliciphyllum*. In such instances close identity is not implied. Where evidence is more convincing, form-genera like *Menispermites, Sabalites,* and *Zingiberites* are used. This practice is not established or standard, however, and due caution in interpreting lists of genera must be exercised. Nevertheless, we can glean from the multiplicity of Cenozoic floras certain generalizations which contribute to an understanding of the history of angiosperms and the existing vegetation.

If we exclude from consideration doubtful form-genera, such as *Laurophyllum* and *Celastrites* from their supposed living counterparts, we find that in the Atlantic Coastal Plain, 40 per cent of the upper Cretaceous (Ripley) genera are unknown in the early Eocene. There is thus a gradual, though very marked, difference between the two. A similar difference is recognized between the Paleocene and Cretaceous floras of the Rocky Mountain region (Table 11).

The Eocene flora, by elimination of the older types and development of new genera, shows a further modernization. Whereas the

TABLE 11

The Cenozoic—Approximate Correlation of Representative Floras

Period	Atlantic Coastal Plain	Rocky Mountain Region	Pacific Coast	Europe	Other notable floras
Pliocene	Citronelle	Ogallala	Mt. Eden	Teglian (Holland)	Japan, Java, Sumatra
Miocene	Alum Bluffs	Weiser Creede Florissant(?)	Payette Latah Mascall	— — Oeningen (Switzerland)	Trinidad, Manchuria, Japan
Oligocene	—	Florissant(?) White River	John Day Bridge Creek Weaverville	Amber (Samland) Hamstead (England) Bembridge (England) Isle of Wight *	Chile
Eocene	Brandon(?) Claiborne Jackson Wilcox	Green River Yellowstone	Puget Sound Goshen Clarno Chalk Bluffs Wasatch	— London Clay —	Greenland, Spitsbergen, Alaska
Paleocene	—	Fort Union Upper Denver Raton	—	Sezanne (France) Gelinden (Belgium)	—

* Fig. 58.

upper Cretaceous floras nearly everywhere can be interpreted as warm-temperate, the Cenozoic shows a gradual diversification of environments, segregation of forest types, and definite endemic associations (Fig. 58).

The floristic analysis of existing vegetation, as Asa Gray pointed out long ago, leads directly to the mid-Cenozoic. The ecological interpretation of fossil floras, a necessary partner to any such approach, was proposed by Clement and developed by Chaney.

CENOZOIC FLORAS OF WESTERN NORTH AMERICA

The Eocene floras of Oregon and California appear to be tropical with their closest living counterparts in Central America, from Mexico to Venezuela, and indicate an annual rainfall of 80″ minimum, with freedom from frosts. Eocene floras from Washington appear to be somewhat less tropical, finding their equivalents in temperate rain forests. The genera suggesting this relationship are *Acer, Alnus, Betula, Cornus, Fraxinus,* and *Populus.* The Eocene floras of the Rocky Mountain region likewise appear to be less tropical than contemporary floras from California and Oregon.

The Miocene floras of western North America show a greater homogeneity than do those of the Eocene and at the same time indicate more temperate conditions. In these floras there are three main elements, two of which have disappeared gradually. The major element is composed of types which find their modern equivalents among Pacific Coast types. The second element includes those which are closely allied with forms now found in eastern North America. The third element is composed of forms now found in eastern Asia. Typical of the Pacific element are *Sequoia* and *Umbellularia;* of the eastern American element, *Liquidambar, Juglans, Fagus,* and *Crataegus;* and of the Asiatic element, *Ailanthus, Libocedrus, Ginkgo, Glyptostrobus,* and *Trapa.* The upper Miocene Austin flora from the Blue Mountains of Oregon has these elements in the following proportion: Pacific Coast, 65 per cent; eastern North American, 22 per cent; Asiatic, 12 per cent.

The Kenai flora of Alaska, considered by Hollick and others to be of Eocene age, includes such genera as *Diospyros, Ficus,* and *Magnolia;* but the most conspicuous and widespread element of this flora comprises such genera as *Acer, Betula, Carpinus, Castanea, Corylus, Fagus, Ginkgo, Juglans, Liquidambar, Myrica (Comptonia), Platanus, Populus, Prunus, Quercus, Salix, Sequoia, Taxodium, Tilia,*

Fig. 58. (See next page for caption.)

Trapa, and *Ulmus.* The abundance of *Sequoia* emphasizes the temperate aspect of this flora, which with slight modifications has been recorded from various other Eocene localities in the Arctic, including Greenland and Spitsbergen. Not only are most of the genera represented in the existing flora of Canada, but many are still represented in the existing flora of Alaska.

The significant feature about these Eocene Arctic floras is that they show a comparable northward swing both of their northern and southern limits, which in turn is comparable to the northward advance of the Jackson flora, which is usually considered to be of the same age. Berry compared the geographic ranges of these two floras and recognized the enormity of this shift. From such observations we can begin to comprehend the dynamics of floral change. The Jackson flora reaches Latitude 37° North. The most similar existing flora to that of the Jackson ranges to Latitude 26° North, and then only under the influence of warm ocean currents.

THE CENOZOIC OF EASTERN ASIA

The significance of older Cenozoic floras of Siberia, together with those of Manchuria, Korea, and adjacent parts of northeastern Asia, has been summarized by Kryshtofovich, who concludes that nowhere in this region during the Cenozoic were there even subtropical conditions. As late as the Lower Miocene it was occupied by a deciduous forest composed of temperate types such as *Fagus, Ulmus, Alnus, Betula, Corylus, Populus, Juglans, Comptonia,* and *Trapa.* Kryshtofovich points out the similarity of this flora to that from the Eocene of Alaska, and the marked difference between it and the subtropical floras of older Cenozoic age in western Europe. The early part of the Cenozoic period probably did not have the great uniformity of climate over a wide range of latitude as has been frequently pictured by earlier writers. The fossil plant record indicates that there were considerable differences in temperature and humidity along the Pacific Coast of North America.

Fig. 58. The Oligocene flora of the Isle of Wight. Among the angiosperm genera in this rich flora are found: Abelia (Ab), Acanthus (Ac), Aldrovanda (Al), Acrosticum (Am), Brasenia (Ba), Catalpa (Ca), Cinnomomum (Cn), Clematis (Cs), Engelhardtia (Ea), Equisetum (Eq), Ficus (F), Fagus (Fg), Incarvillea (I), Melissa (Ml), Papaver (P), Sparganium (Sg), Stratiotes (St), and Zizyphus (Z). (Drawn by Edward Vulliamy. By permission from Plant Life Through the Ages, by A. C. Seward. Copyright, 1931, Cambridge University Press, London.)

CENOZOIC FLORAS BASED UPON
POLLENS, SEEDS, AND FRUITS

The Green River flora, the largest Eocene flora of the Rocky Mountain province, shows several interesting relationships. Not only is there a rich flora based upon fossil leaves and fruits but also abundant microfossils. More than forty genera have been recognized on the basis of pollen grains (Wodehouse).

The pollens include aquatic types such as *Potamogeton, Peltandra,* and *Myriophyllum.* Conifers are represented by *Pinus, Abies, Picea, Glyptostrobus,* etc. Among other gymnosperms are *Dioon* and *Ephedra,* while among the predominant dicotyledons are such genera as *Liriodendron, Hicoria, Juglans, Engelhardtia, Ailanthus, Alnus, Betula, Carpinus,* and *Tilia.* The majority of genera present are anemophilous.

Since most of these may be classified as temperate, a situation may be reconstructed in which the leaves of the lowland subtropical plants were mingled in the adjacent lake sediments with wind-borne pollen grains from plants on the adjacent uplands where conditions were more temperate. The remains of a cactus of the *Opuntia* type have been found in the Green River shales of Utah.

There are three floras of early Cenozoic age in Europe which are noteworthy because their peculiar modes of preservation have enriched our knowledge of the ecology of the times: the Eocene London Clay flora, the Oligocene Baltic Amber flora, and the Miocene flora from Oeningen, Switzerland.

The London Clay is a marine-estuarine deposit formed by the burden of a large Eocene river flowing from the west. The muds contain many fossils of fruits, seeds, and driftwood. Their preservation is usually by lignitization and pyritization. The most common plant from this deposit is a stemless palm, *Nipa* (*N. burtini*), also found in the Eocene of Belgium. The living *Nipa* grows in the brackish estuaries of Malaya and Australia. More than a dozen species of palms are known from London Clay. The aspect of the flora is distinctly tropical, the chief members belonging to the ANACARDIACEAE, SAPOTACEAE, MENISPERMACEAE, LAURACEAE, ICACINACEAE, BURSARACEAE, and FLACOURTIACEAE. It has been estimated that three-fourths of the ninety genera (exclusive of incertae sedis) are extinct. The total number of recognized species is about three hundred. Approximately 60 (of the 314) species could not be attributed to a family, and 20 other references were doubtful. Deposits containing large numbers of seeds and fruits are also found in Vermont (Eocene or Oligocene) and Germany (Miocene).

The Brandon (Vermont) lignitic flora represents a nonalluvial swamp deposit. Recent investigations by Barghoorn, Spackman, and Traverse on pollens, woods, and seeds which comprise the flora indicate a warm temperate association, with *Glyptostrobus, Engelhardtia, Liquidambar, Planera, Mimusops, Cyrilla,* and *Gordonia* predominating.

One of the most interesting known plant occurrences of Cenozoic age is that of the amber-bearing beds of East Prussia. Amber is the resinous exudation of certain fossil coniferous trees (*Pinus succinifer*) which oozed out from wounds made by damaged or decayed branches or boring insects. This product slowly hardened and often fell to the forest floor, where it accumulated over long periods of time. The same process can be observed at the present day in the case of the copal of Africa and the Kauri-gum of New Zealand. In addition to the insects and other small animals, amber naturally often enclosed fragments of plants: leaves, twigs, wood, flowers, and seeds have all been found in amber. Some of the flowers are almost perfectly preserved and can be compared with living genera (Figs. 59 and 60). Small cones of *Abies* and stamens of *Quercus* are very commonly preserved. The memoirs by Conwentz, and Goeppert and Menge on the Amber flora are praiseworthy. The irreplaceable classic collection of amber plants and animals at Koenigsberg was destroyed during World War II.

The most celebrated Miocene flora is that from Oeningen along the German-Swiss border (Lake Constance). This plant assemblage contains more than 700 nominal species, and beds of similar age in France, Germany, Czechoslovakia, and Hungary swell the total number of contemporary forms to almost 1000 species. There are a few striking features of the flora: one-sixth of the species are monocotyledons, one-eighth are cryptogams, one-eighth conifers, and the remainder dicotyledons of a mixed hardwood type. Surprisingly there are no undoubted representatives of the RANUNCULACEAE, CRUCIFERAE, LABIATAE, or COMPOSITAE. The chief families are MAGNOLIACEAE, FAGACEAE, ACERACEAE, LAURACEAE, LEGUMINOSAE, SALICACEAE, and MORACEAE. Very similar Oligocene-Miocene floras occur in North America, as at Florissant (Colorado).

Fig. 59. *Antidesma*. A flower (Euphorbiaceae) preserved in Baltic amber. Oligocene. (Redrawn from Conwentz.)

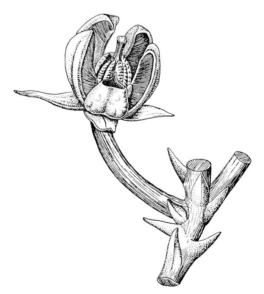

Fig. 60. *Andromeda*. A flower (Ericaceae) preserved in Baltic amber. Oligocene. (Redrawn from Conwentz.)

The chief conclusion to be drawn from this survey of selected Cenozoic floras is that the angiosperms had by Miocene time become thoroughly modernized. This is not only true with respect to the families and genera present but also of the spatial distribution of the so-called hardwood mesophytic forest. Both in eastern North America and in the Northern Pacific Basin there lived trees very like those existing today in the same region.

From the voluminous but disorganized literature concerning Cenozoic plants from the Southern Hemisphere, we can recognize broad similarities between the existing vegetation and Cenozoic floras in approximately the same regions. Berry's work on the early and middle Cenozoic of South America, for example, indicates an indigenous flora which has continued on into the present. The Miocene and Pliocene floras are primarily significant in the problem of the origin of the existing flora.

Bibliography

A very good introduction to the ecological-floristic approach to Cenozoic floras may be gained by consulting Berry 1937, Chaney 1936, and Macginitie 1941, listed below. A more readable account will be found in Knowlton 1927.

BERRY, E. W. 1937. Tertiary floras of Eastern North America, *Bot. Rev.* 3: 31-46.
——. 1938. Tertiary flora from the Rio Pichileufu, Argentina. *Geol. Soc. Am. Spec. Pap.* 12.
CHANEY, R. W. 1936. "The succession and distribution of Cenozoic floras around the Northern Pacific Basin," in *Essays in Geobotany in Honor of William Albert Setchell.* University of California Press, Berkeley.
CONWENTZ, H. 1886. *Die Flora des Bernsteins.* Vol. 2. Verlag Wilh. Engelmann, Leipzig.
DUIGAN, S. L. 1951. A catalogue of the Australian Tertiary flora, *Proc. Roy. Soc. Vict.* n.s. 63: 41-56.
FLORSCHÜTZ, F. 1949. "Het wisselend aspect van het bos sinds de Krijtperiode," in BEEKMAN. *Hout in Alle Tijden.* Vol. 1. Beekman, Deventer.
GOEPPERT, H. R., and A. MENGE. 1883. *Die Flora des Bernsteins.* Verlag Wilh. Engelmann, Leipzig.
KNOWLTON, F. H. 1927. *Plants of the Past.* Princeton Univ. Press, Princeton.
MACGINITIE, H. D. 1941. A Middle Eocene flora from the Central Sierra Nevada. *Carn. Inst. Wash. Publ.* 534.
REID, E. D., and M. E. CHANDLER. 1933. *The Londay Clay Flora.* British Mus. Nat. Hist., London.
SANBORN, E. I., S. S. POTBURY, and H. D. MACGINITIE. 1937. Eocene flora of Western America. *Carn. Inst. Wash. Publ.* 465.
SHUKLA, V. B. 1944. On *Sahnianthus,* a new genus of petrified flowers from the Intertrappean beds at Mohgaon Kalan in the Deccan, *Proc. Nat. Acad. Sci. India* 14: 1-39.
TRAVERSE, A., and E. S. BARGHOORN. 1953. Micropaleontology of the Brandon lignite, an early Tertiary coal in Central Vermont, *Jour. Paleont.* 27: 289-293.
WALTHER, J., and J. WEIGELT. 1934. Die eozane Lebenwelt in der Braunkohle des Geiseltales, *Nov. Act. Leop.* n.f. 1.

20

ORIGIN OF THE EXISTING FLORA

The existing flora is the sum total of the living vegetation of the world. This vegetation is segregated into fairly recognizable natural geographic units or provinces which are known not only to the phytogeographer, but also to the casual observer. However, in the existing flora there are many anomalous features which have interested taxonomic and the floristic botanists (Fig. 61).

Asa Gray recognized nearly a century ago that the flora of eastern Asia resembles greatly that of eastern North America. More recently a very similar and more localized flora has been recognized in the Balkan region.

The general affinities of the European flora are with Asia and are very unlike the eastern American.

Again, the existing flora of Australia is surprisingly isolated, but with its chief relationship Malayan (Melanesian and New Zealandian).

ANTIQUITY OF THE EXISTING FLORA

The problems of the antiquity or origin of the existing flora rest upon the fact that most of the living genera of woody plants had in past geologic times more extensive geographic distributions than they have at present. Hence Asa Gray postulated an extensive late Cenozoic flora, covering Asia and North America, which was broken up by the influence of the Pleistocene glaciation, and of which only remnants have persisted in those regions of the northern hemisphere where the flora could migrate southward and remigrate northward with the return of more equable conditions. He called attention to the strong Mexican element in the existing flora of western United States. Gray had knowledge of the paleobotanical information of his time, but little was or is known of the Cenozoic plants of central Asia.

We have already noted three great aspects of the history of the angiosperms in Cenozoic times. The first of these is the Cretaceous-Eocene radiation which resulted in the spread of the rapidly diversifying angiosperms from some (unknown) center of evolution in the northern hemisphere southward by three great routes: (1) through Africa, (2) through India, Malaya, the East Indies, to Australia and New Zealand, and (3) through Central America to South America. The second of the aspects of angiosperms which is important in this problem is the great modernizing of the floras in lower Cenozoic times. The families and genera become increasingly similar to those now living. The third aspect is the remarkable Miocene flora of the northern hemisphere with its mixed hardwood forests which greatly resemble existing units of vegetation ("association"). There were, to be sure, latitudinal and altitudinal zonations, but the plant associations became differentiated, organized, and relatively stabilized.

The origin of the existing flora is to be found in this development.

PHYSICAL CHANGES DURING THE LATER CENOZOIC

The geological events of post-Miocene time were the primary causes of the segregation or formation of the geobotanical provinces recognized today.

Already by the Miocene, Australia and New Zealand had been severed from the Asian land mass. Rich faunas and floras have been found at numerous localities, but their contents are unlike those of the northern hemisphere. Age determinations are accordingly controversial. By Pliocene times much of Australia had become arid, although a noteworthy fauna of birds and giant marsupials is known from Lake Callabonna in South Australia.

In the northern hemisphere great physical changes were also taking place. There was a general tendency toward cooler conditions. This was, at least in part, due to the relatively rapid rise of land in widespread provinces. The Rocky Mountains and the Sierra Nevadas continued to rise, the Wasatch Mountains were uplifted, and general elevation occurred along the whole North Pacific Basin (the Cascadian Revolution). Along eastern North America the rise was gentle, probably only amounting to one or at most several hundred feet.

Bering Strait was closed by a mountain range with fairly mature topography, permitting a general migration of plants and animals over the exposed land. The shore-line migration and interchange

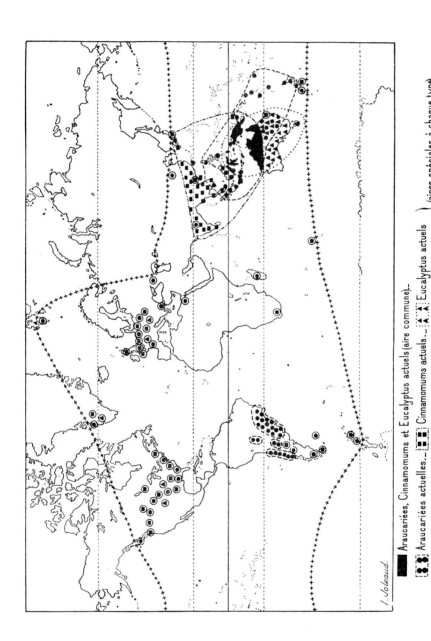

Araucariées, Cinnamomums et Eucalyptus actuels (aire commune).—

Araucariées actuelles.— Cinnamomums actuels.— Eucalyptus actuels ⎫
◎ ● Araucariées fossiles.— ◉ Cinnamomums fossiles.— ④ Eucalyptus fossiles ⎬ (aires spéciales à chaque type)
+++ Limites nord et sud de l'aire de dispersion des Araucariées fossiles.

I. Joleaud.

Fig. 61. (See next page for caption.)

of Japanese and Californian marine invertebrate faunas during Miocene-Pliocene times is well known.

In Europe at the close of the Miocene there was a general retreat of the sea, leaving most of what is now Belgium and northeastern France still under water. In England, however, there was some submergence of the eastern coast. The Mediterranean was considerably more extensive than at present, covering part of Italy, Greece, Spain, and Algeria.

Briefly then, the gradual cooling of climate which was accompanied by widespread diastrophic movements had profound effects upon the rainfall and hence the vegetation of the time.

The floras of the early Cenozoic were relatively homogeneous, although regional and ecological differences are recognized. In post-Miocene times this homogeneity disappeared and there occurred a segregation of floral associations. Orogenic movements were responsible for the breakup of the old established order.

PLIOCENE FLORAS OF WESTERN NORTH AMERICA

In western North America there was an extensive uplift—the Cascade-Sierra Nevada revolution commencing in late Miocene and continuing in the Pliocene. The immediate effect on interior America was decreased rainfall. The Great Basin became more arid and the awesome Colorado River system increased erosion.

Axelrod, who studied nearly a score of small Pliocene floras from the Great Basin and border region, has shown that the effects upon vegetation were no less striking. With increasing aridity the more mesophytic broad-leaved plants of northern origin were eliminated and their place taken by an arid north Mexican element. Thus at present sagebrush occupies much of the area inhabited in Miocene times by a woodland association.

Clements and Chaney have pointed out that the woodland association was established in Miocene times and that the present-day climax associations of the Southwest were segregated from this ancient complex. The three modern communities, oak-juniper (southwestern United States and northern Mexico), piñon-juniper (Great Basin and Colorado Plateau), and digger pine (California) were segregated in the Pliocene. A comparable segregation of

Fig. 61. Comparison of present and fossil distributions of Araucariaceae, Cinnamomum, and Eucalyptus. An example of the application of paleobotanical data to paleogeography and floristics. (By permission from Atlas de Paléogéographie, by L. Joleaud. Copyright, 1939, by Paul Lechevalier, Paris.)

coniferous associations had been recognized by Chaney, Clements, and Mason. Braun has interpreted excellently the deciduous forests of eastern North America from a similar point of view.

OTHER REPRESENTATIVE PLIOCENE FLORAS

The best known of the eastern North American Pliocene floras is the Citronelle flora found in southern Alabama. It includes only eighteen species, three of which, *Taxodium distichum*, *Quercus nigra*, and *Planera aquatica*, are living in the region at the present time. The others, although considered to be extinct, are closely related to nearby living forms. These include *Betula*, *Fagus*, several evergreen oaks, a small-fruited hickory, a black gum (*Nyssa*), and, more or less doubtfully, *Fraxinus*, *Prunus*, *Vitis*, and a supposed *Yucca*. Perhaps the most interesting plant present in this association is the water chestnut (*Trapa*), which is represented by typical large-horned fruits. This plant, living especially in shallow ponds, is no longer a native of the New World. Several species of *Trapa*, based also on the fruits, are known from beds of Eocene and Miocene age in western North America, but it appears to have had its last natural occurrence in the Pliocene.

The most completely investigated Pliocene floras of Europe occur along the Dutch-Prussian border. In the area between the Maas and the Rhine, where these rivers leave the highlands and enter the plains of the Netherlands, they have cut through a series of terraces composed mainly of estuarine sands and clays. The floral sequence is of considerable interest.

The lowest and oldest of these floras, of Middle Pliocene age, is called the Reuverian flora. The plants recovered are chiefly seeds and fruits, many of them being of minute size. About 300 species of plants have been found, but sixty-nine of these could not be placed in a family. Of the remaining 230 species, some 175 species were identified with considerable certainty. The closest agreement with this flora is to be found in plants now living on the mountains of western China and its allied geographical provinces (Japan, the Himalayas, Tibet, and to a lesser extent, the Malay Peninsula). This conclusion is not only based upon absolutely identical species (in the genera *Gnetum*, *Stewartia*, *Magnolia*, *Zelcova*, *Prunus*, etc.), but to a great number of related species. There are a few species found in the Reuverian flora that are still living in Europe. Others are more closely related to existing European forms than to those of China, such as *Picea excelsa, Quercus robur, Corylus avellana, Carpinus betulus,* and *Vitis vinifera.*

Nearly thirty of the Reuverian plants are found, either in identical or closely related forms, in North America, including *Naias marina, Alisma subcordatum, Hicoria alba, Brasenia purpurea,* and *Liriodendron tulipifera.* Several of these North American species are no longer living in Europe.

The upper of the two Dutch Pliocene floras, known as the Teglian flora, is of Upper Pliocene age. It comprises about one hundred thirty species, most of which differ from those of the Reuverian flora, although a few species persist. A few are common to Asia, but on the whole the flora finds its closest relationship to the existing flora of central Europe. It suggests a much cooler temperature than that indicated by the Reuverian flora.

Reid and Reid interpreted the sequence of floras by a fragmentation theory which is compatible with the paleontological history of the later Cenozoic and which conforms generally with the old theory of Asa Gray.

FRAGMENTATION OF THE LATE CENOZOIC FLORA

The Miocene and early Pliocene floras were practically circumpolar in distribution and generally spread over the northern hemisphere with the zonations already indicated. The oncoming of colder conditions probably forced the plants southward. Presumably there were three principal avenues for migration or escape, and these were determined by the prevailing direction of the mountain systems. One avenue of migration was along the lowlands of eastern Asia by way of the great valley systems and the coastal plains. It has been suggested that the richness of the existing flora of China is due to the intermingling or persistence of northerly species with those already established.

In North America the north-south trend of the mountain ranges permitted fairly free migration, and many species of plants which came by this route and those which are relict in place enrich the American flora. This is the explanation for the marked similarity between the floras of eastern North America and eastern Asia, first observed by Asa Gray and since demonstrated by many others. This resemblance extends not only to many genera with closely related species, but also to a considerable number of identical species. A study of the flora of the Island of Yezo, which lies to the north of the main island of Japan, discloses that more than 26 per cent of its plants are found also in North America.

The third migration route for the floras of the north, as they were forced southward by the increasing cold, was down the Scandinavian Peninsula and adjacent areas into central and western Europe, but here the physiography is very different from that of North America and eastern Asia. The great mountain systems, i.e., the Alps, Pyrenees, Carpathians, Balkans, and Caucasians, all trend east and west and thus prevent further southward migration. Many of the northerly Miocene and Pliocene plants actually reached western Europe, as is shown by their presence in the Reuverian flora, but, as the cold increased, they were forced against the mountain barriers and perished.

The Teglian flora of the late Pliocene is very different from the Reuverian flora, and apparently had two centers of origin, one from Scandinavia, and the other from the mountains of central Asia. It was a cool-temperate assemblage, and hence when it was pushed southward by the advancing cold, much of it was able to survive.

There are two important conclusions which may be drawn from these selected studies of late Cenozoic floras. They show the so-called cosmopolitan mixed hardwood flora so typical of the upper Miocene of the northern hemisphere, and they also show—what is more important—the segregation and recognition of definite plant associations, well established in the earliest Pliocene.

The great extent of this mixed hardwood forest was marked throughout by the same genera and, to some extent, species. Braun has termed this original undifferentiated climax as the panclimax of the Tertiary.

The elevation of mountains and the cooling of climate caused a segregation of "northern" and "southern" types and a great diversification of habitats. This became evident already in the Pliocene. In North America shrinkage in the extent of the forest from the west due to increasing aridity of the interior coincident upon the rising Rocky Mountains resulted in segregation of communities on a basis of moisture requirements of their constituent species, and retreat eastward of those of highest demands. Glaciation to the north resulted in a southward crowding of the temperature belts of vegetation, and, particularly, in the destruction of vegetation over the glaciated territory. Thus there are two great movements of the floral elements, the original shrinkage of deciduous forest away from the interior and its retreat from the north. The result of the first great movement was: (1) the retreat of the most mesophytic species from the western portion of deciduous forest and the consequent increased dominance of species of lesser moisture requirements, establishing there the prevalence of the oak-hickory type, an association-segregate of the original mixed hardwood forest; and (2) the localization in the Appalachian mountains and plateau region of remnants of the mixed forest of the late Cenozoic. This remnant was not greatly disturbed in the southern Appalachian region by the southward migrations of the Pleistocene. It then served as a center of dispersal northward and of repopulation of glaciated territory.

Segregation of smaller units from the original undifferentiated climax may have been brought about by the retreat of certain species and persistence of others, those persisting constituting a segregate. The oak-hickory association of the Ozarks and adjacent territory may have formed in this manner.

It has been possible to reconstruct the vegetation of the Cenozoic and more recent successive peneplains of the Appalachian region, despite the destruction of relict associations by human occupancy (Braun).

The association-segregate may have arisen by the advance of species and by increase in range, climate and migration capacity then exerting selective influences bringing about the separation. Thus in the northward return of deciduous forest, relatively few species appear to have gone very far, and from the mixed mesophytic forest of the southern Appalachian region the beech-maple climax association of the northern part of the deciduous forest has developed. This development has gone on more or less contemporaneously in Europe as well as in America, for there a beech-maple association is also climax over a considerable area. The beech-maple association, arising as an association-segregate from the undifferentiated mixed climax, has become really one of the important associations of the deciduous forests of the north temperate zone.

The existing flora is therefore only the vegetation which now covers the inhabitable portions of the earth. Genetically it is the inheritance from extinct genera and species of the Cenozoic; geographically it contains fragments of widely distributed Miocene-Pliocene floras, together with units changed in content and distribution. An example of this interpretation is the *Taxodium* swamp association known since Miocene times (Fig. 62).

Fig. 62. (See next page for caption.)

The terms "fragment," "remnant," or "relict," as used by many authors, are highly connotative. Living *Ginkgo* and *Metasequoia* are remnants of once greater races. They are survivors against odds. But there are larger units of vegetation which similarly represent fragments of more extensive associations and floras. The geologically unmolested floras of New Caledonia, the Amazonian flora of Brazil, New Zealand, and many others, provide clues which the paleobotanist cannot afford to ignore.

Bibliography

AXELROD, D. I. 1940. Late Tertiary floras of the Great Basin and border areas, *Bull. Terr. Bot. Club* 67: 477-487.

———. 1940. The Mint Canyon flora of Southern California, *Amer. Jour. Sci.* 238: 577-585.

———. 1950. Studies in later Tertiary paleobotany. *Carn. Inst. Wash. Publ.* 590.

BATALLER, J. R., and G. DEPAPE. 1950. Flore oligocene de Cervera (Catalogne), *An. Esc. Per. Agric. Esp. Agro. Serv. Tec. Agric.* 10: 5-60.

BERRY, E. W., and A. HOLLICK. 1924. A later Tertiary flora from Bahia, Brazil. *Johns Hopkins Univ. Stud.* 5.

BRAUN, E. L. 1935. The undifferentiated deciduous forest climax and the association segregate, *Ecology* 16: 514-519.

CERNJAVSKI, P. 1933. Beiträge sur Kenntnis der Pliozänenflora in der Umgebung von Glogovac in Kroatien, *Bull. Serv. Geol. Roy. Yugoslavie* 2: 1-12.

CHANEY, R. W. 1935. A Pliocene flora from Shansi Province, *Bull. Geol. Soc. China* 12: 129-142.

DORF, E. 1930. The Pliocene floras of California. *Carn. Inst. Wash. Publ.* 412.

KRYSHTOFOVICH, A. N. 1929. Evolution of the Tertiary flora in Asia, *New Phytol.* 28: 303-311.

———. 1935. A final link between the Tertiary floras of Asia and Europe, *New Phytol.* 34: 339-344.

MIKI, S. 1937. Fossil plants from the *Stegodon* beds and the Elephas beds near Akashi, *Jap. Jour. Bot.* 8: 303-342.

REID, C., and E. M. REID. 1915. The Pliocene floras of the Dutch-Prussian border, *Meded. van de Rijksops. van Delfstoffen,* No. 6.

SCHONFELD, G. 1947. Holzer aus dem Tertiär von Kolumbien, *Abh. Senck Naturforsch. Ges.* 475: 1-53.

SELLING, O. H. 1947. On the Late Quaternary history of the Hawaiian vegetation. *Bishop Mus. Spec. Publ.* 39.

SMITH, P. A. 1937. The submarine topography of Bogoslof, *Geogr. Rev.* 27: 630-636.

Fig. 62. A Miocene *Taxodium* swamp. Reconstruction of a brown coal swamp environment commonly encountered in the lower Cenozoic of the northern hemisphere. The trees are the cypress *Taxodium* with "knees" exposed above water level. Some of the standing trunks found during mining operations in eastern Germany measure more than 5 meters in diameter. It should be evident that reconstructions of vegetation of the Cenozoic are strongly influenced by knowledge of the living counterparts. (By permission from *Prehistoric Animals,* by J. Augusta and Z. Burian, no date. Spring Books, London.)

21

POLLEN ANALYSIS AND FLORISTICS—KEYS TO FLORAL CHANGE

The plants of the Pleistocene were specifically identical with those living at present—with few exceptions. The chief differences between the various Pleistocene floras and those of the present are in spatial distribution. At first glance it might be assumed therefore that a study of Pleistocene sediments and their contained plants has little to offer the paleobotanist. Quite the contrary is true. The process of floral change and the effects of environmental change can be studied on a grand scale.

Since the Pleistocene is the most recent geological period and the plant species and communities are known to us, we can observe the geological processes when they are severe and rapid. The problems of extinction, migration, and distribution of floras and faunas become, not speculation, but matters of direct observation.

CONDITIONS OF THE PLEISTOCENE

The Pleistocene was a relatively cold and climatically unsettled period with relatively long warm intervals alternating with colder intervals. The later phase of the Pliocene was marked by rapid cooling so that the North Polar ice cap reached a size equivalent to its present extent. It is not known, for instance, whether the great extinction of plants and animals took place at the end of the Pliocene or during the Pleistocene.

The climate near the margin of ice during the glacial stages— that is, when the ice sheets increased in size and pushed southward —was probably like that of southern Greenland. Progressively away from the ice, conditions were more equable. Tundra formed a narrow zone along the margin of the ice sheet. The tundra in central Europe was bordered by steppes, although this does not seem to have been true in North America. In North America there are extensive deposits of loess, which indicate a drier climate than now prevails. Beyond the tundra and steppe belt was a more or less broken deciduous forest. As world climatic conditions became more equable and warmer, the ice melted, the whole succession of plant zones moved northward with the ice, and conversely, as conditions became more rigorous and colder, the whole succession moved southward. This gradual process of floral extension and retraction is the history of Northern Hemisphere Pleistocene phytogeography. Interpretation of chronology is at present controversial and many long-accepted conclusions have been questioned. Arbitrarily we shall follow conventional opinion.

The several glacial stages can be roughly correlated over Europe and North America. Usually a scale, like the following, is used to indicate the relationship between the glacial and warmer "interglacial" stages.

Alpine Europe	North America
Postglacial	
Wurm	Wisconsin
Riss-Wurm	Sangamon
Riss	Illinoian
Mindel-Riss	Yarmouth
Mindel	Kansan
Gunz-Mindel	Aftonian
Gunz	Nebraskan

Attempts to correlate stages of North America and Asia with those of Europe are arbitrary and tentative; they cannot be accepted at face value. As research has progressed, many local differences have been recognized. Some geologists argue that there was a single glaciation. Nothing comparable to the detailed, indeed elaborate, European Pleistocene chronologies has been established in the United States. The geographical areas involved are not comparable in extent nor are the unbroken sedimentary sequences. The Pleistocene of Scandinavia shows distinctive differences from that of Alpine Europe, as do Mediterranean sediments. More remote effects like the "Pluvial" stages of Africa are even more difficult to correlate.

FOSSIL PLANTS OF THE PLEISTOCENE

There are four chief sources of botanical information regarding the plants of the Pleistocene: (1) macroscopic, (2) pollen analyses of peats and clays, (3) relict plants, and (4) the inferential studies based on the present floras of Arctic and sub-Arctic regions.

The number of interglacial macroscopic floras is surprisingly small. Many years ago Wettstein described a fairly large assemblage from Germany, of which more than 70 per cent of the species live in the same district at present, and the remainder are found in the typical Pontic European floral element. In the Don Valley near Toronto there is a flora of interglacial plants (age still disputed) made up entirely of living species, a few being now restricted slightly to the south. Such studies have only emphasized the similarity to nearby extant floras.

It is largely through the development of palynology—the study of spores and pollens—that our knowledge of the Pleistocene and post-Pleistocene has reached its present state. The methodology of pollen analysis has proved its dependability and is with increasing ingenuity being applied to Cenozoic and Paleozoic sediments.

Spores and pollens are characterized by a relatively thick wall or membrane divided into two, occasionally three coats. The outer layer is known as the exine, the inner as the intine. The exine is frequently ornamented or sculptured. The ornamentations are of great variety, and many descriptive names have been used to distinguish and classify pollens according to type of sculpturing. The chemical nature of the membranes is such that they are extremely resistant to acids, alkalis, and organic solvents, therefore resistant to bacterial metabolism—a property which not only accounts for the abundance of fossil pollens but also permits maceration and manipulation of the sediments to recover the pollens. For a comprehensive study of fossil pollens, the reader is referred to Erdtman's *Introduction to Pollen Analysis*.

POLLEN ANALYSIS

The fundamental assumption in pollen analysis is that the pollen content of a peat (or other sediment) is more or less characteristic of the plant associations which grew in the immediate vicinity. The great abundance of pollens of *Salix, Typha, Corylus,* CYPERACEAE, etc., bears out the general thesis, for these plants are characteristic of bog habitats. On the other hand, the buoyancy of pollen, which permits transport for great distances, and the relative abundance of spores and pollens in the upper air and over the oceans far removed from land must be reconciled or accounted for. In practice this source of error can be minimized. In the statistical analysis of results, the numerical abundance of species is plotted and interpreted. In the presentation of data the pollens of certain genera are omitted from the calculation of percentages and only "significant species" are included. Plants which live in proximity to the deposit are omitted on the assumption that they will show a false ratio of abundance (e.g., *Typha*, ERICACEAE). Similarly, those which produce a prodigious quantity of pollen (*Corylus*) and those which cannot readily be identified by genus or species are excluded. To the last named category belong "salicoid" pollen, GRAMINEAE, etc. The significant tree pollens are calculated on the basis of 100 per cent, while the other constituents are added to the results.

Various, indeed, many, methods for isolating spores and pollens have been devised. All of them have certain objectives in common: (1) maceration of the sample to separate the pollens from the colloidal material in which they are embedded, (2) deflocculation of the matrix, and (3) concentration of the pollen content (by centrifuging the suspension). Some of the methods have additional stages to hydrolyze the polysaccharides and to dissolve the mineral crystallites which may be present.

There is considerable difference of opinion concerning the effects of different reagents on the pollen grains. The most drastic treatment, used by Erdtman, results in almost complete solution of all constituents except the exines and thereby yields a very clear spore concentrate. On the other hand, Geisler has used an alcohol method which leaves the pollens virtually unaffected but at the same time fails to remove the detritus. A brief comparison of the methods in common use may be found in Erdtman (1943).

In the study of fossil pollen in peat, the following method will, in most cases, give good results. The peat is first bleached by chlorine (to remove the lignin component); then acetolyzed (to remove the cellulose and other polysaccharides).

Starting with a wet peat, it should be dried, preferably in a vacuum over concentrated sulphuric acid. It should then be powdered by rubbing it through a brass mesh. About two-tenths of a gram of the powdered material will generally be found sufficient for an ordinary pollen analysis. The powder is collected in a centrifuge tube and suspended in a mixture of 4 ml of glacial acetic acid and 1 ml of concentrated hydrochloric acid. After adding three or four drops of sodium chlorate solution (1 part to 2 parts of water), the powdered peat is, as a rule, bleached in a few seconds.

The tube is then transferred to a centrifuge. After centrifuging, the fluid is decanted and the sediment washed first with water and then with glacial acetic acid. Finally, acetolysis is accomplished by placing the sediments in a mixture of 9 ml acetic anhydride (technical) and 1 ml of concentrated sulphuric acid. The tube is placed in a waterbath and the content heated to the boiling point and then transferred to the centrifuge. After centrifuging, the fluid is decanted, the sediments washed with water, then with diluted glycerin, and finally transferred to glycerin jelly. Reference slides can be made by using glycerin jelly, or the remaining residue may be stored, in glycerin, in small tubes for future investigation.

The nature of the sample may necessitate modification of the method. For instance, dilute hydrochloric or nitric acid may be used initially to remove calcium carbonate or to disintegrate compact peat, which cannot be powdered readily by rubbing against a metal mesh. Hydrofluoric acid may be used to dissolve silica; and in some cases, after acetolysis, a second chlorine treatment (followed by staining, e.g., with safranin) or washing with a cold 0.5 per cent caustic soda solution may improve the result.

POST-PLEISTOCENE FLORAS OF NORTHERN EUROPE

The vegetational history of postglacial time is best known in northern Europe. Archeological and geological studies, as well as paleobotanical, have provided extensive information. Thus the sequence of climatic, floral, and cultural changes over the past twenty thousand years is rather fully understood. The chief features are suggested by Table 12.

Widespread and prolonged postglacial tundra conditions are indicated by remains of *Dryas, Betula nana,* and *Salix* far south of the ice front. Generally this association was succeeded by a period in which *Pinus* predominated, variously accompanied by *Betula* and *Corylus.* The pine was followed by *Quercus,* the hazel frequently persisting on into the oak period.

The classic chronological succession of floras in the Riss-Wurm has been worked out by Jessen and Milthers from pollen studies in Jutland and northwestern Germany. The earliest clays contain an Arctic (and sub-Arctic) association with *Betula nana,* species of *Salix,* and *Dryas.* This is followed by a gradually milder climate with *Pinus silvestris, Betula pubescens, Ulmus,* and considerable aquatic vegetation. The next stage (peat) contains a mixed-hardwood association with *Quercus, Tilia, Corylus, Alnus*, etc., which indicate quite temperate climate. The fourth phase is cooler with *Picea, Pinus silvestris, Populus tremula, Betula pubescens*, and *Betula nana*. This tendency is further developed with a return to the *Betula nana* heath, which is correlated with the advance of ice in Scandinavia. This cold phase is of short duration, and is followed by the maximum development of the mixed hardwood forest, with occasional records of *Trapa, Brasenia*, etc. This is gradually replaced by *Betula nana* heaths and is the result of the final advance of the Scandinavian ice sheet.

TABLE 12

Postglacial History of Northern Europe

Climatic Stages	Vegetation	Cultural Stages	Estimated Ages
POSTGLACIAL			
Sub-Atlantic Cold, wet	Beech dominant	Historic	–
Sub-Boreal Warm, dry	Mixed oak forest, diminishing beech, pine increasing	Neolithic	2000 B.C.
Atlantic Warm, wet	Mixed oak forest dominant	–	–
Boreal Warmer, dry	Hazel maximum, pine decreasing	Mesolithic	–
Pre-Boreal	Birch, pine	–	5000 B.C.
LATE GLACIAL			
Arctic Cold	Upper Dryas	–	8000 B.C.
Sub-Arctic Warmer	Birch, pine	Upper Paleolithic	15,000 B.C.
Arctic Cold	Lower Dryas flora	–	–

The hypothesis, then, that the vegetation moved south before the advancing ice and subsequently returned north, is only in small part true. There were actually many fluctuations in temperature and moisture. The resulting phases have been given suggestive names: preboreal, boreal, Atlantic, subboreal, sub-Atlantic. The Atlantic or middle period was considered as a climatic optimum, warm and humid, between the very continental boreal and subboreal. The sub-Atlantic represented a return of humidity. The stages so set forth were associated with a definite stratigraphy and archeology, and have been dated with great accuracy through the varve-counting method of De Geer.

Postglacial history, as Von Post recognized, may be divided into three periods: (1) a period of increasing warmth, (2) a period of maximum temperature, and (3) a period of decreasing temperature. There are in addition lesser fluctuations of various climatic factors. Under some conditions minor fluctuations have doubtless been extreme enough to produce recognizable effects.

Somewhat similar conditions prevailed in eastern North America, although precise correlation between the two continents is not yet possible. Deevey has traced the sequence in Connecticut and Sears has described the vegetational change of Ohio and Indiana. A large number of isolated deposits have been studied (cf. Hansen). Eastern United States has a continental climate while in northwestern Europe the climate is influenced by oceanic factors.

FLORISTICS AND POSTGLACIAL HISTORY

These and other studies have shown that conditions following the last glacial stage have not returned to an equilibrium—if indeed an equilibrium is ever possible. The fluctuations in climate, cyclic and long-term, do not admit any such notion as climatic equilibrium. The existing vegetation is not a static flora, but a flora that is constantly changing even though the changes occur at rates which to casual observation seem imperceptibly slow. In this light the study of floristics assumes added meaning.

The third source of information concerning the changes in existing floras is then the study of the relict plants (literally, "left behind"). Many students of floristics have made contributions from this point of view. Outstanding are Fernald, Ostenfeld, Podpera, and Czechzott. Fernald termed the phenomenon of relict distribution "relic-endemism."

Fernald's studies were chiefly in areas of northern and eastern America and of Europe which were near or north of the southern limits of the continental ice sheets of the Pleistocene. These regions retain some peculiar relict species of "a flora which apparently was widespread in mid-Pleistocene time but which already shows obvious signs of senility and of relic-endemism." It is necessary to recognize two assumptions in thus reasoning a "widespread mid-Pleistocene" flora and "obvious signs of senility."

In North America the earlier advances of Pleistocene continental ice sheets were probably much more extensive than the latest of Wisconsin glaciation. Although our knowledge of the limits of the different ice advances is incomplete, it is recognized that the Arctic Archipelago, most of Alaska, the Torngat Mountains of northern Labrador, and considerable areas about the Gulf of the St. Lawrence were not crossed by the continental ice sheets, or had only local extensions from them; while the region south of the Arctic continental coast, extending from central Labrador, western Gaspé, New Brunswick, and Nova Scotia west across the Canadian plains was overridden and scoured by ice. In eastern North America the Wisconsin glaciation, ending perhaps 15,000 to 20,000 years ago, extended south to Nova Scotia, southern New England, Long Island, New Jersey, Pennsylvania, and the Ohio Valley. Within those latitudes there were areas in which the Wisconsin glaciation was largely ineffective in removing the accumulated rock debris and in rounding off the sharp crests, as for example, the Gulf of St. Lawrence (Gaspé, the Magdalen Islands, Newfoundland, Anticosti and the Mingan Islands, and the southeastern corner of Labrador) and the Torngat region of northern Labrador.

Fernald recognized in these areas the presence of hundreds of species, which in eastern America are known nowhere else—and which he interpreted as relicts of the flora which was widespread across the boreal regions during the last interglacial stage. Such isolations in the regions uninvaded by the latest continental ice are indicated by *Polystichum mohrioides, Senecio resedifolius, Lesquerella arctica, Erigeron compositus,* and *Crepsis nana;* and restriction to unglaciated Arctic America of *Oxytropis arctobia.* With these plants, chiefly of western America, now isolated on the unglaciated areas about the Gulf of St. Lawrence or in northern Labrador, there are many endemics which are closely related to species of remote geographic range, rather than to species of the adjacent continental region. Such endemics are illustrated by *Salix calcicola,* an eastern representative of the northwestern *S. richardsonii.*

These relict species are closely confined to the localities which were not invaded by the last continental ice, and they have shown no strong tendency to extend their ranges into the adjacent and recently deglaciated areas. "Thus, in Newfoundland, where the Wisconsin ice seems to have had its greatest development in mountain-ravines and near the central and southeastern sections of the island, the plants of the unglaciated or only anciently glaciated western area remain localized in that area; and in Gaspé and northern Labrador they show a parallel restriction to the unglaciated spots.

Such evidence indicates that this flora was aggressive and made a rapid spread about the boreal regions of America in the long inter-glacial epoch preceding the Wisconsin glaciation; but that it now consists of already waning types, too old or too conservative to spread into closely adjacent and virgin soils" (Fernald).

In Europe a very similar situation is to be observed. The signs of the earlier glaciations were mostly obliterated by the later and most extensive continental sheets, which covered Iceland and Ireland and all but southernmost England and eastward reaching the Ural. The last ice sheet left southern Ireland and most of England undisturbed and eastward merely crossed the White Sea. This last advance, that was nearly synchronous with the Wisconsin, failed to invade the northern borders of Norway and the Kola Peninsula or the region eastward; and southward it left western Denmark and the area to the west, including the Faroe Islands, almost untouched, and invaded only a portion of Iceland.

Fernald observed that "since the beginning of the long interglacial epoch which preceded the latest continental ice-sheets of North America and of Europe, the following regions have had only local glaciation or have remained unglaciated: western North America including most of Alaska, the Arctic Archipelago, northwestern Greenland and many nunataks along the coast of Greenland, north-ern and southeastern Labrador, and the region from Newfoundland to northern Cape Breton and Gaspé, much of Iceland, the Faroe Islands, the British Isles, much of Denmark, and the region south-ward, and the Arctic border of Europe. It is, therefore, significant that at least 100 species which in America are restricted to or which center upon the area uninvaded by the last continental ice-sheet should occur in Europe, likewise, only in the areas which were there not covered by the Great Baltic Glacier or should definitely have their centers of distribution at these points. This considerable flora, which, in Europe as well as in America, occurs only outside the areas which were invaded by the latest continental ice-sheets, is well illustrated by *Epilobium latifolium* L., *Lomatogonium rotatum* (L.) Fries, *Campanula uniflora* L. and *Eutrema Edwardsii* R. Br. In Europe, as in America, these plants, now persisting as relics from the earlier Pleistocene flora, have rarely invaded the closely adjacent regions (in Europe the Scandinavian Alps) which were denuded by the last continental glacier and which, one would suppose, would offer most attractive habitats for them. The situation in Europe is, then, quite parallel with that in America, for in Europe, just as in America, the arctic species seem to be so ancient as to have lost their capacity for pioneering."

Not all students of floristics agree with the Fernald hypothesis, but the underlying principle—the existence of unglaciated (i.e., last glaciation) areas with endemic or relict floras is now generally recognized. The methodology as yet has not been used in enough instances to test its validity for broad problems.

Podpera has made an extensive study of the botanical elements in the steppes adjacent to the Ural Mountains. The general thesis in his investigation is that in the steppes along the Ural Mountains there are species of plants which occur as relict plants in isolated localities in Central Europe. This European steppe flora extends from the Caspian Sea and the Volga River to the branches of the Urals. The area has been termed in history the "European Gate." There are four chief components: Mediterranean, Pontic-oriental, Asiatic-steppe, and Sub-Arctic Steppe.

Czechzott has similarly investigated the existing flora of northern Asia Minor because of its large number of well-known endemics. There are several elements in the flora which range from steppe, to pine and fir communities, to alpine associations. There are several geographic elements represented and the history of the flora dates to Miocene-Pliocene (Sarmatian-Pontian) times.

The papers of Podpera and Czechzott are, strictly speaking, floristic studies and do not attempt to recognize change in progress, but rather the effects of past change. The implications, however, are clear.

Hultén in an ambitious history of Arctic and boreal floras during the Quarternary period, grouped the boreal vegetation into several elements: the continental Eurasiatic, the Arctic-Pacific, the Atlantic-Pacific, the Asiatic-Pacific, the Arctic-Montane, and the boreal circumpolar. These are not relict plants but plant communities which have repopulated the region. Hultén of course was dealing with great areas which were practically covered by ice during the maximum Pleistocene glaciation. Thus he says, "All plants of this area radiate from districts that were not completely buried under the ice-sheet of the maximum glaciation. In other words: the plants have spread over the arctic and boreal belt from the refugia close to the ice, where they were left in possession of a small part of their earlier area and where they were able to survive the severe conditions of the maximum glaciation." He adds, "Such a group constitutes an evolution of a fragment of the earlier vegetation which was more or less isolated within a certain district by the ice of the maximum glaciation." Hultén advances evidence showing that there is presently in progress an interchange of species between Kamchatka and Alaska by way of the Aleutian Islands.

Fernald and Hultén hold to a "nunatak hypothesis" of the repopulation of glaciated areas. A nunatak is an island of elevated exposed land that protrudes through (i.e., which is not covered by) a field of ice. Since many nunataks support plant communities, it is believed that as the ice retreated during the Pleistocene, large nunataks were the refugia of plants which subsequently survived and repopulated the area.

CLIMATIC FLUCTUATIONS IN HISTORICAL TIMES

It is evident that the many postglacial changes are manifestations of a very complex and fluctuating process. Pollen studies have demonstrated a considerably warmer period since the retreat of the ice some 20,000 years ago. As a matter of fact, there were minor periods of warmth as recently as 1000 years ago.

The evidence upon which this last observation is based is too voluminous to consider more than most briefly. The data are of three chief sources: archeological (i.e., from excavation), historical (i.e., from recorded history); and from recognizable changes in the flora.

During the recent investigations in the old Norse settlements in Greenland, there was found irrefutable evidence of a past warmer climate. The historical and ethnological work has been done principally by Nørlund, Hansen, and Roussel (see various papers in the *Meddelelser om Grönland*). Among the noteworthy observations, dating 700-900 years ago, are: human burials made in unfrozen ground, tree roots that penetrated coffins and skeletons, extensive use of wood, a buried layer of leaf mould, and the foundations of barns constructed to hold a hundred head of cattle. The chief sites in Greenland that have furnished these remains are Herjolfsnes, Sandnes, and Brattahild (see also *Crania Groenlandica*, Hansen and Fürst, 1915).

In North America there has been observed the existence of relict prairie in western Pennsylvania, Ohio, and in the central states. The evidence suggests that the extent of prairie was formerly greater than at present. Raup has recognized floral and climatic changes in southern New England. He noted that "numerous woodland plants common to the more southern Appalachians have a scattered distribution in the uplands of New England, indicating a former, more continuous range." In peat bogs of recent age, there occur many stumps of the swamp white cedar, characteristic of the more southern Atlantic Coastal Plain, which attained much greater size than do living individuals in this region. He cites archeological and zoological evidence of equal interest.

These two examples, demonstrating marked fluctuations in climate within historical times, are no less remarkable than an observation by Sir Arthur Keith (*New Discoveries Relating to the Antiquity of Man*, pp. 145-146):

"In the central part of Northern Transvaal there is an arid area known as Springbok Flats. At present it is so parched with drought that it provides only the scantiest sustenance for living things. On its withered surface lie millions of stone arrow-heads and scrapers left by men who hunted over it, at a time, we may be sure, when it was green and well-stocked with game."

Dorf (1959) has recently presented a critical review of evidence concerning intense and widespread effects of climatic changes on plant and animal distribution.

The avid interest of paleobotanists, geologists, archeologists, and others in the Pleistocene and post-Pleistocene is indicated by an enormous output of technical papers (cf. Erdtman annual reviews of literature on palynology, a journal *Pollen and Spores,* and by such notable books as Zeuner *Dating the Past* (first ed. 1946, third ed. 1952).

Thus it is possible to observe slow but progressive changes in distribution in the existing flora. The present flora is not static, it is ever changing in space, content, and, without doubt, inheritance. That this movement is largely motivated by climatic changes seems self-evident. From the observable factors in this process, it may be argued that past migrationary movements were induced by geological factors of comparable magnitude. This is merely another application of Hutton's concept of geological processes—that they are the commonplace changes that go on about us, magnified by the cumulative effects of time and continued change.

Bibliography

ANTEVS, E. 1928. The last glaciation. *Amer. Geogr. Soc. Res. Ser.* 17. New York.

BRAUN, E. L. 1950. *Deciduous Forests of Eastern North America.* Blakiston Division, McGraw-Hill Book Co., Inc., New York.

CAIN, S. A. 1939. Pollen analysis as a paleo-ecological research method, *Bot. Rev.* 5: 627-654.

———. 1944. *Foundations of Plant Geography.* Harper & Bros., New York.

CZECHZOTT, H. 1937. The distribution of some species in Northern Asia Minor and the problem of Pontide, *Mitt. K. Naturwiss. Inst. Bulgarien* 10: 43-68.

DEEVEY, E. S. 1943. Additional pollen analysis from Southern New England, *Amer. Jour. Sci.* 241: 717-752.

———. 1944. Pollen analysis and history, *Amer. Scientist* 32: 39-53.

DORF, E. 1959. Climatic changes of the Past and Present, *Contrib. Mus. Paleont. Univ. Mich.* 13: 181-210. A remarkable summary of the present and recent past, with extensive bibliography. Thought-provoking and critical.

ERDTMAN, G. 1943. *An Introduction to Pollen Analysis.* A Chronica Botanica Publication. The Ronald Press Co., New York.

FERNALD, M. L. 1925. Persistence of plants in unglaciated areas of Boreal America. *Mem. Gray Herb. Harvard Univ.* 2. Reprinted from *Mem. Amer. Acad. Arts and Sci.* 15. A part of this chapter is based upon this great floristic classic.

———. 1929. Some relationships of the floras of the Northern Hemisphere, *Proc. Int. Congr. Pl. Sci.* 2: 1487-1507.

———. 1931. Specific segregations and identities in some floras of eastern North America and in the Old World, *Rhodora* 33: 25-63.

FIRBAS, F. 1939. Vegetationsentwicklung und Klimawandel in der mitteleuropäischen Spat- und Nacheiszeit, *Naturwiss.* 27: 81-89, 104-108.

GLEASON, H. A. 1922. The vegetational history of the Middle West, *Ann. Amer. Assoc. Geogr.* 12: 39-85.

GODWIN, H. 1959. Studies of the Post-glacial history of British vegetation. *Phil. Trans. Roy. Soc. Lond.* B. 242:127-149.

HULTÉN, E. 1937. Outline of the history of Arctic and Boreal Biota during the Quarternary period. Tryckeri Aktiebolaget Thule (Stockholm).

JESSEN, K., and V. MILTHERS. 1928. Stratigraphical and paleontological studies of interglacial freshwater deposits of Jutland and North-West Germany. *Danmarks Geol. Unders. Raek.* 48.

KOIDZUMI, G. 1919. Genetic and floristic phytogeography of the Alpine flora of Japan, *Bot. Mag., Tokyo,* 33: 193-222.

PODPERA, J. 1923. Geobotanical analysis of the plant areas in the steppes adjacent to the Ural mountains, *Publ. Fac. Sci. Univ. Masaryk* 27: 3-68.

PURI, G. S. 1947. Fossil plants and the Himalayan uplift, *Jour. Ind. Bot. Soc.,* Iyengar Mem. Vol. (1946) 1947: 167-184.

RAUP, H. M. 1937. Recent changes of climate and vegetation in southern New England and adjacent New York, *Jour. Arnold Arbor,* 18: 79-117.

SEARS, P. B. 1935. Glacial and post-glacial vegetation, *Bot. Rev.* 1: 37-51.

VAN ROYEN, W. 1937. Prehistoric droughts in the Central Great Plains, *Geogr. Rev.* 27: 637-650.

ZEUNER, F. E. 1952. *Dating the Past.* 3d ed. Methuen & Co., Ltd., London.

Attention is called to G. Erdtman's "Literature of Palynology" published annually in *Geologiska Foreningens: Stockholm Forhandlingar.* This series was first issued biennially, commencing with 1927. It serves as a check list of current research in this field. The project was initiated and has been continued by Dr. Erdtman.

22

FOSSIL PLANTS AND EVOLUTION

The plants living today have been developed from ancestors living in the geological past. This phenomenon of biological continuity is the basic fact of botanical evolution. The process of progressive change is poorly understood and the causes and methods of evolution are not known. Paleontology demonstrates two great factors in the history of life, great expanses of time and cumulative change, concepts which have tantalized philosophers since the days of Thales. Paleontology illustrates change from simple to complex, continuity of species, kinship of great groups, and extinction of great groups.

EVOLUTION THEORIES

There are two major theories of organic evolution which have profoundly directed the course of philosophical biology. The first of these is the theory of Lamarck (1744-1829) and the second that of Darwin (1809-1882).

Lamarck's theory of evolution held that the environment acted on the internal structure of the organism in such manner that it adapted to and changed with the changing environment. This theory, depending as it does upon the changes induced upon the individual, implies inheritance of acquired characters.

Lamarck denied all catastrophes in geology or sudden changes in organic life and believed in gradual change without any sharp breaks either in the continuity of terrestrial history or in the evolution of animals and plants. All that is needed, in his opinion, to effect any evolutionary change is matter, space, and time.

Lamarck was the first person to give us a biological concept of the "tree of life," or phylogeny. Classifications before his time had been simply numerical successions of groups arranged one above another. With the development of the idea of a tree of life, there followed a new concept of extinction of past races of animals and plants.

The Lamarckian theory of evolution may be stated somewhat crudely as follows:

1. The internal forces of life tend to increase the size of an organism, not only as a whole, but in every part as well.
2. Each organ or part is the outcome of a new movement, which in turn is initiated by a new and continuous need or want.
3. The development of an organ is in direct proportion to its use. Continued use modifies the organ little by little until its full development is attained, while disuse has the opposite effect, the organ diminishing until only a vestige remains or it disappears altogether.
4. Some part of the "experience" that has been acquired by an individual organism during lifetime is transmitted by heredity to its offspring.

The Neo-Lamarckian School. Lamarck's second and third postulates, especially, have a measure of truth in them, but the crucial point in the theory is the validity of the last premise, and therein has been the impediment to any general acceptance. There has developed a group of investigators who are in a sense the followers of Lamarck and to whom the name Neo-Lamarckian has been given. Among the chief adherents are many paleontologists who see continually before them indisputable evidences of adaptation which seem to imply the action of mechanical forces in their production. Belief in the inheritance of acquired characteristics has been unfashionable for some decades, but a tendency to reappraise the problem is evident in critical literature. That acquired modifications influence more or less profoundly the development of every being is more or less true, and in many instances repetition of acquired effects, generation after generation, gives rise to ontogenetic series which simulate the phylogenetic. The development of new species from cosmic and other types of radiation, or in response to chemical stimulation (fungicides, hormones, etc.), or to climatic factors are now primary data of science. One can no longer deny categorically or dogmatically that some form of acquired inheritance is possible. Indeed, acquired inheritance is essential.

Darwinian Evolution. In the *Origin of Species* (sixth edition, 1880), Darwin says that the modification of species "has been

effected chiefly through the natural selection of numerous, successive, slight, favorable variations; aided in an important manner by the
inherited effects of the use and disuse of parts; and in an unimportant manner—that is, in relation to adaptive structures, whether past
or present—by the direct action of external conditions, and by the
variations which seem to us in our ignorance to arise spontaneously."

Darwin pointed to five factors in his theory of evolution: (1)
natural selection by (2) inheritance, (3) variation, (4) "fitness," and
(5) adaptability. These are manifest by the "survival of the fittest"
in the "struggle for existence." The Neo-Darwinian school of
thought accepts these tenets, but adds the concept of "mutation,"
derived from the experimental data of genetics.

St. Hilaire (1772-1844) and deVries (1848-1935) have also influenced evolutionary thought because they believed that the change
from one species to another may have been by sudden "saltations."
Whereas Lamarck and Darwin attempt to find intermediate forms
between species, i.e., species undergoing change, St. Hilaire and
deVries suggested that intermediate forms may not exist. St. Hilaire
had no experimental evidence to support his theory, but he is
notable for anticipating the mutation theory of deVries.

Genetic experiments during the past fifty years have cast a whole
new light on the mechanisms of inheritance and the requirements
of a satisfactory evolution theory. Morphogenesis is probably
beyond the abilities of paleobotany, but the student is urged to
consult a good reference work in this field.

It must be recognized that the study of paleobotany is, in every
decade, colored to a great degree by prevailing evolutionary concepts. Paleontologists are almost in agreement that the Darwinian
approach to evolution is essentially compatible with the facts of the
fossil record. But again, it is necessary to note that it seems that
the environment has had a profound effect upon the organism, that
the changing environment is accompanied by changing organisms,
and that extinction follows severe or long-continued change (that is,
the organism can no longer keep pace with the process of change).
Thus merely on the face of the record it appears that some type of
natural selection is intimately related to the changing environment.

There are other aspects of evolutionary speculation which have
either obtained support from the study of fossil plants or have
affected the philosophy of paleobotany.

THE THEORY OF RECAPITULATION

In 1866 Haeckel (*Generelle Morphologie d. Organismen*) pro-pounded the theory that during individual development organisms tend to recapitulate their racial history. "This great generalization gradually emerged from a mass of observed facts in the field of animal embryology and palaeontology, during the time when the theory of evolution was still fighting its own struggle for recognition and it helped to a great extent in the acceptance of evolution itself as a guiding principle in biology" (Sahni). In the plant kingdom there are many examples which support a theory of recapitulation. The ferns, conifers, and the RANALES afford typical instances.

On the basis of stelar anatomy, ferns may be classified into three groups: the protostelic, siphonostelic, and dictyostelic. These terms have reference to the type of stele of the plant in its adult condition, no matter what the juvenile conditions may be. It is an established fact, based on many developmental studies, that even in a dictyostelic fern the vascular system is initially a protostele, giving off simple traces to the juvenile leaves. As the plant grows, the protostele expands, acquires a pith, and gives off traces in a typical siphonostelic manner. In the adult phase with its fully developed leaves, the siphonostele becomes a dictyostele. Similarly, the siphonostelic ferns are not siphonostelic to start with, but pass through a protostelic phase. Only in the protostelic form does the juvenile type of structure persist throughout life.

From independent evidence, evidence that has nothing to do with the facts of ontogeny, we may conclude that the protostele, sipho-nostele, and dictyostele are progressive stages in an evolutionary sequence, at least in a general way recapitulative of the ancestral history.

It would appear from a consideration of vascular anatomy of the stem, that the concept of recapitulation is applicable to a wide range of structures in the FILICALES, such as the development of the leaf-trace, which has followed a course of evolution somewhat parallel to that of the axial cylinder. In the first place the leaves successively formed during the ontogeny of the fern show an increasing elabora-tion in their vascular supply, an elaboration that roughly keeps pace with the stelar advance in the stem. Secondly, the same kind of sequence is sometimes repeated, although in a more or less abbreviated form, even in the development of the individual leaf of the adult type.

Jeffrey believed that the first ring of the secondary wood in living ARAUCARINEAE shows in the abundance of parenchyma, a condition persisting throughout the secondary wood in Mesozoic representatives of the family. "The situation here indicated is of great value and wide validity not only for the gymnosperms but also for the dicotyledons." Such opinions defy proof or disproof, but they are stimulating arguments.

MIGRATION, ISOLATION, AND EXTINCTION

An entirely different approach to the study of the evolution of plants is from the vantage point of distribution and its attendant problems of migration, isolation, and relict phenomena. Probably the most general expression of this problem is that by Willis (*Age and Area*). The weakness in this great work is that the conclusions are based upon a statistical study of existing plants without due consideration of geological history.

Plant Migration. One fact which stands out clearly from the study of Pleistocene and late Cenozoic floras in western Europe and along the Atlantic Coastal Plain is that at different geological times different floras have occupied the same locality. By "different floras" is meant different assemblages of plants which have lived in the past, as they do in the present, in regional, or in ecological association, more especially in climatic association.

For example, the Pliocene-Pleistocene succession of northern Europe shows at the close of the Pliocene period a temperate flora almost identical with that now inhabiting parts of England. At a later period there existed a flora composed of plants now inhabiting colder regions—subarctic, alpine, or cold temperate.

Evidence of this kind can scarcely be interpreted otherwise than as indicating the movement of plant assemblages, under the influence of climatic change; in other words, migration.

E. M. Reid has criticized the theory, asking, "If migration has occurred, how has it been brought about?" Willis suggested that newly arrived, or newly formed, species tend to spread outward in all directions from their point of arrival, or point of origin, like rings formed by casting a stone in a pool. In such a tendency there may be a motive force; but migration is a directed movement, and the com-

bined evidence of geology and paleobotany indicates that the direct-
ing force is change of climate, water table, or some other critical
factor. Change of climate, acting ecologically, works as a driving
process, so that movement, instead of being general or haphazard,
becomes a movement in one direction, i.e., migration. Botanists have
gradually recognized the magnitude of present-day floral changes.

Extermination. The study of western European Pliocene floras
led to the recognition of an extinct Tertiary flora in West Europe.
This flora, which Reid called the Chinese–North-American plant
association, is now represented by two living plant associations: the
one, the forest-belt flora of the East Asian mountains; the other,
the allied flora of parts of North America. As discussed in earlier
chapters, there is much evidence from recent and fossil botany and
geology to show that all three are either migrant floras, branches of
a common polar or circumpolar flora, which migrated southward in
late Tertiary time under the influence of a cooling climate in the
northern hemisphere, or are remnants of a more general flora. In the
end there resulted the complete extermination of the European
branch and the isolation of the other two.

In the history of the flora there are exemplified two kinds of
extermination, both of which are concerned with the question raised
by the study of age and area. In the first place there is regional
extermination; no living trace being left, in the region where such
extermination occurs, of the life that has been. In the second place,
there is specific extermination; the species being eliminated, but an
allied one taking its place.

Regional Extermination. Regional extermination, as illustrated
by the history of the Chinese–North-American flora, may be of
different degrees.

1. It may be confined to one region only. For example, the
genera *Magnolia, Liriodendron, Menispermum,* and *Nyssa* have been
exterminated in Europe, but have survived in east Asia and North
America, though they are now represented by different species in the
two regions. Survivals of this kind in Japan and North America,
which are many, led to the recognition by Asa Gray of the fact that
the floras of Japan and Atlantic North America are allied.

2. Extermination may have occurred in two out of the three
regions. Thus *Phellodendron, Actinidia,* and *Zelkowa* have been
exterminated in Europe and probably in North America, but survive
in eastern Asia. *Dulichium, Karwinskia,* and *Proserpinaca* have been

destroyed in Europe and probably in eastern Asia, but survive in North America. When such regional distribution has occurred, there is nothing to indicate in the present how wide the distribution may have been in the past, or to say whether genera are survivals or not.

3. Extermination may have taken place in all three regions, or in other words, the flora has been completely annihilated and in the present there is no remnant of the older flora. We have numerous instances of such extermination in the case of species—extinct species of *Dulichium, Euryale, Liriodendron,* and so on, far too numerous to name here; but we have also in all probability instances of genera exterminated in the many undetermined fossil forms which would appear to belong to living families but cannot be placed in living genera.

The genera *Sequoia* and *Metasequoia* once inhabited Europe, eastern Asia, the Arctic regions, and large areas of North America; now *Sequoia* is confined to the Pacific coast of California and *Metasequoia* to China. *Euryale* was once represented by many species scattered throughout Europe; now it survives as a single species only in parts of China and Assam. Or again, with individual species; *Liriodendron tulipifera, Nyssa sylvatica, Pilea pumila,* and *Dulichium spathaceum* were once all inhabitants of western Europe; now they are confined to the North American continent.

There are various other aspects of the study of migration and distribution. Perhaps the most suggestive theory of ancient distributions is that which developed out of Wegener's theory of continental drift, which postulates a single great continental mass that later broke apart to form the present continents.

According to the tenets of the theory of continental drift, the land mass underwent great "westward" horizontal drifting; Australia and Antarctica began to separate in middle Jurassic time and drifted southeastward. In the early Cretaceous the Americas began to move westward, and finally in the Pleistocene, Greenland and Newfoundland were separated from Norway and Great Britain. Diels has reviewed the evidence of the distribution of the existing floras which Wegener and Irmscher had cited in support of the theory. He pointed out that the flora of Atlantic America is related to that of eastern Asia—not to that of Europe. Yet at the time when this flora developed (late Miocene) Atlantic America was 200° distant from Asia.

However, paleobotanical evidence does not unequivocally support the theory. The upper Cretaceous radiation of angiosperms demonstrates that Australia, Malaya, and India were in general proximity, but western America and eastern Asia were also in proximity. Berry could "see no record of a former union (of South America and western Africa) in anything we know of their stratigraphy, floras, and faunas." More remotely in geological time we know of the Gigantopteris flora restricted to the North Pacific province—on both sides of the ocean. The riddle of large-scale migration cannot be explained by this ingenious hypothesis. As interesting as these problems may be, and the paleobotanical evidence relevant to them, the answers may never be solved.

The actual fossil record, however, is a source of tangible data which has as its chief quality chronological succession. The Devonian antedates the Carboniferous. The Mesozoic precedes the Cenozoic. In the cases of those groups of plants which have left good records or long histories, the evidence of paleobotany as to what is "primitive" and what is "advanced" is the most trustworthy evidence. The terms "primitive" and "advanced," "undifferentiated" and "specialized" are, however, tinted glasses through which a person sees a landscape—not as it really is, but colored. The paleobotanist reads the record from the past toward the present, not backward. There is no mystery concerning "very specialized" types that occur in the Devonian. They do occur; they are not anachronisms. Man's dismay is his ignorance.

The fact of progressive change throughout geological time in the direction toward "complexity" from "simplicity" is equally true in the several subdivisions of paleontology—paleobotany, invertebrate paleozoology, and vertebrate paleozoology. To a considerable degree interpretation colors the reading of chronology and the reading of biological succession. Each generation of paleontologists is influenced by the intellectual "isms" of the times.

Time is manifest by change, and biological change is intimately associated with geological change.

Bibliography

ABEL, O. 1929. *Palaeobiologie und Stammesgeschichte*. Fischer, Jena.
DUTOIT, A. L. 1927. A geological comparison of South America and South Africa. *Carn. Inst. Wash. Publ.* 381.
———. 1957. *Our Wandering Continents*. Hafner Publishing Co., New York.

HUXLEY, J., A. C. HARDY, E. B. FORD et al. 1954. *Evolution as a Process*. George Allen & Unwin, London.

LIBBY, W. F. 1955. *Radiocarbon Dating*. 2d ed. University of Chicago Press, Chicago.

LULL, R. S. 1929. *Organic Evolution*. 2d ed. The Macmillan Co., New York.

SAHNI, B. 1925. Ontogeny of vascular plants and the theory of recapitulation, *Jour. Ind. Bot. Soc.* 4: 202-216.

SCHENK, H. G. 1940. Applied paleontology, *Bull. Amer. Assoc. Pet. Geol.* 24: 1752-1778.

STEBBINS, G. L. 1950. *Variation and Evolution in Plants*. Columbia University Press, New York.

WILLIS, J. 1922. *Age and Area*. Cambridge University Press, London. In many respects more satisfying than his later *Birth and Spread of Plants*, 1949.

23

A REASONABLE PHYLOGENY

It is a fitting close to this review of the paleobotanical record, and the biological principles it interprets, to consider a reasonable phylogeny.

The establishment of a concept of evolution, suggesting, as it does, the ultimate common ancestor, necessitates a genealogy of plant groups. The facts of kinship are in practice designated by classification, particularly in taxonomic groups of greater ordinal value than genera.

It has been amply demonstrated in this survey that in the near past there lived many species and genera which have now become extinct, and that, as one searches the record of the remoter past, families, orders, classes, and phyla gradually "disappear" until in the early Paleozoic only marine thallophytes are known to us. Yet this record is not merely the appearance, dominance, and elimination of types; it is the course of evolution—specialization, modification, and diversification.

Lam, a distinguished student of the logic and philosophy of phylogeny, draws an interesting distinction between the method of taxonomy and phylogeny. "Taxonomy is the expression of momentary relations between concrete or abstract items . . . it is nothing but classification. In Taxonomy we can never speak of kinship, but merely of resemblances and differences. The distinguishing factor of Taxonomic schemes are cross-sections through phylogenetic schemes." Lam observes that taxonomy is static and its symbols of expression are two-dimensional, but phylogeny is dynamic and its symbols are three-dimensional. Thus the usual expression of phylogenetic relationships is in the form of a "tree of life" with a large trunk, many large branches, and a great number of small twigs.

The paleobotanist must, however, begin at a logical beginning in his phylogeny. The roots of the tree of life are buried in the prehistory of the Proterozoic—mere speculation supplies the inferential early stages in plant evolution. A reasonable phylogeny based upon the paleobotanical record should use with caution the vogues of current morphology. Groups of plants, of which no fossil representatives are known, and which are taxonomically "isolated," hold little importance for the present.

Eighty per cent of the paleontological record, in point of time, lies in back of the beginning of the Devonian. Actually, the vascular plants concerning which we have some definite biological knowledge are first known in the upper Silurian, yet we have Cambrian and Pre-Cambrian spores and fragments which invalidate, by their very existence, any neat scheme based upon later records. The main trends of plant evolution as indicated by the fossil record may be expressed in the following narrative of events.

The thallophytes of the Pre-Cambrian and even the Silurian and the lower Devonian belong, so far as their remains permit determination, to the several major groups now recognized by botanists. The CHLOROPHYCEAE and RHODOPHYCEAE appear to have been well represented. We can say no more than that.

THE NEMATOPHYTES

The earliest plant group which is of significance in the study of plant phylogeny is the Silurian and Devonian NEMATOPHYTALES described by Lang, and independently recognized by Chiarugi. These plants are still incompletely known, but they are most suggestive of a relationship between brown algae and vascular plants. The genus *Nematophyton*, the best-known member of the order, has a large stem without definite organization of tissue. In *Nematothallus* there are cuticularized spores of the pteridophytic type. Possibly also belonging to this group is the curious bifid thalloid plant known as *Protosalvinia* (= *Foerstia*), though some paleobotanists hold it to be an alga. In this genus there are produced large cuticularized spores borne in tetrads. The group does not include plants with vascularized tissues, but rather plants with thalloid bodies fairly certainly adapted to the land habit. The spores were borne within the heavy walled tip of the body, there not being a differentiated sporangium.

CAMBRIAN SPORES

The resistant spore (i.e., the cuticularized or cutinized spore) is an essential feature for a terrestrial plant. Cambrian spores with the tetrad scar were recognized first in the Swedish kolm or oil-shale (Darrah, 1937) and more recently in Russia, India, and Canada. At least eight Cambrian occurrences have been reported. These ancient structures indicate the antiquity of this development and force a measure of caution in generalizing about Devonian plants.

THE PSILOPSIDS

With the discovery of the Rhynie flora and the recognition of the PSILOPHYTALES, the common ancestry for all vascular plants became a matter within the bounds of speculation. In *Rhynia* and *Horneophyton* the undifferentiated plant body consists of slender leafless axes or shoots, dichotomously branched, and terminal columellate sporangia producing resistant spores in tetrads. The axis was truly protostelic. In *Psilophyton* the plant body is some-what more elaborate in having spiny emergences which function as leaves. The plant body is covered with cuticle provided with stomata. *Asteroxylon* was clothed with small scalelike leaves. The stele in *Asteroxylon mackiei* was actinostelic and in *Asteroxylon elberfeldense* siphonostelic.

Thus far in the PSILOPHYTALES there are four basic attainments: (1) the upright aerial photosynthetic axis, (2) the necessary differentiation of internal tissues for support of the upright habit, (3) the terminal sporangium producing resistant spores, and (4) potential leaves, or at least homologues of leaves. It is to be noted that even within this small group there are three stages in the development of the stele correlated with the requirements of increasing size: protostele—actinostele—siphonostele.

The perplexing problem concerning the PSILOPHYTALES is the boundary of the group. There are many nearly contemporaneous Devonian plants which have simple dichotomously branched axes and terminal sporangia and are thus closely allied to the RHYNIACEAE and PSILOPHYTACEAE. Some of these however are particularly significant. *Drepanophycus* (*Arthrostigma*) has small emergence-like leaves which may be arranged with spiral or verticillate phyllotaxy. At least one form appears to have sporangia borne in the axils of spirally disposed leaves. *Hyenia* has a more or less psilophytean habit with short dichotomously branched "leaves" arranged in whorls. *Calamophyton*, another Devonian plant, was very like *Hyenia* excepting that the axis was jointed or articulated. The sporangia are borne terminally in clusters of two or four. Strikingly suggestive is the occasional occurrence of loose cones formed by the distal grouping of fertile tips.

The remarkable late Silurian genus *Baragwanathia* has an apparent relationship to *Drepanophycus* but its leaves were large (up to 4 cm in length) and numerous.

Protopteridium is a small plant constructed essentially upon a dichotomous plan, like *Pseudosporochnus* or *Psilophyton* but with determinate pinnate branching terminal, some of these pinnate branches being fertile.

The plant body has been differentiated along three phyletic lines: (1) the dichotomous axis with spirally disposed segments (leaves), (2) the dichotomous axis with verticillated segments, and (3) the axis with determinate pinnate branching—still without differentiated leaves.

The propriety of including all of these within the psilophytalean complex is open to grave question, but together they demonstrate a homogeneity that suggests close kinship. It is this relationship which has given rise to the acceptance of the *Psilophyton* group as suggestive or representative of the ancestral stock of all vascular plants. The telome theory of Zimmermann was inspired by the psilopsids.

The *Psilophyton* complex may be called the Mid-Devonian "level of attainment." The relatively new land plant was a dichotomous axis with differentiation of telomes, in the service of the several necessary functions. None of the early diversifications from the prototype progressed far beyond their common heritage. The vegetation modifications were more rapid and profound than the reproductive ones. Sporangia with homospores were, with very few exceptions, still terminal in position. There is scarcely any suggestion of a strobilus, although the fertile tips become localized to certain branches, as in *Hyenia* and in *Protopteridium*. But the axis has evolved in three independent lines, two of which are provided with small leaves, probably arising by the modification of emergences ("enations" in a broad sense), and the third with large leaves probably arising by cladification.

The psilophytes have been termed the PSILOPSIDA and are defined as dichotomous, leafless, and rootless plants with terminal homosporous sporangia. From this group there evolved the LYCOPSIDA, SPHENOPSIDA, and PTEROPSIDA.

THE LYCOPSIDS AND SPHENOPSIDS

The lycopsid body plant is constructed on the dichotomous plan with spirally disposed microphyllous leaves. Strictly speaking, naked terminal sporangia are not known among the fossil lycopsids, although the strobilus was a later development. The stem was protostelic or siphonostelic. The sporangia are borne upon sporophylls.

The sphenopsid body is constructed on a more or less dichotomous plan with articulated axes and microphyllous leaves borne in verticils. Among all of the older sphenopsids the naked sporangia are borne terminally, and on small pedicels (i.e., they are sporangiophoric rather than sporophyllic). The sphenopsids are either protostelic or siphonostelic. Both the lycopsid and sphenopsid groups, in their later members, bear strobili and microphyllous leaves. The articulate nature of the axis in the sphenopsids is the most apparent point of difference. Recently the recognition of the NOEGGERATHIALES has rendered this relationship somewhat controversial. The habit in this order is anisophyllous and the leaves spirally disposed, i.e., the stem is nonarticulated, but the fructification is of the sphenopsid (*Sphenophyllum*) type. However, the stachyosporic versus the phyllosporic fructification was probably achieved or differentiated in the psilopsid complex, and the strobilus evolved independently in each phyletic line. The sphenopsid leaf may have had a different origin from that of the lycopsids. The sphenopsids never attained the seed habit.

THE PTEROPSIDS

The pteropsids were the only plants to attain great size constructed on elaborations of the stele. The stele was interrupted by branch and leaf gaps and the siphonostele became (ontogenetically becomes) a dictyostele. The pinnate body with terminal sporangia is characteristic of the primitive ferns. The COENOPTERIDALES include very simple ferns exhibiting interesting stages in the cladification of telomes to form leaves. The classification of Paleozoic ferns has not progressed far enough to become standardized. There is a tendency for the terminal sporangia to give way to marginal and finally to superficial placement. All higher plants are pteropsids because of their fundamental body plan.

DIVERGENCE OF THE GYMNOSPERMS

The pteridosperms are the "first" plants to develop true seeds and true pollen (the microspore with the enclosed gametophyte composed of a few cells or nuclei). The general habit was superficially filicinean.

The pteropsid body is, in the earlier forms, dichotomous with some of the branches with determinate growth, expressed in the pinnate habit. The sporangia are terminal but borne on pinnate branches. There are no differentiated leaves in the earliest members. The pteropsids are generally megaphyllous, the large leaves arising by cladification. The family ZYGOPTERIDACEAE is noteworthy in this connection.

Each of these lines of descent deserves some further comment. The best known Paleozoic lycopsids are the LEPIDODENDRACEAE, which attained great size with only a scanty supply of xylem but with considerable cortex. The LEPIDODENDRACEAE are important because they attained the condition of heterospory. The sporangia are borne in large strobili and the spores are differentiated into megaspores and microspores. In some forms the megaspores were reduced in number to eight, four, and ultimately to one functional spore per megasporangium. This megaspore was sometimes provided with integuments and thus simulated the seed habit. There were two deficiencies in this seedlike structure: the sporophyll was shed with the sporangium, and the megaspore apparently fell to the ground and developed without a resting period. Among the Paleozoic lycopsids there are smaller forms belonging to the SELAGINEL-LACEAE and LYCOPODIACEAE.

The spenopsids have never been important members of the vegetation, excepting perhaps in mid-Carboniferous times. Usually the sporangia are grouped into strobili which are in general homosporous. Heterospory is attained in the CALAMITACEAE. A well-developed cambium produced secondary tissues. Thus from an ancestry out of the Devonian filicinean complex developed the most primitive gymnosperms. The fructification is typically non-strobiloid, but the variety of its modifications is great. The cupulate seed has been considered to be of great portent because cupular structures appear among later gymnosperms. No one knows, as yet, what the cupule really is, or whether all cupular organs are homologous.

The retention of fernlike characters in the pteridosperms and their obvious relationships with the living and fossil cycads has led to the common belief that the cycadophytes have a fern ancestry. The CYCADALES and BENNETTITALES have strobilar fructifications, the older BENNETTITALES being bisporangiate, with the microsporic and megasporic structures arranged in spiral flower-like construction. The CYCADALES are monosporangiate and are probably an aberrant offshoot from a pteridospermic or early bennettitalean stock. The remarkable Triassic MICROFLORAE are important bennettitaleans because they possessed small bisporangiate flowers and smooth branched stems, and small, entire deciduous leaves.

There is another line of gymnosperms which developed from the early pteropsids in Devonian times. This is a phyletic line of large arborescent plants producing compact secondary wood and blade-leaves or needle-leaves. This group possessed a cambium, as in the pteridosperms. The first group to differentiate from this phyletic line was the CORDAITALES, which are characterized by monosporangiate strobili composed of spirally arranged segments, winged pollen, and small winged bilaterally symmetrical seeds with dicotyledonous embryos. The secondary wood of the CORDAITALES is composed of tracheids with multiseriate hexagonal bordered pits on the radial walls. The CORDAITALES have much in common with the GINKGOALES, although the anomalous cupulate ovule of *Ginkgo* has been compared with the pteridospermic ovule.

The conifers were differentiated from a cordaitalean ancestry during late Carboniferous times. The earliest conifers, the VOLTZIALES, are represented by *Lebachia* and several related genera. They possess cordaitean-like seeds, similar construction of the sterile bracts accompanying the terminal ovule, normally winged pollen, and wood of the *"Dadoxylon"* type. Three major groups differentiated from the VOLTZIALES during early Mesozoic times: the TAXINEAE, the ABIETINEAE, and the ARAUCARINEAE, which have the number of ovules reduced to one and the bract and ovuliferous scale fused.

The several orders of the gymnosperms have been variously classified into larger units. Nathorst and Chamberlain used the terms "CYCADOPHYTA," and "CONIFEROPHYTA." Jeffrey used the terms "ARCHIGYMNOSPERMAE" and "METAGYMNOSPERMAE," and Seward proposed the adjectival designations "manoxylic" and "pycnoxylic" to suggest fundamental differences in wood structure among the main groups of gymnosperms. The term manoxylic applies to the cycadean type of wood, which is porous, loose in texture, and more parenchymatous in structure. The term pycnoxylic refers to the compact wood of the coniferous type. Sahni proposed the name "stachyosperm" for the coniferophytes because the seeds are borne upon the stem, and the name "phyllosperm" for the cycadophytes because the seeds are borne upon leaves. Sahni's terms, now commonly used as "phyllosporic" and "stachyosporic," seem to correspond to the underlying divergence and thus have the greatest usefulness. It is a significant fact that all four of these attempts to recognize lines of kinship among the gymnosperms are in complete agreement; they recognize the existence of only two main divisions: the cycad type and the conifer type.

THE ANGIOSPERMS

The angiosperms or flowering plants arose from some gymnosperm stock. The angiosperm is typically bisporangiate, and the ancestry is to be found among the cycadophytes. In the MICROFLORAE of the bennettitaleans there occurs the approximation of a complete flower, and Wieland (and many others) have used this occurrence to indicate a phylogenetic relationship between the BENNETTITALES and the strobilar ranalean complex.

Paleobotanical evidence lends support to the hypothesis that the ranalean complex is most primitive among the angiosperms, although not unequivocally. The occurrence of Triassic palms would favor a monocotyledonous ancestry. The widespread occurrence of homoxylous woods in the Cretaceous and lower Cenozoic, and leaves of the TROCHODENDRACEAE, further suggest a ranalean origin.

The paleobotanical record has not thus far contributed much toward an understanding of evolution within the angiosperms. We can accept, however, that the monocotyledons, although they differentiated early, evolved from the dicotyledons, and that the herbaceous habit was derived from the woody habit. The herbaceous habit was attained independently in many families as a mass response to climatic-ecological stimulation. It is possible that this grand-scale evolution in the space of a geologically short time is an example of a phenomenon that has happened many times in the geological past.

ISOLATED PLANT GROUPS

There are intentionally omitted from this survey considerations of the existing PSILOTACEAE, the GNETALES, and the fungi. Undoubted fossils of the PSILOTACEAE are not known, so that the paleobotanist has no basis for linking them with the PSILOPHYTALES, which became, apparently, extinct in the Devonian. The status of the putative primitive nature of the plant body in the PSILOTACEAE is controversial, although there is a strong tendency to accept the family as a persistent remnant of the PSILOPSIDA. A few fossil leaves have been attributed to the GNETALES, but they are insufficient evidence upon which a case can legitimately be made. There are a number of well-characterized fossil fungi, but in all cases where reproductive structures are known, they are referable to existing families. To the paleobotanist the fungi represent a mode of nutrition and indications of environmental conditions.

The bryophytes have an unbroken geological history dating from the Carboniferous, but the two main divisions, the MUSCI and the HEPATICAE were already differentiated. It has been noted that the columellate sporangium of certain RHYNIACEAE may denote a kinship between the earliest tracheophytes and the bryophytes. The evidence is too meager to permit any more than flimsy hypothesis.

PHYLOGENETIC HISTORY

The phylogenetic history of the plant kingdom can be stated, not only in terms of taxonomy, but also in the terms of morphology. There are a number of fundamental inventions or developments in the history of the tracheophytes:

1. The invasion of land by an undifferentiated thalloid plant (not later than Silurian, perhaps as early as Cambrian).
2. The simple upright undifferentiated and protostelic axis (apparently Silurian).
3. Enlargement of the plant body, with specializations toward a division of labor—sterile and fertile (apparently late Silurian).
4. Origin of the photosynthetic leaf (Silurian).
5. Specializations in the service of support, with the resultant secondary body (Devonian).
6. Development of the strobilus (Devonian).
7. The development of heterospory (Devonian, if not earlier).

8. Retention of the gametophyte within the megaspore, within the megasporangium, where fertilization takes place, with the ultimate attainment of (a difference only in degree) the seed (probably upper Devonian).

9. The evolution of the pollen grain. The same tendency as the retention of the megagametophyte (Carboniferous, if not earlier).

10. Evolution of the bisporangiate flower (Triassic).

11. Attainment of the condition of angiospermy (Jurassic or Triassic).

12. Evolution of the herbaceous habit (Cretaceous, but chiefly Cenozoic).

This phylogenetical scheme, stripped of many interpretative hypotheses, may be expressed in the accompanying diagram (Fig. 63).

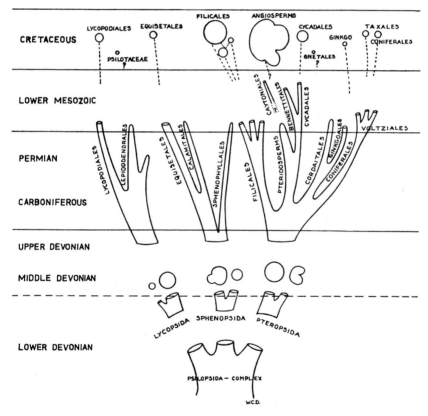

Fig. 63. A phylogenetic scheme of vascular plants. The branches express probable origins of the major groups. The cross-sections in mid-Devonian and Cretaceous times indicate the relative taxonomic isolation of each group.

THE OUTLOOK

Thus the study of paleobotany has given an integrated and organized picture of the history of the plant kingdom. The gaps in the fossil record are many, but there is optimistic hope for the future. At the turn of the century the pteridosperms were unknown; a few decades ago the Rhynie flora was discovered and the CAYTONIALES were recognized. Still more recently the Silurian flora from Victoria and the NEMATOPHYTALES were understood for the first time. Within the past two decades the VOLTZIALES have proved to be the key to conifer evolution. Meanwhile the slow accumulation of less spectacular pre-Devonian and early Mesozoic discoveries weaves a colorful tapestry of plant history. Who can yet appraise *Pentoxylon* or *Rhacophyton* or gauge the portentous discovery of Proterozoic microorganisms?

Hugh Miller wrote in 1857 in his *Testimony of the Rocks:* "We see only detached bits of that green web which has covered our earth ever since the dry land first appeared; but the web itself seems to have been continuous throughout all time."

Bibliography

It is difficult to select a small number of supplementary readings which will provide a guide to the range of current speculation in plant phylogeny. The following are conservative and suggest dissatisfaction with accepted opinions:

BERTRAND, P. 1947. *Les végétaux vasculaires.* Masson et Cie, Paris.
BOWER, F. O. 1935. *Primitive Land Plants.* Macmillan & Co., Ltd., London.
BROWNE, I. M. 1935. Some views on the morphology and phylogeny of the leafy sporophyte, *Bot. Rev.* 1: 383-404, 427-447.
HEIM, R., *et al.* 1952. Evolution et phylogenie chez les végétaux. *Colloq. Inter. Cent. Rech. Scien.,* Paris.
JEFFREY, E. C. 1917. *Anatomy of Woody Plants.* Chicago University Press, Chicago.
LAM, H. J. 1936. Phylogenetic symbols, past and present, *Acta Biotheor.* A 2: 153-194.
———. 1947. A new system of the Cormophyta, *Blumea* 6: 282-289.
———. 1952. Dynamic paleobotany. *C. R. 3e Congr. Strat. Geol. Carb.,* Heerlen, 1951, 1952: 385-395.
WARDLAW, C. W. 1952. *Phylogeny and Morphogenesis.* St. Martin's Press, Inc., New York.
ZIMMERMANN, W. 1930. *Die Phylogenie der Pflanzen.* Fischer, Jena.
———. 1949. *Geschichte der Pflanzen.* Fischer, Stuttgart.

The student who wishes to examine an extreme, even heretical, point of view should consult:

GREGUSS, P. 1955. *Identification of Living Gymnosperms on the Basis of Xylotomy.* Akademiai Kiado, Budapest.

AUTHOR INDEX

Abbott, M. L., 87, 96
Abel, O., 269
Agassiz, L., 190
Andrews, H. N., 16, 19, 77, 78, 81, 86, 113, 123, 165
Arber, E. A. N., 161, 211, 217
Arnold, C. A., 16, 19, 66, 81, 109, 113, 139, 157, 165
Arnold, J. R., 30, 31
Augusta, J., 131, 247
Axelrod, D. I., 241, 247

Bailey, I. W., 181, 182, 212, 216, 217, 218
Barghoorn, E. S., 33, 34, 40, 42, 93, 96, 152, 237
Bataller, J. R., 247
Bayer, A., 228
Bell, W. A., 139, 228
Benson, M., 76
Bernard, C., 31, 66
Berry, E. W., 19, 136, 160, 176, 218, 225, 228, 233, 237, 247, 268
Bertrand, C. E., 33, 148, 159
Bertrand, P., 19, 48, 49, 66, 87, 101, 105, 108, 109, 113, 116, 117, 139, 148, 152, 280
Binney, E. W., 15, 101
Blumenbach, J., 14
Bochenski, T., 81
Bold, H. C., 12
Bose, A., 40
Bowen, R. N. C., 11
Bower, F. O., 12, 112, 280
Braun, E. L., 242, 245, 247, 260
Brongniart, A., 14, 15, 103, 190
Brown, R. W., 113, 207
Browne, I., 66, 86, 96, 280
Buckland, W., 166
Burian, Z., 131, 247

Cady, G. H., 152
Cain, S. A., 260
Calder, M. G., 81
Carruthers, W., 15, 167, 169, 175
Cernjavski, P., 247
Chamberlain, C. J., 174
Chandler, M. E., 237

Chaney, R. V., 136, 185, 231, 237, 241, 242, 247
Chiarugi, A., 38, 271
Clements, F. E., 231, 241, 242
Conant, J. B., 30
Conway, V., 224, 228
Conwentz, H., 236, 237
Cookson, I. C., 51, 55, 56
Cooper, J. R., 66
Corda, A., 15
Corsin, P., 113, 139
Craft, W. N., 56
Cross, A. T., 96, 123, 152
Cuvier, G., 8, 14
Czechzott, H., 254, 257, 260

Darrah, W. C., 16, 19, 26, 28, 31, 40, 42, 77, 81, 96, 102, 113, 139, 152, 165, 203, 218, 272
Darrow, B. S., 183, 189
Darwin, C., 261, 262, 263
Darwin, E., 14
Daugherty, L. H., 195, 203
Davis, C. A., 153
Dawson, J. W., 41, 42, 54, 55, 59, 66
Deevy, E. S., 254, 260
DeGeer, E. H., 253
DePape, G., 247
deVries, H., 263
Diels, L., 267
Dillon, G. W., 72, 74, 104, 206, 207, 208, 209
Dorf, E., 3, 12, 55, 56, 94, 216, 228, 247, 259, 260
Duigan, S. L., 237
Duparque, A., 144
DuToit, A. L., 269

Edwards, W. N., 19, 203, 217
Emberger, L., 16, 19, 217
Engelhardt, H., 176
Erdtman, G., 217, 250, 251, 259, 260
Ettingshausen, C., 15, 176, 227

Felix, C. J., 165
Fenton, C. L., 37, 40
Fenton, M. A., 37, 40
Fernald, M. L., 136, 254, 255, 256, 257, 258, 260

Firbas, S., 260
Fischer, F., 29
Florin, R., 159, 164, 165, 167, 177, 179, 189
Florschütz, F., 237
Ford, E. B., 269
Foster, A. S., 12
Frič, A., 228
Fujii, K., 209, 218
Fürst, R., 258

Ghosh, A. K., 40, 152
Gifford, E. M., 12
Gleason, H. A., 260
Godwin, H., 260
Goeppert, H. R., 14, 15, 20, 24, 31, 59, 181, 235, 237
Goldring, W., 61
Gordon, W. T., 81, 151
Gothan, W., 16, 19, 139, 183, 189
Gowan, J., 165
Graham, R., 81
Grand'Eury, F., 84, 86, 158, 159
Grant, W. M., 40
Gray, A., 231, 238, 243, 266
Greguss, P., 280
Gulbranson, E. A., 30
Gümbel, C., 24
Gunderson, A., 218
Gwynne Vaughan, D., 101, 113, 201

Haeckel, E., 264
Hall, J., 36
Halle, T. G., 16, 19, 27, 28, 31, 42, 47, 115, 118, 120, 139, 203
Hallier, H., 215
Hanna, G. D., 40
Hansen, H. P., 258
Hanson, S., 254
Harder, E. C., 40
Hardy, A. C., 269
Harris, T. M., 39, 40, 122, 123, 164, 165, 167, 177, 195, 202, 203, 207
Hartung, W., 96
Heer, O., 15, 176, 195, 215, 224
Heim, R., 280
Hirmer, M., 16, 19, 37, 80, 83, 85, 92, 101, 171
Høeg, O. A., 34, 62, 66, 164
Hoffmann, E., 19
Hollick, A., 231, 247
Hoskins, J. H., 96, 123
Hsu, J., 66
Hulten, E., 257, 258, 260
Hutton, J., 157, 259
Huxley, J., 269

Irmscher, E., 267

Jeffrey, E. C., 27, 28, 31, 34, 83, 148, 152, 154, 178, 181, 184, 265, 280
Jennings, O. E., 55
Jesson, K., 252, 260
Johnson, J. H., 40
Joleaud, L., 241
Jongmans, W. J., 16, 86, 96, 137, 139, 144, 146, 152
Joy, K. W., 24
Jurasky, K. A., 152
Just, T., 217

Keith, A., 259
Kern, E. M., 113
Kidston, R., 36, 42, 46, 47, 55, 96, 110, 113, 118, 139, 165, 201
Knowlton, F. H., 136, 228, 237
Knox, E. M., 153
Koidzumi, G., 260
Konno, E., 96, 189
Koopmans, R., 21, 146, 152
Kosanke, R. M., 149, 153
Krasser, F., 176
Kraus, G., 181
Kraüsel, R., 19, 31, 47, 50, 53, 56, 59, 61, 66, 90, 91, 94, 176, 177, 189
Kryshtofovich, A. N., 16, 19, 53, 136, 233, 247
Kuyper, B., 29, 31

Lacey, W. S., 24
Lam, H. J., 55, 270, 280
Lamarck, J. B., 187, 261, 262, 263
Lang, W. H., 31, 36, 38, 40, 42, 46, 47, 51, 55, 56, 165, 271
Leclercq, S., 26, 31, 55, 66, 96, 98, 99, 113
Lederer, E., 30
Lesquereux, L., 15, 135, 219, 228
Levittan, E. J., 93, 96
Libby, W. F., 8, 30, 31, 269
Lignier, O., 167, 173
Lindley, J., 157
Long, A. G., 115, 123
Lull, R. S., 269
Lundblad, B., 81, 203
Luther, M., 13
Lutz, J., 139
Lyell, C., 142

MacBride, T. H., 168
Macginitie, H. D., 237
McLean, R. C., 75, 82
Mägdefrau, K., 16, 19, 125, 195, 201, 221
Mamay, S. H., 40, 113

Marion, A., 176
Marshall, C., 153
Maslen, A. C., 157
Mason, H., 189, 242
Menendez, C. A., 113
Menge, A., 235, 237
Meschinelli, A., 176
Miki, S., 185, 186, 247
Miller, H., 280
Mithers, V., 252, 260
Moret, L., 19

Nathorst, A. G., 21, 42, 66, 89, 163, 167
Nier, A. O., 30
Nørlund, J., 258

O'Donnell, H. J., 153
Ogura, Y., 123
Oishi, S., 199, 203
Oliver, F. W., 114, 120, 123
Ostenfeld, C., 254

Pannell, E., 81
Parkin, J., 211, 217
Parks, B. C., 153
Parsons, J., 14
Peck, R. E., 37, 40
Penny, J. S., 189
Pia, J., 37, 40
Pilger, R., 178
Pliny, 13
Podpera, J., 254, 257, 260
Potbury, S. S., 237
Potonié, H., 16, 19, 66, 114, 139
Puri, G. S., 260
Pythagoras, 13

Raistrick, A., 153
Rasky, R., 40
Raup, H. M., 258, 260
Read, C. B., 66, 113
Reid, C., 243, 247
Reid, E. M., 237, 243, 247, 265, 266
Renault, B., 148, 159
Roos, C., 144, 146, 153
Roussel, J., 258

Sahni, B., 17, 113, 139, 177, 178, 197, 203, 218, 264, 269
St. Hilaire, I., 263
Sanborn, E. I., 237
Saporta, G., 15, 164, 167, 176, 220
Schenk, A., 163
Schenk, H. G., 269
Scheuchzer, J., 13
Schimper, W. P., 15, 19, 176, 181
Schonfeld, G., 247

Schopf, J. M., 76, 82, 123, 142, 150, 153
Schuchert, C., 11, 136
Schultes, R. E., 94
Schultze, M., 24
Schuyer, J., 153
Scott, D. H., 16, 19, 76, 77, 83, 94, 114, 118, 120, 123, 157
Sears, P. B., 260
Sellards, E. H., 25, 114
Selling, O. H., 96, 247
Sen, J., 152
Seward, A. C., 16, 19, 127, 135, 183, 197, 219, 224, 228, 233
Shukla, V. B., 237
Simpson, J. B., 189, 203, 204, 207
Sinnott, E. W., 113, 204, 216, 217, 218
Sitholey, R. V., 31, 204
Smith, A. F., 247
Smith, G. M., 12
Smith, W., 6, 14
Solms-Laubach, H., 16, 20, 31, 167
Spackman, W., 153
Spegazzini, C., 183
Srivastava, P. N., 197
Stadnichenko, T., 149
Stebbins, G. L., 269
Steere, W. C., 40
Sternberg, H., 179
Stewart, W. N., 82
Stipanicic, P. N., 113
Stockmans, F., 56, 139
Stopes, M. C., 21, 144, 145, 153, 208, 209, 218, 228
Straus, A., 38
Suess, E., 133
Swamy, B. G. L., 212, 217

Takhtajian, A. L., 218
Teixiera, C., 139
Tertullian, 13
Thales, 261
Thiessen, R., 34, 149, 153
Thomas, H. H., 55, 87, 96, 122, 123, 167, 171, 177, 218
Thompson, W. P., 218
Traverse, A., 157, 165, 237
Treibs, A., 29, 30
Turner, H. G., 147
Twenhofel, W. H., 11
Tyler, S. A., 33

Unger, F., 15

van der Hammen, L., 65
Vankrevelen, D. W., 153
VanRoyen, W., 260

Velenovsky, J., 228
Verdoorn, F., 12, 186
Viniklar, L., 228
Voight, E., 31
VonPost, E. L., 254

Walcott, C. D., 32, 33
Walkom, A. B., 204
Walther, J., 237
Walton, J., 16, 19, 21, 25, 31, 82
Ward, L. F., 19, 166, 204
Wardlaw, C. W., 12, 280
Wegener, A., 136, 267
Weigelt, J., 237
Weiss, E., 86, 88
Wesley, A., 29, 31
Wettstein, R., 213, 250
Weyland, W., 16, 47, 51, 53, 61, 66, 90, 91, 94
White, D., 120, 139, 144, 145, 150, 153

White, I. C., 139
Wieland, G. R., 167, 168, 169, 174, 177, 183, 184, 189, 204, 211, 212
Williamson, W. C., 15, 86, 87, 170
Willis, A. J., 24
Willis, J. C., 265, 269
Witham, H., 14, 15, 157
Wodehouse, R., 234

Xanthus of Sardis, 13
Xenophanes, 13

Yabe, H., 199
Yokoyama, M., 176, 199

Zalessky, M. D., 132, 139, 150
Zeiller, R., 16, 93, 140, 164, 204
Zeuner, F. E., 9, 11, 259, 260
Zimmermann, W., 12, 83, 171, 172, 178, 273, 280

SUBJECT INDEX

(Numbers in *italic* refer to illustrations.)

Abelia, 232, 233
Abies, 182, 234, 235
Abietites, 225
Acanthus, 232, 233
Acer, 223, 231
Aceraceae, 235
Acitheca, 105
Acmopyle, 185
Acrostichides, 201
Acrostichum, 232, 233
Actinidia, 266
Actinostrobus, 187
Adiantites, *126*, 127
Adiantum, 112
Aftonian, 249
Agathis, 154
Age of the earth, 8
Ailanthus, 231, 234
Albion, 222
Aldanophyton antiquissimum, 53
Aldrovanda, 232, 233
Alethopteris, 103, *104*, 117, 118, 119, 131
   norini, 121
Algae, 33 ff.
Algal coals, 148, 149, 150
Alisma subcordatum, 243
Allegheny, 129
Alloiopteris, 111
Alnus, 231, 233, 234, 253
Amaranthaceae, 216
Amber, 13
Amber flora, 234, 235
Amyelon, 158
Anacardiaceae, 234
Anachoropteris, 100, 102, 109, 111
Andromeda, 236
Androvettia, 225
Aneimites, 129
Aneurophyton, *44*, 45, 58, *60*, 61, 64, 109,
   110, 114
   germanicum, 53, 54, *60*, 61
Angiopteris, 106
Angiosperms, origin of, 205 ff.
Ankyropteris, 100, 102, 111
   corrugata, 102
Annularia, 87, 89, 96
Anomozamites, 172, 173
   muelleri, 176
Antholithus zeilleri, 162

Anthracite, 147
Anthracoporella, 34
Anthraxylon, 144
Antidesma, 236
Appalachian revolution, 131
Aptian, 222
Arachnoxylon, 100
Aralia, 217, 223, 229
Araliopsis, *208*, *220*, 223, 229
Araucaria, 184
   excelsa, 188
Araucariaceae, 178, 181, 184, 240, 241
Araucariopitys, 181, 182
Araucarioxylon, 181, 188, *193*, 195
   arizonicum, 181, 195
Araucarites, 183
   windhauseni, 183
Archaeocalamites, 86, 88, 89, 95
Archaeopteris, *44*, 45, 59, 109, 110, 111
   114, 125
   latifolia, 109
Archaeosigillaria, *44*, 45, 58, 68, 79
Archaeothrix, 33
Arthrostigma, 42, 59, 64, 272
Arthrotaxus, 185, 187
Articulatae, 83
Artisia, 154
Artocarpus, 203, 223
Asclepiadaceae, 219
Ascomycetes, 37, 38
Aspidiaria, 73
Aspidiophyllum, 206, *207*, 226
Aspidium, 112
Asterocalamitaceae, 84, 95
Asterocalamites, *126*, 127
Asterophyllites, 87, 96
Asteropteris, 100
Asterotheca, 105, 106
Asteroxylaceae, 64
Asteroxylon, 47, *48*, 49, 50, 58, 59, 63, 64,
   272
   elberfeldense, 47, 50, 53, 54, 272
   mackiei, 42, 47, 49, 51, 272
Astromyelon, 87
Atane flora, 223
Atlantic coastal plain floras, 221
Aulacotheca, 51, 115, 117
Azolla, 111, 112
   intertrappea, 113

285

Bacteria, 32
Baiera, 132, *156*, 162, 163, 164, 195, *196*, 197, 199
  paucipartita, 163
  taeniata, 163
Baragwanathia, 51, 53, 58, 63, 64, 67, 68, 273
  longifolia, 51
Baragwanathia flora, 51, 58
Barrandeina, 58
Basidiomycetes, 38
Beania, 175
  spectabilis, 163
Beech-maple forest, 245
Bennettitales, 154, 158, 166 ff., 211, 212, 276, 277
Bennettites, 167
Bensonites, 102
Berberidaceae, 215
Bergeria, 73
Betula, 231, 233, 234, 242, 252
  nana, 252, 253
  pubescens, 252, 253
Betulaceae, 205
Bjuvia, 175
Blue-green algae, 32, 33
Boghead coals, 34, 148, 149
Bothrodendraceae, 69
Bothrodendron, 69, *70*, 71, 75
  mundum, 75
Botryococcus braunii, 34
Botryopteris, 100, 102, 111, 113
  globosa, 102
Boulaya, 115
  fertilis, 115
Bowenia, 175
Bowmanites, 92, 96
Brachyphyllum, 225
Brandon flora, 235
Brasenia, 232, 233, 253
  purpurea, 243
Broggeria, 58
Brown coal, 142, 143, 246, 247
Bryophytes, 39
Bucheria, 58, 64
Bucklandia neirsteinensis, 176
Bunter, 192
Buriadia, *134*, 135
Bursaraceae, 234

Cactus, 234
Calamitaceae, 84, 95, 275
Calamites, 84, 85, 86, 87, 88, 95, *128*, 129, *130*, 131, 155
Calamocladus, 87
  (*Asterophyllites*) *charaeformis*, 87
Calamophytaceae, 64, 83, 95

Calamophyton, *44*, 45, 58, 63, 64, 84, 89, 95, 272
  primaevum, 53, *90*
Calamostachys, 88, 89, 96
  binneyana, 88
  casheana, 88
Calathiospermum scoticum, 122
Calciferous, 129
Callipteridium, 131
Callipteris, 132, 133
Callithamniopsis, 34
Callitris, 185
Callitropsis, 185
Callixylon, 58, 59, 155, 157, 158, 165
  newberryi, 66
  zalesskyi, 157
Calymmatotheca, 117
Camasia, 37
Cambrian spores, 271
Campanula uniflora, 256
Capparites, 225
Carbon[14], 9, 30
Carboniferous floras, 124 ff.
Cardiocarpon anomalum, 76
Cardiocarpus, 161
  spinatus, 165
Cardiopteris, *126*, 127, 129
Carnoconites, 199
Carpinus, 231, 234
  betulus, 243
Cascadian revolution, 239
Castalia, 207
Castanea, 231
Catalpa, 232, 233
Caulopteris, 106, *108*, 109, 113, *130*, 131
Caytonanthus, 122, 123
Caytonia, 122, 123, 211
Caytoniaceae, 122, 123
Caytoniales, 211, 212, 218, 280
Cedroxylon, 181, 182
Cedrus, 182, 187
Celastrites, 229
Celastrophyllum, 229
Cenomanian, 220, 222
Cenozoic floras, 229 ff.
  fragmentation of, 243
Cephalopteris, 98, 111
Cephalotaxaceae, 178, 185
Cephalotaxus, 187
Ceratium, 34
Ceratozamia, 175
  vicetinus, 176
Chaetocladus, 34
Charophytes, 36
Cheiropteris, *194*, 195
Cheirostrobaceae, 84, 95

Cheirostrobus, 93, 94, 95
  pettycurensis, 94
Chemical methods, 29
Chlamydothrix, 32
Chlorococcales, 34
Chlorophyceae, 33, 271
Chorionopteris, 111
Cingularia, 88, 131
  typica, 88
Cinnamomum, 203, 217, 223, 226, *232,* 233, 240, 241
Citronelle flora, 242
Cladophlebis, 111, 195, 201, 203
  denticulata, 195
Cladoxylales, 98, 111
Cladoxylon, 44, 45, 59, 98, 109, 110, 111
  scoparium, 53
Clarain, 144, 145, 146
Classification of plants, 11
Clathropteris, 199, 202
Clavator, 36
Clematis, 232, 233
Clepsydropsis, 58, 59, 100, 111
Climaciophyton, 94
Climatic fluctuations, recent, 258
Coal
  algal, 148, 149, 150
  paleobotany of, 141 ff.
Coal balls, 127
Coalification, 150, 151, 152
Codiaceae, 34
Codonospermum, 22, 115
Codonotheca, 114, 115
Coenopteridales, 98, 111, 274
Collenia, 37
Colpodexylon, 68
Colpoxylon, 117
Comanchian, 190
Compactions, 4
Compositae, 216, 235
Compressions, 4
Comptonia, 231, 233
Conemaugh, 129
Coniferales, 158, 178 ff.
Conifers
  Cenozoic, 225
  Cenozoic radiation, 184
  woods, 181, 182
Coniopteris, 201
Conostoma, 115
Continental drift theory, 267, 268
Convolvulaceae, 216
Cooksonia, 64
Coorongite, 149
Cordaianthus, 158, 159, 160, 161
  penjoni, 158, 159
  pitcairnei, 160

pseudofluitans, 160
  shuleri, 22, 159, 160
  zeilleri, 160
Cordaicarpus, 160, 161
Cordaitaceae, 155
Cordaitales, 127, 154 ff., 180, 188, 276
Cordaites, 126, 127, *128,* 129, *130,* 131, 134, 135, 154, *156, 157, 159,* 180
Cornus, 223, 231
Corylus, 231, 233, 250, 251, 252, 253
  avellana, 243
Corynepteris, 102, 109, 111
Corystospermaceae, 122, 123
Crataegus, 224, 231
Credneria, 206, 219, *220, 221,* 226
Crepis nana, 255
Cretaceous, 190
  floral succession, 219, 222, 223
  Rocky Mountain floras, 226
Cretovarium, 201
  japonicum, 210
Crossotheca, 115, 117, *118,* 119, 122, 162
  hughesiana, 115
Cruciferae, 235
Cryptomeria, 185
Cryptophycus, 36
Cryptozoon, 35, 36
  protiferum, 36
Ctenis, 195
Culm, 129
Cunninghamia, 183, 185
Cupressaceae, 178, 181
Cupressoxylon, 181
Cyathea, 111
Cyathotrachus, 105, 109
  altissimus, 22, 106
Cycadaceae, 175
Cycadales, 154, 158, 162, 166, 174, 211, 276
Cycadeoidea, 166, 167, 168, 172, 173, *193, 198,* 199, *200,* 201
  dacotensis, 168
  dartoni, 168, 173, 174
  ingeni, 173
  jenneyi, 173
  micromela, 173
  moreri, 174
  wielandi, 168
Cycadites escheri, 176
Cycadofilices, 114
Cycas fujiana, 176
Cyclocrinus, 34
Cyclostigma, 58, *125*
Cyperaceae, 205, 250
Cyperacites, 225
Cyrilla, 235
Czechanowskia, 163, 164, 165

Dadoxylon, 188, 276
Dakota flora, 222, 226
Dalbergia, 203, 224
Dammara, 184
Danaeopsis, 194, 195
Danian flora, 222
Dasycladaceae, 34
Dasyporella, 34
Deccan trap, 192
Degeneria, 218
Delesserites, 35
    salicifolia, 36
Denver flora, 219, 220
Devonian floras, 57
Dewalquea, 225
Diastrophism, 8
Dicksonia, 112
Dicranophyllum, 132, 164
Dicroidium, 122
Dictyophyllum, 199
Dictyozamites, 173
Dimeripteris, 58
Dimorphosiphon, 34
    rectangulare, 34
Dioon, 175
Dioonicarpidium, 194, 195
Diospyros, 217, 223, 226
Diplolabis, 100
Diploporaceae, 34
Dipteridaceae, 199, 202
Dipteris, 202
Dipterocarpaceae, 208
Diselma, 185
Disko flora, 203
Dogger, 195
Dolerotheca, 115, 117, 119, 123
Dombeyopsis, 226
Drepanophycaceae, 64, 68
Drepanophycus, 42, 53, 54, 58, 59, 63, 64, 68, 80, 81, 272, 273
Drimys, 197, 212, 218
Dryas, 252, 253
Dryoxylon, 201
Duisbergia, 58
Dulichium, 266, 267
    spathaceum, 267
Durain, 144, 145, 146

Elberfeld flora, 53, 58
Electron microscopy, 29
Emplectopteris triangularis, 121
Encephalartos, 175
    gorceixianus, 176
Engelhardtia, 232, 233, 234, 235
Enigmophyton, 62, 64
    superbum, 62
Eoangiopteris, 105

Eospermatopteris, 60, 61, 110, 114
Ephedra, 234
Ephedrites, 188
Epilobium latifolium, 256
Equisetaceae, 84, 95
Equisetites, 96, *194,* 195, *198,* 199
Equisetum, 83, 84, 86, 87, 95, 96, 98, 224, *232,* 233
    arvense, 83
    giganteum, 83
Ericaceae, 236, 251
Erigeron compositus, 255
Ernestiodendron, 179, 180
Etapteris, 100, 109, 111, *126,* 127
Eucalyptus, 217, 223, 240, 241
Euphorbiaceae, 216, 236
Euryale, 267
Eusporangiate ferns, 100, 111
Eutremia edwardsii, 256
Evolution theories, 261 ff.
Existing flora, origin, 238 ff.
Extermination of floras, 266, 267

Fagaceae, 227, 235
Fagoxylon, 201
Fagus, 231, *232,* 233, 242
Ferns, 97 ff.
    Devonian, 97
    eusporangiate, 100, 111
    Mesozoic, 201
Ficophyllum, 229
Ficus, 217, 223, 226, 231, *232,* 233
Filicales, 111, 264
Film technique, 21, 22, 23, 24
Fitzroya, 187
Flacourtiaceae, 234
Floral provinces, Paleozoic, 135
Florissant flora, 215, 235
Floristics, 248 ff.
Foerstia, 38, 58, 271
Folienia, 187
Form genus, defined, 73
Fox Hills, 222
Fraxinus, 226, 231, 242
Fungi, 38
Furcula, 208
    granulifera, 202, 207
Fusain, 144, 145, 146

Gangamopteris, 133, *134,* 135
Gault, 222
Geinitzia, 221, 225
Geminella, 34
Geological time scale, 6, 7
Germanophyton, 62, 64
    psygmophylloides, 62

Gigantopteris, 131, 132, 135, 136
Gilboa fossil forest, *60*, 61
Ginkgo, 162, 163, 164, 223, 226, 231, 241, 276
   adiantum, 226
   biloba, 161, 163, 165
Ginkgoales, 154, 161, 162, 163, 187, 276
Ginkgoites, 163, *196*, 197, *200*, 201, 203
Ginkgophyllum, 62, 64, 164
Girvanella, 33
Gleichenia, 111, 117
Gleicheniaceae, 112
Gloeocapsa, 150
Gloeocapsomorpha, 33
Glossopteris, 127, 133, *134*, 135, 136, *196*, 197
Glossopteris flora, 133
Glyptostrobus, 185, 187, 231, 234, 235
Gnetales, 178, 195, 211, 213, 278
Gnetopsis, 115, 122
Gnetum, 242
Gondwana floras, 133, 134, 135, 136
Gondwanaland, 195
Gondwanidium, *134*, 135
Gordonia, 235
Grahamland flora, 195
Gramineae, 251
Green River flora, 234
Grewiopsis, 226
Ground sections, 20
Gunz, 249
Gyrogonites, 36

Hagiophyton, *108*, 109, 113
Halimeda, 34
Hamamelidaceae, 208
Hausmannia, 199, 203
Hedeia, 52, 58
   corymbosa, 52
Hepaticae, 39, 278
Herbaceous habit, 214
Hercynian revolution, 131
Heterangium, 115, 117
Hicoria, 234
   alba, 243
Homoxylon, 197, 218
   rajmahalensis, 197, 218
Hornea, 42
Horneophytaceae, 64
Horneophyton, 42, 45, 46, 47, *48*, 49, 50, 64, 272
   lignieri, 42, 43, 45
Hostimella, 51, 58, 62
Hyenia, *44*, 45, 58, 59, 63, 64, 84, 89, 95, 272, 273
   elegans, 53, *91*
Hyeniaceae, 64, 83, 95

Hymenophyllaceae, 112
Hypnum, 39

Icacinaceae, 234
Illinoian, 249
Impressions of fossil plants, 4
Incarvillea, *232*, 233
Incrustations, 4
Infrared photography, 26
Inversicatenales, 98, 100, 111
Iridopteridales, 100, 111
Iridopteris, 100, 111
Isle of Wight flora, 233
Isoëtaceae, 69
Isoëtes, 67, 69, 77, 79, 81
Isoëtites, 69, 81

Jackson flora, 224, 233
Juglandoxylon, 201
Juglans, 223, 224, 226, 231, 233, 235
Jungermannites, 39
Juniperus, 223
Jurassic, 190

Kansan, 249
Karwinskia, 266
Katmai, 3
Kaulfussia, 106
Kenai flora, 231
Kerosene shales, 34, 148, 149
Keteleeria, 182
Keuper, 192
Kimmeridgian, 195
Klukia, 202
Knorria, 73
Kolm, 29, 34, 272
Kuckersite, 33, 34, 150

Labiatae, 235
Laccopteris, 112, *196*, 197, 202, 203
Lagenostoma, 115, 117, 119, *120*, 123
   lomaxi, *120*
Lance flora, 222, 226
Laramide revolution, 191
Laramie flora, 219, 222
Larix, 182
Lauraceae, 203, 205, 227, 234, 235
Laurophyllum, 225, 226
Laurus, 223, 226
Lebachia, 170, 180, 276
   piniformis, 179, *180*
Lecrosia, 180
Leguminosae, 216, 227, 235
Leguminosites, 225

Lepidocarpaceae, 69
Lepidocarpon, 69, 75, 76, 77, 79
  lomaxi, 76, 77
  magnificum, 77, 78
  wildianum, 77
Lepidocystis, 79
  glabrum, 77
Lepidodendraceae, 68, 71, 275
Lepidodendron, 29, 59, 68, *70*, 71, *72*, 73, 74, 79, *126*, 127, *128*, 129, *130*, 131, 133, 144
  corrugatum, 127
  johnsonii, 74, 81
  selaginoides, 74, 75
  vasculare, 74
Lepidodendropsis, 79, 127
Lepidophloios, 69, 73, 79
  wunschianus, 82
Lepidophyllum, 73
Lepidopteris, 122, 162, *196*, 197
  natalensis, 122
  ottonis, 122
Lepidostrobophyllum, 73
Lepidostrobus, 73, 76
  foliaceus, 75
  oldhamius, 75
  veltheimianus, 75
Leptostrobus, 164, 183
Lescuropteris, 131
  moorei, 121
Lesquerella arctica, 255
Liassic, 195
Libocedrus, 231
Lignite, 142, 143, 150
Liliaceae, 210, 219
Linopteris, 103, *104*, 111
Liquidambar, 231, 235
Liriodendron, 203, 207, 212, 223, 226, 266, 267
  tulipifera, 243, 267
Liriodendropsis, 223
Lithothamnion, 36
Liverworts, 39
Loganella, 64
Lonchopteris, 103, 131
London Clay flora, 234
Lunz flora, 192
Lycopodiaceae, 69, 275
Lycopodites, 69, 78, 81
Lycopodium, 59, 67, 69, 96
  lucidulum, 79
Lycopsida, 69 ff.
Lycostrobus, 196, 197
Lyginopteris, 114, 115, 117, 119, *126*, 127, 155
Lyginorachis, 117
Lythraceae, 216

Maceration techniques, 24, 25
Macrocycas, 175
Macrostachya, 88, 96
  heterosporoides, 88
  thompsonii, 88
Macrotaeniopteris, 192, 195
Magnolia, 203, 207, *221*, 223, 226, 235, 242, 266
Magnoliaceae, 203, 205, 206, 207, 219, 235
Magnoliales, 211, 215
Magothy, 222, 223
Malm, 195
Marattiaceae, 102, 104, *108*, *109*, 111, 112, 199
Marattiales, 111
Marchantites, 39
Mariopteris, 103, *104*, *105*, *108*, 109
  muricata, *109*, 110
Marpolia, 33
Marsilia, 175
Matonia, 111, *200*, 201, 202
  pectinata, 202
Matoniaceae, 112, 201, 202
Matonidium, 112
Mazocarpon, 76, 77
  oedipternum, 76, 82
  shorense, 76
Medicine Bow flora, 222, 226
Medullosa, 115, 117, 119
Megaphyton, 106, *108*, 109, 113
Melissa, *232*, 233
Menispermaceae, 203, 234
Menispermum, 266
Mertensides, 112
Mesa Verde, 222
Mesolithic, 253
Mesoxylon, 157, 158, 161
  sutcliffii, 157
  Thompsonii, 157, 165
Mesozoic floras, 190 ff.
  subdivisions of, 190
Metacedroxylon, 182
Metaclepsydropsis, 100
Metacupressinoxylon, 182
Metasequoia, 185, *186*, 189, 247, 267
Miadesmaceae, 69
Miadesmia, 69, 76, 77
  membranacea, 76
Microcachrys, 185
Micrococcus, 32
Microcycas, 175
Microflorae, 169, 177, 211, 212, 214, 276, 277
Microtome methods, 27
Migration, 265, 266
Mimusops, 235

Mindel, 249
Mississippian, 124, 129
Mitrospermum, 161
Monocotyledons, 210, 215
Monograptus, 57
Monongahela, 129
Mont Pelée, 3
Moraceae, 235
Mosses, 39, 278
Myeloxylon, 117
Myrica, 231
Myriophyllum, 234
Myrtaceae, 227

Naiadito lanceolata, 39
Naias marina, 243
Namurian, 129
Nathorstina, 69, 79, 81
Nebraskan, 249
Nelumbium, 201, 207
Nematophycus, 38
Nematophytales, 38, 271, 280
Nematophyton, 38, 58, 62, 271
Nematothallus, 38, 271
Neocalamites, 193, 194, 196, 197
Neolithic, 253
Neuropteridium, 133
Neuropteris, 103, *104,* 114, *116,* 117, *126,*
    127, *128,* 129
    decipiens, 129
    heterophylla, 116, 117, 121
    obliqua, 121
    ovata, 121
Neuropterocarpus, 117, 119
New Albany flora, 58, 59
Newlandia, 37
Nilssonia, 175, 199, *200,* 201
Nilssoniales, 175, 214
Nipa, 234
    burtini, 234
Noeggerathiales, 94, 131, 274
Noeggerathiopsis, 133, *134,* 135
Norimbergia, 202
Nucellangium, 81
Nunatak hypothesis, 258
Nymphaeaceae, 203, 207, 215
Nyssa, 201, 242, 266
    sylvatica, 267

Oak-hickory forest, 245
Odontopteris, 103, *116,* 117
    reichi, 116, 117
Oeningen flora, 235
Oil shales, 149
Oligocarpia, 111, 112
Onychiopsis, 112, *200,* 201

Oolitic, 195
Ophioglossales, 111
Opuntia, 234
Oscillatoria, 33
Oscillatoriaceae, 33
Osmunda, 201
Osmundaceae, 110, 201
Osmundales, 111
Osmundites, 110, 111
Otozamites, 173, 195
Oxfordian, 195
Oxytropis arctobia, 255

Pachytesta, 117, 119, *120*
    olivaeformis, 120
Pachytheca, 58
Palaeocycas, 175
Palaeonitella, 36
Palaeopitys milleri, 54, 165
Palaeoporella, 34
Palaeostachya, 88
Palms, Triassic, 183, 202, 207, 208
Palyssia, 183, 188
Pangaea, 136
Papaver, 232, 233
Pararaucaria patagonica, 184
Parícutin, 3
Parka, 38
Patoot flora, 223
Patuxent, 222
Peat, 142
Pecopteris, 103, *104, 106, 107, 108,* 109,
    111, 118, 121, 131
    miltoni-abbreviata, 121
    pluckeneti, 121
    wongii, 121
Peel technique, 21, 22, 23, 24
Pelourdea, 196, 197
Peltandra, 234
Peltaspermaceae, 122, 123
Pennsylvanian, 124, 129
Pentoxyleae, 197, 203
Pentoxylon, 197, 208
    sahnii, 197
Peridiniales, 34
Permian floras, 132
Petrifications, 4, *22*
Petrified Forest, Arizona, 195
Phaeophyceae, 34
Phellodendron, 266
Pherosphaera, 187
Phycomycetes, 33, 37
Phylloglossum, 67, 69
Phyllophorales, 98, 100, 111
Phyllosperm, 277
Phyllospore, 277

Phyllotheca, 94, 133, *134*, 135
Phylogeny, 270 ff.
Physostoma, 115, 119
   elegans, 22
Picea, 182, 234, 253
   excelsa, 243
Pila, 33, 148, 149
   bibractensis, 148
Pilea pumila, 267
Pilgerodendron, 185
Pinaceae, 178, 182
Pinakodendron, 79
Pinoxylon, 182
Pinus, 182, 185, 223, 225, 234, 252
   succinifer, 235
   sylvestris, 252, 253
Pityaceae, 155
Pityoxylon, 181, 182
Pitys, *126*, 127, 157, 158
Plagiopus, 39
Plagiozamites, 131
Planera aquatica, 242
Planoxylon, 181, 182
Plantago, 215
Platanaceae, 203, 205
Platanophyllum, 226, 229
Platanus, 203, 223, 231
Platyphyllaceae, 62, 64
Platyphyllum, 62, 64, 164
Pleistocene, 248 ff.
Pleuromeia, 69, 79, *80*
Pleuromeiaceae, 69
Pliocene floras, 241, 242, 243
Pluvial stages, 249
Pocono, 129
Podocarpaceae, 178, 181, 183, 185, 188
Podozamites, 195, *196*, 197, 225
Pollen analysis, 250, 251, 253
Polypodiaceae, 201
Polypodiopsis, 185
Polypodium, 111, 112
Polystichum mohrioides, 255
Polytrichum, 39
Populus, 231, 233
   tremuloides, 253
Poroxylaceae, 155
Poroxylon, 155, *156*, 157, 158
Porphyrins, 29
Portlandian, 195
Post-glacial history, 253
Potamogeton, 234
Potomac, 222
Potoniea, 117
Pottsville, 129
Prepinus, 184
Price flora, 129
Primicorallina, 34, 35

Primneste, 36
Proaraucaria, 183
   mirabilis, 183, 184
Prorhyniales, 66
Proserpinaca, 266
Proteaceae, 227
Proterozoic plants, 32, 33
Protocalamites pettycurensis, 86
Protocedroxylon, 181, 182
Protodammara, 225
Protolepidodendraceae, 64, 68
Protolepidodendron, 59, 63, 64, 67, 68, 70, 71, 81
   scharyanum, 59
Protophyllocladus, 225
Protophyllum, 201, 219, 226
Protopiceoxylon, 181, 182
Protopteridaceae, 64
Protopteridium, 54, 58, 62, 63, 64, 97, 98, 111, 112, 273
   thompsonii, 62
Protosalvinia, 38, 59, 271
Prototaxites, 38, 62
Prunus, 231, 242
Psaronius, 106, *107*, *108*, 109, *126*, 127, *134*, 135
Pseudobornia, 125
   ursina, 89
Pseudoborniaceae, 83, 95
Pseudolarix, 182, 185
Pseudosporochnaceae, 64
Pseudosporochnus, 58, 61, 63, 64, 273
Pseudotsuga, 182, 187
Pseudovoltzia, 181
Psilophytaceae, 64
Psilophytales, 272, 273, 278
Psilophyton, 41, 42, *44*, 45, 52, 58, 59, 63, 64, 272, 273
Psilopsida, characterized, 54
Psilotaceae, 278
Psilotum, 54
Psygmophyllum, 62, 64, *126*, 127, *134*, 135, 164
Pteridophylls, 103, *104*
Pteridosperms, 114 ff.
   Mesozoic, 122
Pterophyllum, 173, *194*, 195
Pteropsida, defined, 97
Pteruchus, 122, 123
Ptilophyllum, 173
Ptilozamites, 199
Ptychocarpus, 105, 106, 109
   unitus, 106

Quercus, *221*, 231, 235, 252
   nigra, 242
   robur, 243

Rachopteris, 126, 127, 129
Radiographic methods, 28
Rajmahal Hills flora, 197
Ranales, 212, 225, 226, 264
Ranunculaceae, 168, 215, 225, 235
Raritan, 222, 223
Raumeria reichenbachiana, 177
Recapitulation theory, 264
Reinschia, 33, 148, 149
Relict endemism, 187, 247, 254
Reuverian flora, 242, 243, 244
Rhabdocarpus, 119, 121
Rhabdoporella, 34
Rhacophyton, 63, 64, 98, 99, 111, 280
    zygopteroides, 98, 99
Rhaetic floras, 192, 195, *196,* 197, 199
Rhamnus, 224, 226
Rhodea, 111, 129
Rhodophyceae, 36, 271
Rhynia, 44, 45, 47, 49, 50, 64, 272
    gwynnevaughani, 42, 43, 45, *46, 48,* 49
    major, 42, 43, 45, *46, 48,* 49, 51
Rhyniaceae, 64, 278
Rhynie flora, 42, 43, *48,* 49
Ripley, 222
Riss, 249
Rivularia, 33
Rotodontiospermum, 115
Rubiaceae, 216

Sabalites, 220, 229
Sabulia, 208
Sagenopteris, 196, 197, 201
    phillipsi, 123
Sahni Institute of Paleobotany, 17
Sahnianthus, 237
Salicaceae, 205, 235
Saliciphyllum, 229
Salix, 221, 231, 250, 252, 253
    calcicola, 255
    richardsonii, 255
Salvinia, 111, 112
Salviniaceae, 112
Salviniales, 111
Sangamon, 249
Saportea, 132
Sapotaceae, 234
Sassafras, 223, 226
    montana, 226
Saxegothaea, 185
Schilderia adamanca, 195
Schizaea, 111
Schizaeaceae, 202
Schizolepis, 183, 188
Schizomycetes, 32
Schizoneura, 133, *134,* 135
Schizopodium, 64

Schizothrix, 33
Sciadopitys, 185
Scolecopteris, 105
Scoresby Sound flora, 195
Scythophyllum, 194, 195
Sedimentation, 8
Selaginella, 67, 69, 96
Selaginellaceae, 69, 275
Selaginellites, 69, 78, 81
    amesiana, 78
Senecio resedifolius, 255
Senonian, 221, 222
Sequoia, 181, 185, 186, 187, *221,* 223,
    225, 226, 231, 233, 267
    sempervirens, 183
Sigillaria, 68, 70, 71, 73, 79, *126,* 127,
    128, 129, 131, *134,* 135, 138, 144
    sulcata, 76
Sigillariaceae, 68, 71
Smilax, 210
Solenhofen flora, 34, 197
Solenopora, 36
Sparganium, 210, *232,* 233
Spencerites, 69
Sphaerocarpales, 39
Sphaerostoma, 117
Sphagnites, 39
Sphenolepidium, 200, 201
Sphenophyllaceae, 83, 95
Sphenophyllostachys, 92, 93
    dawsoni, 92, 93
Sphenophyllum, 91, *92,* 93, 95, 96, *126,*
    127, *128,* 129, 131, *134,* 135, 274
    cuneifolium, 93
    fertile, 93
    plurifoliatum, 93
Sphenopsids, 83 ff.
Sphenopteridium, 125
Sphenopteris, 103, *104,* 111, *116,* 117,
    118, 119
    tenuis, 121
Sphenozamites, 194, 195
Sphondylophyton, 94
Splint coal, 144
Sporangites, 149
Sporocarpon, 36
Sporogonites, 47, 64
Stachiospore, 277
Stachyosperm, 277
Stachyotaxus, 178, 183, 188, *196,* 197
Stangeria, 175
Stauropteris, 100, *101,* 102, 111, 112, *126,*
    127
    burntislandica, 101, 102
    oldhamia, 101
Stephanian, 129

Stephanospermum, 115
Sterculia, 209
Sterculiaceae, 209
Stewartia, 242
Stigmaria, 70, 71, 73, 79, *126*, 127
Stigmariopsis, 73
Stipitopteris, 106, 109
Stratiotes, 232, 233
Stromatolites, 37
Sutcliffia, 117
Swedenborgia, 183, 189

Taeniopteris, 103, 131, 132, 172, 173, 175, 197, *198*, 199
   vittata, 171
Taiwania, 185
Tasmanites, 149
Taxaceae, 178, 179, 181, 184, 188
Taxales, 179
Taxodiaceae, 178, 181
Taxodium, 185, 186, 187, 223, 231, 245, *246*, 247
   distichum, 242
Taxoxylon, 181
Taxus, 184
Tcheremkhite, 149
Teglian flora, 243, 244
Telangium, 117
Telome theory, 63, 64
Tethys Sea, 135
Tetracentraceae, 212
Tetracentron, 197, 218
Tetrastichia, 115, 117
Thamnocladus, 34, *35*
Thamnopteris, 110
Thaumatopteris, 199, 202
Thin sections, 20
Thinnfeldia, 122
Thujopsis, 185
Thursophyton, 42, 50, 63
   milleri, 42
Thyllopteris, 182
Thyrsopteris, 112
Tilia, 231, 234, 253
Tingia, 94, 96, 131
Tingiostachya, 96
Tmesipteris, 54
Todea, 201
Todites, 195, 201
   goeppertianus, 201
   rhombifolius, 201
   williamsonii, 201
Torbanite, 34
Torreya, 184, 187
Tracheophytes, 11
Transfer techniques, 25, 26, 27
Trapa, 231, 233, 242, 253

Triassic, 190
Trichopitys, 163, 164
   heteromorpha, 164, 165
Trigonocarpus, 117, 119
Triletes, 73
Triphyllopteris, 129
Trochiliscus, 36
Trochodendraceae, 212, 277
Trochodendroides, 201, 224, 226
   arctica, 224
   richardsonii, 224
Trochodendron, 197, 218
Tsuga, 182
Turonian, 222
Tuscaloosa flora, 222, 225, 226
Typha, 223, 250, 251

Ulmannia, 181
Ulmus, 233, 252
Ulodendron, *126*, 127
Ulotrichales, 34
Umbellularia, 231
Umkomasia, 122

Verbenaceae, 216
Vermiporella, 34
Vesuvius, 3
Viburnum, 226
Vicksburg, 224
Voltzia, 132, 183, *194*, 195
Voltziales, 179, 180, 181, 183, 188, 276, 280
Violaceae, 216
Vitis, 226, 242
   vinifera, 243
Vitrain, 144, 145, 146

Walchia, *126*, 127, 132, 133, *156*, 179
Wardia fertilis, 120, 121
Washington, 129
Wealden, 201
Welwitschia, 188
Westphalian, 129
Whittleseya, 115, 117, *118*, 119
Widdringtonia, 185
Wielandiella, 167, 172, 177, *193*, *196*, 197
Williamsonia, 167, 169, *171*, 177, *198*, 199, *200*, 201
   gigas, 169, *170*
   spectabilis, 171
   whitbyensis, 171
Williamsoniella, 167, 177, *193*, *198*, 199
   coronata, 171, *172*, 173
Winteraceae, 212
Wisconsin, 249
Woodworthia arizonica, 195
Wurm, 249

Xyridaceae, 215

Yarmouth, 249
Yarravia, 51, 58, 63, 64
  oblongata, 51
  subsphaerica, 51
Yarraviaceae, 64
Yucca, 242

Zalesskya, 110
Zamia, 175
  mississippiensis, 176
  praecedens, 176
  tertiaria, 176
  wilcoxensis, 176

Zamiophyllum, 201
Zamiostrobus saportanus, 176
Zamites, 173, 176
  epibius, 176
  paleocenicus, 176
  tertiarius, 176
Zelkova, 242, 266
Zingiberites, 229
Zizyphus, 226, 232, 233
Zosterophyllaceae, 64
Zosterophyllum, 52, 58, 64
  australianum, 52
  rhenanum, 52, 53
Zygopteridaceae, 100, 275
Zygopteris, 102, 108, 109